UNDERSTANDING AND OPTIMIZING HUMAN DEVELOPMENT:

FROM CELLS TO PATIENTS TO POPULATIONS

ANNALS OF THE NEW YORK ACADEMY OF SCIENCES

Volume 1038
December 2004

UNDERSTANDING AND OPTIMIZING HUMAN DEVELOPMENT:

FROM CELLS TO PATIENTS TO POPULATIONS

National Institute of Child Health and Human Development
40th Anniversary Scientific Symposium

Editors
STEPHEN G. KALER AND OWEN M. RENNERT

This volume is the result of the **National Institute of Child Health and Human Development 40th Anniversary Scientific Symposium**, presented by NICHD, and held on September 8, 2003, in Bethesda, Maryland.

CONTENTS

Part II. Gene Expression

Part III. Growth and Development

Part IV. Cell Biology

Part V. Neurobiology

Part VI. Social and Behavioral Sciences

Office of the Director
National Institute of Child Health
and Human Development

September 8, 2003

Dear Colleagues,

Forty years ago the National Institute of Child Health and Human Development was created as the eighth Institute of the National Institutes of Health. While signed into law by President John F. Kennedy, it was pediatrician Dr. Robert E. Cooke who conceptualized the Institute, and the President's sister Eunice Kennedy Shriver who lobbied the Congress tirelessly to pass legislation authorizing it. The three shared a vision of the fledgling Institute as a vehicle "to attack the unsolved health problems of children…and to support imaginative research into the complex processes of human development."

The results of this commitment have been remarkable. The nation's infant mortality rate has declined more than 70 percent in those 40 years, much of it attributable to NICHD-sponsored research. Survival rates for low birth weight infants with respiratory distress syndrome have increased from only 5 percent in the 1960s to 95 percent today due to improved respirator technologies and development of exogenous surfactant, resulting from research efforts of NICHD and other Institutes. The rate of sudden infant death syndrome (SIDS) has dropped nearly 50 percent since the NICHD *Back to Sleep* education campaign began in 1994. Maternal transmission of HIV to infants has dropped from 25 percent to just 2 percent in the U.S. as a result of NICHD's efforts in collaboration with other agencies and organizations. The incidence of *Haemophilus influenzae B* meningitis, once the leading cause of acquired mental retardation, has dropped from more than 15,000 cases per year in 1988 to almost none today, as a result of NICHD-led vaccine development. Congenital hypothyroidism, once responsible for many cases of mental retardation, no longer has an impact on cognitive development because of screening techniques used to detect the condition in all newborns and allow treatment to prevent its effects. Infertility that once prevented couples from having babies of their own now can often be treated and reversed. Scientific information about the safety and effectiveness of various contraceptive methods for women and men is now available. Educational, physical, and behavioral treatments for people with mental, developmental, and physical disabilities are now possible.

Today's 40th Anniversary Scientific Symposium highlights some of these as well as other successes, in the voices of some of our finest extramural and intramural scientists. We thank these individuals for joining us here today, and for their hard work and dedication over the decades. We also gratefully acknowledge all the Symposium registrants for joining us to share in this celebration of NICHD at 40.

Sincerely,

Duane Alexander, MD
Director

Preface

This volume of the *Annals* contains the proceedings of a scientific symposium held at the National Institutes of Health in Bethesda, Maryland on September 8, 2003. The occasion was the 40th anniversary of the National Institute of Child Health and Human Development (NICHD). To celebrate this milestone, the Institute organized a meeting to highlight some of the exceptional contributions by NICHD-supported scientists in areas relevant to our research mission.

The scope and breadth of those accomplishments is exemplified by the seven session themes of the symposium, which form the sections of this volume: Clinical Sciences, Gene Expression, Growth and Development, Cell Biology, Neurobiology, Social and Behavioral Sciences, and Reproductive Biology. Throughout its history, the NICHD has supported *fundamental and clinical* research within its intramural division, outside universities, and other institutions throughout the United States and the world.

The symposium offered an opportunity to reflect on the fruits of unfettered scientific inquiry as well as serving to invigorate our current efforts and point us toward the future. With warm appreciation, we acknowledge the participation of twenty-six invited speakers including some of the foremost scientists in the nation whose work has been supported by the NICHD throughout the decades. Sadly, two of these individuals, Celso-Ramón García and Edward Lewis, have passed away in the months since the symposium was held. Their lives and scientific legacies are summarized here, in the *In Memoriam* pages in this volume.

Finally, the NICHD 40th Anniversary Scientific Symposium (<http://dir2.nichd.nih.gov/nichd/40th/index.html>) would not have been possible without the enthusiastic support and advice of the NICHD Director, Duane Alexander, and members of the organizing committee: Christine Bacrach, Hao-Chia Chen, Jeffrey Evans, Mark Klebanoff, Michael Weinrich, and Anne Willoughby.

STEPHEN G. KALER
OWEN M. RENNERT

Ann. N.Y. Acad. Sci. 1038: xi (2004). © 2004 New York Academy of Sciences.
doi: 10.1196/annals.1315.041

In Memoriam:
Celso-Ramón García

Celso-Ramón García, MD, the William Shippen Jr. Emeritus Professor of Obstetrics and Gynecology at the University of Pennsylvania Medical Center, died on February 1, 2004 at the age of 82. Dr. García, with his colleagues Dr. Gregory Pincus and Dr. John Rock, conducted some of the first clinical trials on oral contraceptives. Through the work of this trio, an effective pill was produced; its basic concept remains, though the dosage has been reduced. "The pill" blocks release of a hormone that normally stimulates eggs during ovulation. It was approved for use in the United States by the Food and Drug Administration in 1960, and is one of the most popular methods of contraception today. More than 12 million women use it worldwide.

A New York City native, Celso-Ramón García graduated from Queens College and earned his medical degree from Downstate Medical Center of the State University of New York in 1945. He completed a rotating internship at the Norwegian Hospital in Brooklyn, NY and then served in the Army Medical Corps from 1946 to 1948. Between 1948 and 1953, García trained as a pathology resident, research fellow, and resident in Obstetrics and Gynecology, all at Cumberland Hospital in Brooklyn. In 1953, he was appointed as Assistant Professor of Obstetrics and Gynecology in the School of Medicine, University of Puerto Rico and from 1955 to 1965 at Harvard Medical School, where he served as Chief of the Infertility Clinic at Massachusetts General Hospital.

From 1965 to 1992, Dr. García was professor of Obstetrics and Gynecology, the William Shippen, Jr. Professor of Human Reproduction, and Director of Reproductive Surgery at the University of Pennsylvania School of Medicine, where he also founded the first Women's Wellness Program. In 1992, he was named emeritus professor. In 1995, the Celso-Ramón García Endowed Professorship in Reproductive Biology was established at the University of Pennsylvania.

Ann. N.Y. Acad. Sci. 1038: xiii–xiv (2004). © 2004 New York Academy of Sciences.
doi: 10.1196/annals.1315.002

Dr. García received the 2000 Scientific Leadership Award from the Global Alliance for Women's Health of the United Nations for his efforts in the development of the first oral contraceptive, for developing innovative and holistic programs and surgical interventions in women's health, and for supporting global women's health policy development for all stages of women's lives.

In Memoriam:
Edward B. Lewis

Edward B. Lewis, PhD, Thomas Hunt Morgan Professor of Biology, Emeritus at California Institute of Technology, died on July 22, 2004 at the age of 86. Dr. Lewis was a geneticist who received the 1995 Nobel Prize in Physiology or Medicine for work on *Drosophila melanogaster* that illustrated how genes control embryonic development. Familiar with irradiation as a method of mutagenesis in *Drosophila*, Dr. Lewis also contributed key insights on the association between radiation and leukemia based on his studies of Japanese survivors of the atomic bomb and radiologists exposed to chronic, low-dose irradiation.

Edward Lewis was born in Wilkes-Barre, PA in 1918. As a high school student there, he developed an interest in fruit fly genetics and performed experiments on *Drosophila*. A dedicated flautist, he attended Bucknell University on a flute scholarship but left after one year to study genetics and biostatistics at the University of Minnesota, where he received a bachelor's degree in 1939. Lewis earned his doctorate in genetics from the California Institute of Technology in 1942. He then served in the U.S. Army Air Corps from 1942 to 1946.

Dr. Lewis returned to Caltech as an instructor in 1946, was named assistant professor in 1948, and professor of biology in 1956. He was named the Thomas Hunt Morgan Professor and Chair of Biology in 1966 and retained the chair until his retirement from active faculty duties in 1988. As an emeritus professor, he maintained an active work schedule until shortly before his death.

Dr. Lewis's work and theories illuminated basic concepts of how genes work, although he made his major discoveries well before modern tools of molecular biology were available. He identified a mutant fruit fly with 2 sets of wings, instead of the normal single set, and demonstrated that a specific genetic defect caused the abnormality. Through the years, Lewis isolated many other mutants, mapping genes controlling such traits as eye and limb

Ann. N.Y. Acad. Sci. 1038: xv–xvi (2004). © 2004 New York Academy of Sciences.
doi: 10.1196/annals.1315.003

development to specific locations on the third chromosome in *Drosophila*. In 1957, he demonstrated that these genes were arranged on chromosomes in the same order as they were activated along the body axis during development, a concept known as colinearity.

When Dr. Lewis received the 1995 Nobel Prize in Physiology or Medicine (shared with Eric Wieschaus of Princeton University and Christiane Nüsslein-Volhard of the Max Planck Institute for separate and complementary lines of research), the Nobel Committee's presentation speech noted: "The genes Edward Lewis discovered have in fact the same order in our DNA as in that of the fruit fly, and they work in the same way. The knowledge gained about development of the fruit fly has thus been a prerequisite for the recent advances in understanding how vertebrates develop."

Dr. Lewis was a member of the National Academy of Sciences, the American Academy of Arts and Sciences, the Royal Society (London), and many other prestigious organizations. In addition to the Nobel Prize, Lewis received numerous awards for his scientific contributions, including the Albert Lasker Award for Basic Medical Research in 1991 and the National Medal of Science in 1990. In 2003, he was inducted into the National Institute of Child Health and Human Development's Hall of Honor, an award presented by the NICHD in recognition of researchers it has supported who have made outstanding contributions to their research fields.

History of Intramural Clinical Research at the National Institute of Child Health and Human Development (NICHD)

D. LYNN LORIAUX, MD, PHD

Chairman, Department of Medicine, Oregon Health Sciences University, Portland, Oregon 97201, USA

ABSTRACT: This article reviews the beginnings of the NICHD intramural clinical research program; it focuses on three men, Roy Hertz, Mort Lipsett, and Griff Ross, who were instrumental in providing the intramural research program with the vision and character seen today.

KEYWORDS: NICHD; Roy Hertz; Mort Lipsett; Griff Ross; intramural research program; NIH

My charge is to review the beginnings of the NICHD intramural clinical research program. Of the many leaders who shaped the clinical research effort within the intramural program, I have chosen to discuss the three who I think gave the intramural clinical research effort the vision and character we see today.

The first is Roy Hertz (FIG. 1). Roy was born in Cleveland, Ohio, June 19, 1909. Dr. Hertz began his NIH career in the Nutrition Research Laboratory. In 1946, Hertz was appointed chief of the Endocrinology Section of the National Cancer Institute. His research focus was the effect of antagonists to progesterone and estrogen on the growth of the female tract, focusing on inhibition of growth. This work in hormonal antagonism was a logical extension of his PhD studies. To expand his studies, he concurrently established a clinical research unit at George Washington University in 1949. In 1953, this unit was moved to the NIH and reopened at the Clinical Center. He admitted the Clinical Center's first patient, Charles Meredith, for the study of hormonal effects on prostate cancer. Hertz became the NICHD scientific director in 1965 and was elected to the National Academy of Sciences in 1972. Roy died October 28, 2002 of heart failure. He was one of the giants of the world of medicine. He was the first to successfully treat and cure metastatic chorio-

Some material appearing here derives largely from the author's article *Remembrance: Mort and Griff* (Endocrinology **131**: 1–3, 1992).

Address for correspondence: D. Lynn Loriaux, MD, PhD, Department of Medicine, Oregon Health Sciences University, 3181 S.W. Sam Jackson Park Road, Mail Code L607, Portland, Oregon 97201-3098, USA. Voice: 503-494-1564.

loriauxl@ohsu.edu

Ann. N.Y. Acad. Sci. 1038: 1–6 (2004). © 2004 New York Academy of Sciences.
doi: 10.1196/annals.1315.007

FIGURE 1. Dr. Roy Hertz.

carcinoma. Before his breakthrough, the only cancers that had been cured with drugs were the leukemias and lymphomas and there was a question whether a solid tumor could be cured by drugs alone. Hertz's legacy is all solid tumors that are responding to chemotherapy.

Roy hired Mort Lipsett (FIG. 2) in 1957 and Griff Ross (FIG. 3) in 1960. These two men brought this program to a remarkable fruition in the study of endocrinology. It encompassed the years of the Vietnam War. Mort worked on steroids, and Griff on gonadotropins. Interestingly, it is was Mort who deemed most of medical progress "soft." His greatest work was on steroid metabolic conversions in human beings. Griff did his greatest work on the mechanism of follicular growth in the rat. They worked together in harmony for more than 20 years. Mort told me he and Griff never had an argument.

Mort's father was a pharmacist. His family moved to San Francisco at the beginning of World War II, and Mort went to Berkeley and majored in chem-

FIGURE 2. Dr. Mort Lipsett (*far right*) and NIH Director Donald S. Fredrickson (*far left*) escort First Lady Roslyn Carter during a visit to the NIH clinical Center.

istry. His education was interrupted by the draft, and he served as a medic in the 10th Mountain Division and was twice decorated for valor in combat during the Italian campaign. After the War, he went to USC medical school on the GI bill. An internship was followed by a medicine residency, and Mort then returned to New York to work with O.H. Pearson. His interest led to his position at the NIH in 1957. Mort was a genius. He forgot nothing, could beat three or four competent chess players at a time, was a life master bridge player and could do differential equations in his head. He could toss off whole journals before the rest of us finished the first few pages. Mort loved competition. He was focused on the state of his cardiovascular health. He loved to race up 12 flights of stairs and see who could first decelerate their pulse to 60 beats per minute or less. Some of us never got down to a pulse of 60. Some of us never got up to the 12th floor. Mort used books like an artist uses brushes—he always had a book in hand. He left several of his endocrine texts to me. The pages were clean, no dog ears. He treated books with respect.

Griff on the other hand was born in Mount Enterprise, East Texas. He thought of East Texas as different. He called it the land of tall pines, red dirt, and hook worms. He went to Stephen S. Austin College and to the University of Texas Medical Branch in Galveston. He entered private practice in his hometown, the fourth generation of his family to do so. He was drafted into

FIGURE 3. Dr. Griff Ross (with Dr. Judith Vatukaitis in the background).

the air force in the Korean War and spent two years as a general medical officer in England. When the war was over, Griff took a fellowship in internal medicine at the Mayo Clinic. Griff came to the NIH three years after Mort. Griff read slowly. He disliked competition any more intense than a friendly game of golf with friends. He once told me he belonged to an exercisers anonymous group, a mutual support group composed of close friends; if anyone got the urge to exercise, he could call another who would come and drink with him until the notion passed. Griff's taste in music ran to blue grass, in literature to Steinbeck and Fitzgerald, in food to Texas barbecue, and in drink to martinis without vermouth. He played music by ear and could not read music. He played the saxophone, was an accordionist. He played the harmonica. He was the only man I ever knew who could wear out a harmonica.

The only way Mort and Griff were alike was in their houses, but this was an artifact, since there is only one kind of house in Bethesda. Mort and Griff had different working styles. Mort did not spend time in conversation unless it was centered around a problem of interest. Even then, he would not give it much effort unless there were new data. He would usually take the data sheets from you. He worked best when you were quiet. You could follow his progress by his index finger which moved with his eye. Analysis would begin as he approached the end: "This means such and such" or "you will remember that table in such and such." A JCM would be pulled from the shelf. Tables and figures would be found with pinpoint accuracy. He would copy numbers and make mental calculations. There was some conversation, but it was with himself, not with you.

Griff, on the other hand, liked to worry the data. He would painstakingly study every number, asking question after question about the circumstances surrounding this particular experiment or that "outlier." He would recopy the numbers, rearrange them, metabolize them. There was no quick conclusion, no surgical insight. He would talk about the experiments for days. He would incorporate data from many sources and build a hypothesis. He was Darwinian. Mort left you shaken. Griff left you exhausted. But they synergized. They provided the Clinical Center and NIH with many years of inspired leadership.

Mort and Griff died within months of each other. Mort died of a malignancy. He discovered a tumor when he was unable to make a certain passing tennis shot that had been routine in the past. He ordered a CT on himself and found it. Griff had prostate cancer as an incidental finding. Mort never discussed his illness except to acknowledge the problem and to get on with the issue at hand. Griff talked about his illness at length in a clinical and analytical fashion.

Different as these two men were, they were alike in fundamentally important ways. Both supported science and loved medicine and recognized the difference between scholarship and science. Both understood the sustaining force of science for medicine. Both loved the NIH and those that worked there. Both loved young people and were comfortable in their presence. Both measured the worth of their careers by their accomplishments. Both accepted as a first premise the orchestration of life by molecular messengers. Both found their greatest joy in the discovery of new truths.

This is the legacy of these three fine men: first, a commitment to clinical investigation in its most fruitful form—from bedside to bench. Second: a commitment to nurture clinical investigation across the human condition, boy/girl, man/woman, reproduction, contraception, and old age. And finally: if possible, tackle first the problem with the greatest potential benefit for mankind.

I want to thank you for the honor of speaking at this occasion. I hope what I have said will add to the clinical research presentations to follow. This conference is sure to validate the confidence of these three men in the promise of NICHD.

BRIEF BIBLIOGRAPHIES

Roy Hertz

HERTZ, R. 1971. Biological aspects of gestational neoplasms derived from trophoblast. Ann. N.Y. Acad. Sci. **172**(10): 279–287.

HERTZ, R., D.M. BERGENSTAL, M.B. LIPSETT, *et al.* 1973. Chemotherapy of chorio-carcinoma and related trophoblastic tumors in women. CA Cancer J. Clin. **23**(4): 244–255.

HERTZ, R. 1976. The estrogen-cancer hypothesis. Cancer. **38**(1 Suppl.): 534–540.

HERTZ, R. 1976. Steroid-induced, steroid-producing, and steroid-responsive tumors. Curr. Top. Mol. Endocrinol. **4**:1–14.

KNECHT, M. & R. HERTZ. 1978. Relationship between plasma levels of human chorionic gonadotropin and tumor growth during chemotherapy for human choriocarcinoma maintained in the hamster cheek pouch. Cancer Treat. Rep. **62**(12): 2101–2103

Mort Lipsett

LIPSETT, M.B. 1977. Estrogen use and cancer risk. J. Am. Med. Assoc. **237**(11): 1112–1115.

LIPSETT, M.B. 1980. The social significance of endocrinology. Presidential address. 62nd Annual Meeting of The Endocrine Society. J. Clin. Endocrinol. Metab. **51**(4): 948–951.

CHROUSOS, G.P., A. VINGERHOEDS, D. BRANDON, C. EIL, M. PUGEAT, M. DEVROEDE, D.L. LORIAUX & M.B. LIPSETT. 1982. Primary cortisol resistance in man. A glucocorticoid receptor-mediated disease. J. Clin. Invest. **69**(6): 1261–1269.

LIPSETT, M.B. 1983. NICHD: 20 years of progress in child health research. Child Today **12**(1): 2–7.

LIPSETT, M.B. G.P. CHROUSOS, M. TOMITA, *et al.* 1985. The defective glucocorticoid receptor in man and nonhuman primates. Recent Prog. Horm. Res. **41**:199–247.

Griff Ross

ROSS, G.T., D.P. GOLDSTEIN, R. HERTZ, *et al.* 1965. Sequential use of methotrexate and actinomycin D in the treatment of metastatic choriocarcinoma and related trophoblastic diseases in women. Am. J. Obstet. Gynecol. **93**: 223–229.

WIDER, J.A., J.R. MARSHALL, C.W. BARDIN, M.B. LIPSETT & G.T. ROSS. 1969. Sustained remissions after chemotherapy for primary ovarian cancers containing choriocarcinoma. N. Engl. J. Med. **280**(26): 1439–1442.

ROSS, G.T. 1976. Congenital anomalies among children born of mothers receiving chemotherapy for gestational trophoblastic neoplasms. Cancer **37**(2 Suppl.): 1043–1047.

ROSS, G.T. & M.B. LIPSETT. 1978. Hormonal correlates of normal and abnormal follicle growth after puberty in humans and other primates. Clin. Endocrinol. Metab. **7**(3): 561–575.

ROSS, G.T. 1978. ESPAS: The Endocrine Society Presidential Address Syndrome. J. Clin. Endocrinol. Metab. **47**(4): 922–925.

Mutations in the Synthesis and Action of Estrogen

The Critical Role in the Male of Estrogen on Pubertal Growth, Skeletal Maturation, and Bone Mass

MELVIN M. GRUMBACH, MD

Edward B. Shaw Professor of Pediatrics Emeritus, University of California, San Francisco, San Francisco, California 94143, USA

ABSTRACT: The discovery of males with mutations in CYP19, the gene that encodes aromatase, the enzyme catalyzing the final step in the conversion of androgen to estrogen, and of a man with a mutation in the estrogen receptor α gene has led to increasing recognition of the critical role of estrogen in the male. The diverse roles of estrogen in the male, both circulating and locally synthesized, is supported by extensive studies in male mice generated with disruption of the aromatase gene or the genes encoding the α- and β-estrogen receptor. This presentation focuses on the crucial role of estradiol in the human male on the pubertal growth spurt, skeletal maturation and the cessation of linear growth, and the accrual of bone mass.

KEYWORDS: estrogen; CYP19 mutations; bone mineral; puberty; skeletal maturation; pubertal growth

A great deal of interest, energy, funding, scientific manpower, and excitement has focused on the unlimited potential of translational research from the "bench to the clinic" and the promise of genomics, proteomics, informatics, and nanotechnology—an "endless frontier" and the expectation it will contribute mightily to the future of health care, disease prevention, and the development of new therapeutics. In the overall assessment of advances in biomedical science considerably less interest has been given to "translational" research from the clinic to the bench. The picture I wish to paint for you

Presented at the NICHD 40th Anniversary Scientific Symposium, *Understanding and Optimizing Human Development: From Cells to Patients to Populations,* September 2003.

Address for correspondence: Melvin M. Grumbach, MD, Edward B. Shaw Professor of Pediatrics Emeritus, Department of Pediatrics, 513 Parnassus Ave., S-672, University of California, San Francisco, San Francisco, California 94143-0434.

grumbac@itsa.ucsf.edu

Ann. N.Y. Acad. Sci. 1038: 7–13 (2004). © 2004 New York Academy of Sciences.
doi: 10.1196/annals.1315.008

illustrates how new discoveries have challenged long-held concepts of the role of estrogen in the development, growth, and function of the human male, highlighted the diversity of nonreproductive actions of estrogen in both the male and female, emphasized the role of the extra-gonadal biosynthesis of estrogen from C19 steroid precursors (androgens) in a variety of somatic tissues. This "sea change in conventional wisdom" is a striking demonstration of the interdependence in modern biomedical research of basic science, clinical discovery, and patient-oriented research: a paradigm of the integrated approach and the role of scientific serendipity. "Chance favors the prepared mind."

Consider for a moment that until the past decade in the human being it was widely held that:

(1) estrogen synthesis or responsiveness by the conceptus is essential for implantation and survival of the embryo and fetus;

(2) in the human male, testosterone is the principal sex hormone *directly* involved in the pubertal growth spurt, skeletal maturation, accrual of bone mineral, and maintenance of the skeleton (anti-osteoporotic action);

(3) estrogen has an unimportant and minor role in nonreproductive tissues;

(4) estrogen is not an important regulator of FSH secretion in the male; and

(5) the local conversion in the central nervous system of testosterone to estradiol has an important effect on psychosexual differentiation.

Three key developments are largely responsible for the frameshift in conventional wisdom—the rapid change in the paradigm of the effects of estrogen on the male skeleton (and other somatic tissues).

Louis Pasteur said that the origin of scientific creativity is to know when to be astonished.

(1) In the clinic, the description in 1994 by Smith *et al.* of a man with a homozygous null mutation in estrogen receptor α that caused estrogen unresponsiveness, and of men, boys, girls, and women with severe estrogen deficiency owing to autosomal recessive mutations in the CYP19 gene encoding cytochrome P450 aromatase, in 1994 by Conte *et al.* and in 1995 by Morishima *et al.* and subsequently by others, led to a thorough reassessment of the role of estrogen in the male.

(2) Coincidentally, in the laboratory transgenic mice were generated that had disruption of the gene encoding the estrogen α receptor (so-called αERKO mice) or P450 aromatase, the critical enzyme responsible for the last and irreversible step in estrogen synthesis from androgens.

(3) The third development was the discovery of a second widely distributed estrogen receptor, ERβ, and subsequently the development of the ERβ knockout mouse (βERKO) and of mice with a double KO (αβERKO or DERKO).

Estrogen and androgen are two sides of the same coin. One concept, over a quarter of a century old but almost forgotten, is intracrinology: the conversion in certain extragonadal tissues of C19 steroid precursors to estradiol or to potent androgens. For example, in the male the peripheral conversion of androgen or androgen precursors to estradiol accounts for approximately 80–85% of the total production of estrogen; only about 15% is produced and secreted by the testis.

TABLE 1. Some sites of estrogen action on bone

- **Linear growth:** chondrogenesis—proliferation and differentiation of growth plate chondrocytes—and its link to osteogenesis
- **Skeletal maturation:** the gradual, progressive ossification of the epiphyseal growth plate during puberty, as a postulated consequence of estrogen-induced acceleration of programmed replicative senescence
- **Accrual of bone mass** during puberty and into the third decade
- **Estrogen and the constancy of bone mass in the adult:** remodeling, maintenance, and repair—the osteoclast and the osteoblast and osteocyte

Let us focus in this presentation on the now recognized critical role in the male of estrogen on the pubertal growth spurt, skeletal maturation, and the accrual of bone mass (TABLE 1). This action of estradiol is well illustrated in two cases. One patient, a 24-year-old man had a height of 204.7 cm (+3.75 SD) at the age of 24, eunuchoid skeletal proportions, mild genu valgum, and a bone age of 14 years. He was sexually fully mature and had macroorchidism. He had striking osteopenia of the spine and the lower radius despite a serum testosterone concentration of over 2000 ng/dL and elevated biochemical markers of bone turnover. He was heterosexually oriented. He had insulin resistance and an abnormal lipid profile. His mother exhibited signs of progressive virilization during pregnancy that regressed postpartum. Genomic analysis by Evan Simpson and his group indicated a homozygous single base change in exon IX of the CYP19 gene, a highly conserved region, R375C (TABLE 2).

The patient described by Eric Smith and his associates was 28 years old. Coincidentally he was the same height as our patient and had the same physical findings. His bone age was 15 years at age 28. He had severe osteopenia, increased markers of bone remodeling, insulin resistance, and an abnormal blood lipid profile. In contrast to the aromatase deficient man, his mother did not exhibit signs of virilization during her pregnancy (TABLE 2).

TABLE 2. Comparison of estrogen receptor α deficiency (ERKOα) and of aromatase deficiency

28-year-old male (ERKOα)	24-year-old male with P450arom
Height 204 cm, weight 127 kg	Height 204.7 cm (+3.7 SD), weight 135.1 kg
No acromegaloid features	No acromegaloid features
Eunuchoid skeletal proportions; genu valgum	Eunuchoid skeletal proportions
Normal age of puberty onset	Normal age of puberty onset
Well masculinized; normal testicular size	Well masculinized; testicular volume 34 mL
Bone age 15 years	Bone age 14 years
Severe osteoporosis: increased bone turnover	Severe osteoporosis: increased bone turnover
Psychosexual orientation: heterosexual	Psychosexual orientation: heterosexual
No virilization of mother during pregnancy	Virilization of mother during pregnancy
Insulin resistance; acanthosis	Insulin resistance
Abnormal plasma lipids	Abnormal plasma lipids
No response to high-dose estrogen treatment	Striking response to institution of low-dose estrogen therapy
Inheritance: autosomal recessive	Inheritance: autosomal recessive
Mutation: Arg157X (Exon 2) in ERα gene	Mutation: Arg376Cys (Exon IX) in CYP19 gene

Both disorders—aromatase deficiency and the knockout of the estrogen receptor α are inherited as autosomal recessive traits. Linear growth persisted in these young adults.

Three additional adult males with aromatase deficiency are described, as well as a number of females and younger children. But only one patient with an estrogen receptor α mutation leading to estrogen resistance is known.

All of the adult men presented with delayed bone age, open epiphyses, and osteopenia. They were all tall. The onset of puberty was normal as was its progression. Bone markers indicated an increase in bone remodeling. In contrast to the man with the estrogen receptor α deficiency, estrogen treatment of aromatase-deficient men led to a decrease to normal in the markers of bone turnover, rapid epiphyseal fusion, and repair of the severe osteopenia. In the man we studied with John Bilezikian, three years of estrogen treatment resulted in a striking increase in bone deposition which continued despite cessation of growth within 6 months of therapy, supportive of an anabolic effect on bone. The bone age had increased remarkably from 14 years to about 18 years after 6 months of estrogen therapy, a reflection of the action of estrogen on skeletal maturation in the male.

We now know that estrogen plays a critical role not only in the female pubertal growth spurt but also in that of the male. The pubertal linear growth spurt (skeletal linear growth, not weight) is species specific: it is unique to

Homo sapiens. The adolescent growth spurt first appeared in *Homo erectus* 2. Evolution theorists have proposed that a critical part of our reproductive success as a species is due, in part, to the prolonged pattern of human growth and development, and the delay in attaining full sexual maturity. This appears to be a critical part of the learning and practice of adult behaviors related to sex and child bearing. This unique pattern of growth and development in childhood and adolescence has a striking effect on reproductive advantage and the success of the human species; the human is the most successful mammal in terms of reproductive outcome as assessed by infant mortality among other measures.

Conventional wisdom had dictated that the pubertal growth spurt in the male and epiphyseal fusion was a direct effect of testosterone. We now appreciate that estradiol, generated mainly in extratesticular tissues including the skeleton, is the critical sex hormone in the male in the pubertal growth spurt and skeletal maturation leading to fusion of the epiphysis with the metaphysis

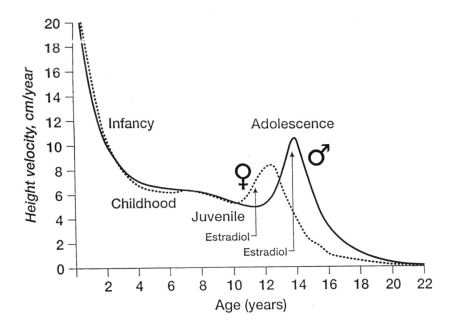

FIGURE 1. The adolescent growth spurt in girls and boys (growth velocity curves). Note the later onset of the pubertal growth spurt in boys and the approximately 2-year difference in peak height velocity and the greater magnitude of peak height velocity compared with girls. The timing of the effects of estradiol is indicated. Progressive epiphyseal fusion terminates the growth spurt and leads to final or adult height. Estrogen accelerates the rate of replicative senescence in the epiphyseal growth plate. Epiphyseal fusion seems to be a consequence of the arrest of growth that terminates the growth spurt and leads to final or adult height. (From Grumbach.[3])

and disappearance of the growth plate. Estradiol is quite likely the dominant sex steroid in bone metabolism in men in the accrual of peak bone mass and in its maintenance and repair. Its action is mainly through the estrogen receptor α.

The pubertal growth spurt coincides with the rise in the concentration of estradiol (FIG. 1). The crucial role of estrogen and not testosterone in this phenomenon is illustrated by the normal pubertal growth spurt of patients with the complete androgen insensitivity syndrome and the remarkable increase in growth velocity in boys (and girls) affected with the aromatase excess syndrome (in which plasma estradiol but not testosterone is elevated).

Jeffrey Baron's group in the Developmental Endocrinology Branch of this Institute has made a seminal contribution to our understanding of the processes of growth plate senescence and of epiphyseal fusion. Using as a model juvenile ovariectomized female rabbits, they showed that the growth plates of animals treated with estradiol exhibited an acceleration of the normal gradual senescent decline in the tibial growth rate, in the rate of chondrocyte proliferation, and in the number of proliferative and hypertrophic chondrocytes. Estrogen increased the *rate* of replicative senescence in the growth plate. Fusion of the epiphysis with the metaphysis appeared to be a consequence of the cessation of growth, not, as many held, the cause of it. We know little about the factors that regulate the control of the lifespan of the chondrocytes and their progenitors and that regulate cell cycle progression and differentiation. Estradiol, while inducing the pubertal spurt in linear growth, leads concurrently to the exhaustion of proliferation and to replicative senescence. This

TABLE 3. Potential use of aromatase inhibitors (or estrogen receptor antagonists) in disorders of growth and sexual maturation to restrain skeletal maturation

Growth disorders or variants of normal growth (to restrain epiphyseal maturation)

    Isolated growth hormone deficiency

    Genetic short stature/constitutional delay in growth

Sexual precocity

    Congenital virilizing adrenal hyperplasia in male and female

        To reduce dose of glucocorticoid

        To inhibit conversion of 19-carbon steroids to estrogens (or estrogen action)

        With/without use of CYP17 inhibitor or anti-androgen

    Testotoxicosis

        To inhibit conversion of 19-carbon steroids to estrogens (or estrogen action)

    McCune-Albright Syndrome

        To inhibit conversion of 19-carbon steroids to estrogens (or estrogen action)

Gynecomastia

    To inhibit estrogen synthesis (or estrogen action)

concept is consistent with the age-dependency of the duration of estrogen exposure to induce epiphyseal fusion. The younger the child when exposed to estrogen (and the lower the bone age), the more years will transpire before disappearance of the growth plate. I have been struck by the similarities of the effects of exogenous estrogen on deer antler growth and the inhibition of regeneration of antlers and the role of estradiol in epiphyseal fusion.

The critical role of estrogen in skeletal maturation has led to the proposal of new therapeutic approaches to the control of growth and bone maturation in a number of disorders of growth and puberty. These approaches aim to suppress estrogen synthesis action by the use of aromatase inhibitors or estrogen receptor antagonists (e.g., SERMS). In pubertal boys it may be possible to suppress skeletal maturation without interfering with the development of male secondary sexual characteristics (TABLE 3).

John Maynard Keyes once said, "The difficulty lies not so much in developing new ideas as in escaping from the old ones." Our discipline is escaping from a long held focus on testosterone as the *principal* sex steroid acting on the male skeleton.

In closing, I want to acknowledge the many contributions of my colleague Felix Conte and our former fellow, the late Akira Morishima; of Evan Simpson and his group, formerly of the University of Texas Southwestern Medical school; and of John Bilezikian of Columbia University College of Physicians and Surgeons, a long-time student of bone metabolism.

REFERENCES

1. BILEZIKIAN, J.P., A. MORISHIMA, J. BELL & M.M. GRUMBACH. 1998. Increased bone mass as a result of estrogen therapy in a man with aromatase deficiency. N. Engl. J. Med. **339:** 599–603.
2. CARANI, C., K. QIN, M. SIMONI, *et al.* 1997. Effect of testosterone and estradiol in a man with aromatase deficiency. N. Engl. J. Med. **337:** 91–95.
3. GRUMBACH, M.M. 2000. Estrogen, bone, growth, and sex: a sea change in conventional wisdom. J Pediatr Endocrinol Metab. **13** (Suppl. 6):1439–1455.
4. GRUMBACH, M.M. & R.J. AUCHUS. 1999. Estrogen: consequences and implications of human mutations in synthesis and action. J. Clin. Endocrinol. Metab. **84:** 4677–4694.
5. MORISHIMA, A., M.M. GRUMBACH, E.R. SIMPSON, *et al.* 1995. Aromatase deficiency in male and female siblings caused by a novel mutation and the physiological role of estrogens. J. Clin. Endocrinol. Metab. **80:** 3689–3698.
6. SMITH, E.P., J. BOYD, G.R. FRANK, *et al.* 1994. Estrogen resistance caused by a mutation in the estrogen-receptor in a man. N. Engl. J. Med. **331:** 1056–1061.
7. WEISE, M. S. DE-LEVI, K.M. BARNES, *et al.* 2001. Effects of estrogen on growth plate senescence and epiphyseal fusion. Proc. Natl. Acad. Sci. USA **98:** 6871–6876.

An Update of Congenital Adrenal Hyperplasia

MARIA I. NEW, MD

Professor, Department of Pediatrics, Director, Adrenal Steroid Disorders Program, Mount Sinai School of Medicine, New York, New York 10029, USA

ABSTRACT: Congenital adrenal hyperplasia (CAH) is a family of autosomal recessive disorders caused by mutations that encode for enzymes involved in one of the various steps of adrenal steroid synthesis. These defects result in the absence or the decreased synthesis of cortisol from its cholesterol precursor. The anterior pituitary secretes excess adrenocorticotrophic hormone (ACTH) via feedback regulation by cortisol, which results in overstimulation of the adrenals and causes hyperplasia. Symptoms due to CAH can vary from mild to severe depending on the degree of ensymatic defect. In the classical form of CAH, there is a severe enzymatic defect owing to mutations in the CYP21 gene. Classically affected female fetuses undergo virilization of the genitalia prenatally and present with genital ambiguity at birth; however, prenatal treatment of CAH with dexamethasone to prevent ambiguity has been successfully utilized for over a decade. In the less severe, late-onset form of CAH, prenatal virilization does not occur. The milder enzyme deficiency was termed nonclassical 21-hydroxylase deficiency (NC21OHD) in 1979 and was later found to be the most common autosomal recessive disorder in humans. Disease frequency of NC21OHD varies between ethnic groups with the highest ethnic-specific disease frequency in Ashkenazi Jews at 1/27. NC21OHD is diagnosed by serum elevations of 17-OHP that plot on a nomogram between the range for unaffected individuals and levels observed for classical CAH and is typically confirmed with molecular genetic analysis. Similar to classical CAH, nonclassical 21-hydroxylase deficiency may cause premature development of pubic hair, advanced bone age, acelerated linear growth velocity and diminished final height in both males and females. Severe cystic acne has also been attributed to nonclassical CAH. Women may present with symptoms of androgen excess, including hirsutism, temporal baldness, and infertility. Menarche in females may be normal or delayed and secondary

This presentation is a slightly modified version of a paper that appeared previously as the following chapter: NEW, M.I. & L. GHIZZONI. 1999. An update on congenital adrenal hyperplasia. *In* Pediatric Endocrinology, 3rd edit., pp. 305–320 (4th edit., pp. 175–192). F. Lifshitz, Ed. Marcel Dekker. New York.

Address for correspondence: Maria I. New, MD, Professor, Department of Pediatrics, Director, Adrenal Steroid Disorders Program, Mount Sinai School of Medicine, 1 Gustave L. Levy Place, Box 1198, New York, NY 10029. Voice: 212-241-7847; fax: (212) 241-5405.

maria.new@mssm.edu

Ann. N.Y. Acad. Sci. 1038: 14–43 (2004). © 2004 New York Academy of Sciences.
doi: 10.1196/annals.1315.009

amenorrhea is a frequent occurence. Polycystic ovary syndrome may also be seen in these patients. In males, early beard growth, acne, and growth spurt may prompt the diagnosis of NC21OHD. Although many males appear to be asymptomatic, they may present with oligozoospermia or diminished fertility. Individuals presenting to dermatology and infertility clinics with symptoms of hyperandrogenemia are rarely screened for NC21OHD. However, with hormonal and molecular genetic screening, previously undiagnosed patients may be identified and can therefore receive glucocorticoid treatment, which has been shown to reverse symptoms within 3 months.

KEYWORDS: congenital adrenal hyperplasia; CAH; steroid synthesis; 21-hydroxylase deficiency; salt-wasting

I. INTRODUCTION

Congenital adrenal hyperplasia (CAH) is a family of inherited disorders of adrenal steroidogenesis. With only one exception, each disorder results from a deficiency in one of the several enzymatic steps necessary for normal steroid synthesis. Since the earliest case of CAH documented in 1865 by the Neapolitan anatomist De Crecchio,[1] numerous investigators have unraveled the mechanisms of adrenal steroid synthesis and the associated enzyme defects responsible for the clinical syndromes.

II. PATHOPHYSIOLOGY

The adrenal glands synthesize three main classes of hormones: mineralocorticoids, glucocorticoids, and sex steroids. FIGURE 1 shows a simplified scheme of the adrenal synthesis of these steroids from the cholesterol precursor molecule. Each enzymatic step is indicated.

The pituitary regulates adrenal steroidogenesis via adrenocorticotropic hormone (ACTH). ACTH stimulates steroid synthesis by acting on the adrenals to increase the conversion of cholesterol to pregnenolone, the principal substrate for the steroidogenic pathways. The central nervous system controls the secretion of ACTH, its diurnal variation, and its increase in stress via corticotropin-releasing factor.[2,3] The hypothalamic-pituitary-adrenal feedback system is mediated through the circulating level of plasma cortisol; any condition that decreases cortisol secretion results in increased ACTH secretion. Cortisol therefore exerts a negative feedback effect on ACTH secretion.

In most forms of congenital adrenal hyperplasia, an enzyme defect blocks cortisol synthesis, thus impairing cortisol-mediated negative feedback control of ACTH secretion (FIG. 2). Oversecretion of ACTH ensues, which stimulates excessive synthesis of the adrenal products of those pathways

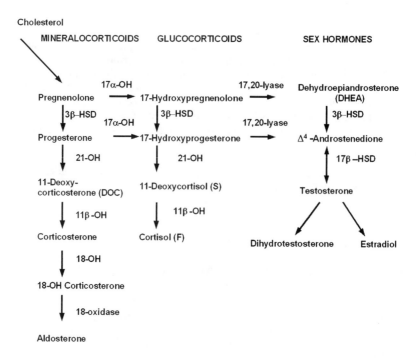

FIGURE 1. Simplified scheme of adrenal steroidogenesis showing abnormal secretion of hormones in congenital adrenal hyperplasia resulting from 21-hydroxylase deficiency. OH, hydroxylase; HSD, hydroxysteroid dehydrogenase.

unimpaired by an enzyme deficiency and causes an accumulation of precursor molecules in pathways blocked by an enzyme deficiency.

The clinical symptoms of the different forms of congenital adrenal hyperplasia result from the particular hormones that are deficient and those that are produced in excess. In the most common case, that of 21-hydroxylase deficiency, the aldosterone and cortisol pathways are blocked and the androgen pathway, which does not involve 21-hydroxylation, is overstimulated. The characteristic virilization caused by 21-hydroxylase deficiency is due to excessive secretion of adrenal androgens.

III. CLINICAL FEATURES

The most prominent clinical feature of 21-hydroxylase deficiency is virilization. Because adrenocortical function begins by month 3 of gestation, a fetus with 21-hydroxylase deficiency is exposed to oversecreted adrenal androgens at the critical time of sexual differentiation. In a female fetus, the

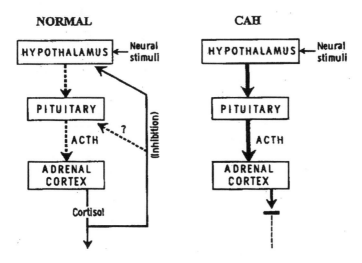

FIGURE 2. Regulation of cortisol secretion in normal subjects and in patients with congenital adrenal hyperplasia. (From Kutten,[133] with permission.)

excessive adrenal androgens masculinize the external genitalia and female pseudohermaphroditism results. In rare cases, the masculinization is so profound that the urethra is penile.[4] The internal genitalia (i.e., uterus and fallopian tubes), which arise from the müllerian ducts, are normal because the female fetus does not possess Sertoli cells of the testes, the source of müllerian-inhibiting factor. The female genital abnormalities are present only in the androgen-responsive external genitalia. Males with 21- hydroxylase deficiency do not manifest genital abnormalities at birth but may demonstrate hyperpigmentation.

The simple virilizing form of 21-hydroxylase deficiency is characterized by excess adrenal androgen secretion, which causes prenatal virilization of the genetic female and postnatal virilization of both boys and girls. In the salt-wasting form, in addition to the excess adrenal androgens, there is aldosterone deficiency causing low serum sodium, high serum potassium, and vascular collapse. In the more severe salt-wasting form, both newborn boys and girls are subject to life-threatening, salt-wasting crises within the first few weeks of life.

The various clinical and biochemical features associated with the different forms of congenital adrenal hyperplasia are indicated in TABLE 1. Continued oversecretion of adrenal androgens as a result of untreated 21-hydroxylase deficiency results in progressive penile or clitoral enlargement; advanced bone age and tall stature in early childhood with ultimate short stature caused by premature epiphyseal closure; early appearance of facial, axillary, and pubic hair; and acne. Girls with congenital adrenal hyperplasia who remain un-

TABLE 1. Clinical and laboratory features of various disorders of adrenal steroidogenesis

Deficiency (syndrome)	Genital ambiguity	Postnatal virilization	Salt metabolism	Diagnostic hormones	Treatment
21-Hydroxylase					
Classic					
Salt wasting	F	Yes	Salt wasting	17-Hydroxyprogesterone (17OHP) Δ^4-Androstenedione (Δ^4-A) Aldosterone	Hydrocortisone (HC), 15–20 mg/m^2/day orally (PO) and fludrocortisone acetate (9αFF), 0.05–0.2 mg/day PO
Simple virilizing (SV)	F	Yes	Normal (↑renin)	17-OHP, Δ^4-A	HC (same; addition of (9αFF) if ↑renin
Nonclassic (symptomatic and asymptomatic)	No	Yes	Normal	17-OHP, Δ^4-A	HC, 10–15 mg/m^2/day or dexamethasone, 0.25–0.5 mg/day h.s., or prednisone 5–10 mg/day
3β-Hydroxysteroid dehydrogenase					
Classic	M (±F)	Yes	Salt wasting	17-OHP 17-Hydroxypregnenolone (Δ^5 17-OHP) Dehydroepiandrosterone (DHEA) Δ^4-A	HC and 9αFF as for SW 21-hydroxylase deficiency
Nonclassic	No	Yes	Normal	17-OHP:DHEA	HC as for nonclassic 21-hydroxylase deficiency

TABLE 1. *(continued)* **Clinical and laboratory features of various disorders of adrenal steroidogenesis**

Deficiency (syndrome)	Genital ambiguity	Postnatal virilization	Salt metabolism	Diagnostic hormones	Treatment
11β-Hydroxylase					
Classic (hypertensive CAH)	F	Yes	Salt retention (PRA↓)	Deoxycorticosterone (DOC) 11-Deoxycortisol (S) Δ^4-A Plasma renin activity	HC, 15–20 mg/m^2/day
Nonclassic	No	Yes	Normal	S; DOC	HC, dexamethasone or prednisone as for nonclassic 21-hydroxylase deficiency
17α-Hydroxylase/ 17,20-lyase	M	No	Salt retention (PRA↓)	DOC Corticosterone (B)	HC, 15–20 mg/m^2/day[a]
Steroidogenic acute regulatory protein (StAR; congenital lipoid hyperplasia)	M	No	Salt wasting	None	HC, 15–20 mg/m^2/day 9αFF, 0.05–0.2 mg/day[a]

[a]With addition of sex steroid replacement at puberty.

TABLE 2. Comparison of classic and nonclassic 21-hydroxylase deficiency

Feature	Classic	Nonclassic
Disease frequency	1:14,000	1:100 all Caucasians 1:27 Ashkenazi Jews
Prenatal virilization	Females	No
Postnatal virilization	Males and females	Variable
Salt wasting	60-75% cases	No
17-Hydroxyprogesterone levels after ACTH challenge	Extreme elevation (>20,000 ng/dl)	Moderate elevation (2,000 - 15,000 ng/dl)
Genotype of CYP21	Severely affected allele/ severely affected allele	Mildly affected allele/ mildly affected allele; or severely affected allele/ mildly affected allele
Associated HLA haplotype	B47;DR7	B14;DR1
Common Mutations:		
Simple virilizing	I172N Intron 2, A → G	V281L P30L P453S
Salt-wasting	Deletion Lg. conversion Intron 2, A → G Exon 3, -8 bp Codons 234-238 Q318 → Stop codon R356W	

treated do not develop breasts or menstruate and are further virilized. In untreated boys, the testes may remain small and there may be infertility, although some untreated men have been fertile.[5]

IV. CLINICAL FORMS OF ADRENAL HYPERPLASIA CAUSED BY 21-HYDROXYLASE DEFICIENCY

Two major phenotypes are recognized in 21-hydroxylase deficiency: classic and nonclassic (late onset; FIG. 3). Within the latter class of patients are those who demonstrate the biochemical defect but lack any overt stigmata of hyperandrogenism. TABLE 2 delineates the differences between classic and nonclassic 21-hydroxylase deficiency.

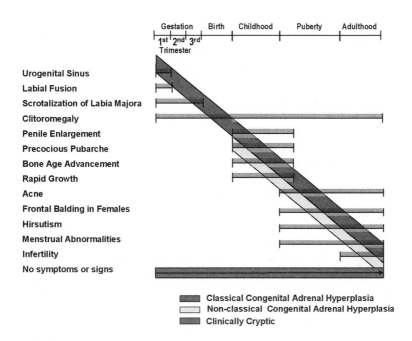

FIGURE 3. Clinical spectrum of steroid 21-hydroxylase deficiency. There is a wide spectrum of clinical presentation in 21-hydroxylase deficiency, ranging from prenatal virilization with labial fusion to precocious adrenarche, to pubertal or postpubertal virilization. During their lifetimes, patients may change from symptomatic to asymptomatic. (From M.I. New, B. Dupont, K. Grumbach & L.S. Levine. 1983. *In* The Metabolic Basis of Inherited Disease, 5th edit. J.B. Stanbury, J.B. Wyngaarden, *et al.*, Eds.: 973–1000. McGraw-Hill. New York. Used with permission.)

A. Classic

Classic congenital adrenal hyperplasia is a well-known genetic disorder transmitted by an autosomal recessive gene. The biochemical and clinical abnormalities of this form of CAH are clearly present in patients both prenatally and postnatally. Progesterone, 17-OH-progesterone, androstenedione, and testosterone are secreted in excess, consequent to increased ACTH stimulation resulting from an inherited 21-hydroxylase deficiency that impairs cortisol synthesis.[14–21] As expected, the urinary excretion of the metabolites of these steroids is also increased.[22,23] Abnormalities in cortisol secretion are also associated with alterations in the secretion of other pituitary hormones such as GH and TSH.[24,25]

In genetic females with congenital 21-hydroxylase deficiency, the developing fetus is exposed to the excessive adrenal androgens, equivalent to the
male fetal level, secreted by the hyperplastic adrenal cortex. External genitalia in the genetic female range from mildly ambiguous to completely virilized. The internal genitalia (uterus and fallopian tubes) are not affected by the
excess androgens. Boys with 21-hydroxylase deficiency do not manifest genital abnormalities at birth. Postnatally, in untreated boys and girls, continued
excessive androgen production results in rapid somatic growth, advanced epiphyseal maturation, progressive penile or clitoral enlargement, early appearance of facial, axillary, and pubic hair, and acne. Without treatment, early
epiphyseal closure and short stature result.[26]

In three-quarters of cases with classic 21-hydroxylase deficiency, salt
wasting occurs, as defined by hyponatremia, hyperkalemia, inappropriate
natriuresis, and low serum and urinary aldosterone with concomitantly high
plasma renin activity (PRA). The increase in the proportion of salt-wasting
cases in recent years may be attributed in part to enhanced ascertainment because of advancements in diagnostic capabilities, as well as increased survival because of the availability of exogenous mineralocorticoid supplements.
Salt wasting results from inadequate secretion of salt-retaining steroids, especially aldosterone. In addition, hormonal precursors of 21-hydroxylase
may act as mineralocorticoid antagonists in the marginally competent sodi-
um-conserving mechanism of the immature newborn renal tubule.[27–29] It has
been observed that an aldosterone biosynthetic defect apparent in infancy
may be ameliorated with age [30,31] and a spontaneous partial recovery from
salt wasting in adulthood was described in a patient with severe salt wasting
in infancy. This variation in the ability to produce mineralocorticoids may be
attributable to another adrenal enzyme with 21-hydroxylase activity.[32] Therefore, it is desirable to follow the sodium and mineralocorticoid requirements
carefully by measuring plasma renin activity in patients who have been labeled neonatally as salt wasters.

Although it has been claimed that salt wasting correlates with severe virilism,[33] it is important to recognize that the extent of virilism may be the same
in simple virilizing and salt-wasting CAH. Thus, even a mildly virilized newborn with 21-hydroxylase deficiency should be observed carefully for signs
of a potentially life-threatening crisis within the first few weeks of life.

B. Nonclassic 21-Hydroxylase Deficiency

An attenuated, late-onset form of adrenal hyperplasia was first suspected by
gynecologists in clinical practice who used glucocorticoids for the treatment
of women with physical signs of hyperandrogenism, including infertility.[34,35]
The first documentation of suppression of 21-hydroxylase precursors in the
urine of such individuals after glucocorticoid therapy was by Baulieu and co-

workers in 1957.[36] The precise diagnosis of a mild 21-hydroxylase defect was made possible when a radioimmunoassay for 17-hydroxyprogesterone (17-OHP) the direct precursor of the enzyme in the adrenal zona fasciculata, was developed.[37] The autosomal recessive mode of genetic transmission of the nonclassic form of 21-hydroxylase deficiency (NC21-OHD) became apparent through family studies of classic 21-OHD.[38-40] The establishment of linkage to HLA[41,42] confirmed the existence of this disorder as an allele of classic 21-OHD.[38,43] The HLA associations for nonclassic 21-OHD[41,44,45] are distinct from those found in classical 21-OHD and differ according to ethnicity.[42,46,47]

The clinical symptomatology of NC21-OHD is variable and may present at any age. NC21-OHD can result in premature development of pubic hair in children; to our knowledge, the youngest such patient was noted to have pubic hair at 6 months of age.[39] In a review of 23 cases presenting for evaluation of premature pubarche, 7 children demonstrated a 17-OHP response to ACTH stimulation consistent with the diagnosis of nonclassic 21-hydroxylase deficiency, a prevalence of 30% in this preselected group of pediatric patients at high risk.[48] Other investigators found 7 of 46 children (15%) with premature pubarche demonstrating an ACTH-stimulated 17-OHP response greater than that of obligate heterozygote carriers of the 21-hydroxylase deficiency gene.[49] Elevated adrenal androgens promote the early fusion of epiphyseal growth plates, and it is common, but not universally found, that children with the disorder have advanced bone age and accelerated linear growth velocity, and ultimately are shorter than the height that might be predicted based on mid-parental height and on linear growth percentiles before the apparent onset of excess androgen secretion.[50]

Severe cystic acne refractory to oral antibiotics and retinoic acid has been attributed to NC21-OHD. In one study of 31 young female patients with acne and/or hirsutism tested with low dose ACTH stimulation after overnight dexamethasone suppression, no cases of 21-hydroxylase deficiency were found.[51] In another study comparing the responses of 11 female patients with acne and 8 (female) control subjects to a 24 h infusion of ACTH, elevated urinary excretion of pregnanetriol in 6 patients was suggestive of a partial 21-hydroxylase deficiency.[52]

Additionally, male pattern baldness in young women with this disorder has been noted as the sole presenting symptom. Severe androgenic alopecia in association with marked virilization has also been reported in an undiagnosed and therefore untreated 59-year-old woman with the simple virilizing form of the disease.[53] Menarche may be normal or delayed, and secondary amenorrhea is a frequent occurrence. The syndrome of polycystic ovarian disease includes a subgroup of women with NC21-OHD. The pathophysiology of this phenomenon probably relates to adrenal sex steroid excess disrupting the usual cyclicity of gonadotropin release and/or the direct effects of adrenal androgens upon the ovary, leading ultimately to the formation of ovarian cysts, which then may autonomously produce androgens.

TABLE 3. Frequency of nonclassic 21-hydroxylase deficiency

Ethnic group	Frequency
Ashkenazi Jewish	1:27
Hispanic	1:53
Slavic	1:63
Italian	1:333
General Caucasian population	1:100

Data obtained from Speiser et al.[46]

Retrospective analysis of the etiologies of hirsutism and oligomenorrhea revealed that 16 of 108 (14%) of young women presenting to this institution for endocrinologic evaluation of these complaints had nonclassic 21-hydroxylase deficiency.[54] In other published series the prevalence of nonclassic 21-hydroxylase deficiency in hirsute, oligomenorrheic women ranges from 1.2% to 30%.[55–59] The disparity in frequency of nonclassic 21-hydroxylase deficiency reported by different authors may be attributed to differences in the ethnic groups studied because the disease frequency is ethnic specific (TABLE 3).

In boys, early beard growth, acne, and growth spurt may be detected. A highly reliable constellation of physical signs of adrenal (as opposed to testicular) androgen excess in boys is the presence of pubic hair, enlarged phallus, and relatively small testes. In men, signs of androgen excess are difficult to appreciate and may theoretically be manifest only by short stature and/or adrenal sex steroid-induced suppression of the hypothalamic-pituitary-gonadal axis, resulting in diminished fertility.

Oligospermia and subfertility have been reported in men with nonclassic 21-hydroxylase deficiency.[60,61] Reversal of infertility with glucocorticoid treatment in three men has been observed.[61–63]

The presence of 21-hydroxylase deficiency can be discovered during the evaluation of incidental adrenal masses.[64] An increased incidence of adrenal incidentalomas has in fact been found in male and female patients with homozygous congenital adrenal hyperplasia (82%) and also in the heterozygote subjects (45%), probably arising from hyperplastic tissue areas and not requiring surgical intervention.[65]

A subset of NC-21OHD individuals are overtly asymptomatic when detected (usually as part of a family study), but it is thought, based on longitudinal follow-up of such patients, that symptoms of hyperandrogenism may wax and wane with time. The gene defect in these so-called cryptic 21-hydroxylase deficient subjects is the same as that found in symptomatic nonclassic patients.

V. PUBERTAL MATURATION IN CLASSICAL CONGENITAL ADRENAL HYPERPLASIA

A. Onset of Puberty

In most patients treated satisfactorily from early life, the onset of puberty in both girls and boys with classic CAH occurs at the expected chronological age.[66–69] The pattern of gonadotropin response to luteinizing hormone-releasing hormone (LHRH) is appropriate for age in prepubertal and pubertal girls with well-controlled CAH.[70,71] Physiologic secretion of gonadotropins, however, may not be entirely normal.[72,73]

True precocious puberty may occur in some well-treated children with CAH, perhaps correlated with bone age. Another setting in which central puberty sometimes occurs in CAH is after initiation of glucocorticoid therapy, producing a sudden decrease in sex steroid levels and leading to hypothalamic activation. LHRH analogs may be employed as an adjunct to therapy with hydrocortisone in such children.[74] Long-term data on final height in a small number of CAH patients suggest that LHRH analogs[75,76] along with growth hormone treatment[77] are not only effective in arresting the pubertal process but also improve final height.

In most untreated or poorly treated adolescent girls and in some adolescent boys, spontaneous true pubertal development does not occur until proper treatment is instituted (TABLE 4).[67,68,78–80] Studies suggest that excess adrenal androgens (aromatized to estrogens) inhibit the pubertal pattern of gonadotropin secretion by the hypothalamic-pituitary axis.[67] The inhibition probably occurs via a negative feedback effect; whether it is primarily at the

TABLE 4. Pubertal disorders in 21-hydroxylase deficiency CAH

Puberty	Classic: Abnormal (poorly treated or untreated)	Classic: Normal	Nonclassic: Abnormal	Cryptic: Normal
Girls	No thelarche; no menarche; secondary amenorrhea or menstrual irregularity; cystic ovaries, anovulation, infertility	None reported	Precocious adrenarche, hirsutism, cystic acne; amenorrhea or menstrual irregularity; anovulation, infertility, cystic ovaries	No abnormalities
Boys	Small testes[a] Decreased spermatogenesis	Normal testicular size Spermatogenesis	Precocious adrenarche Cystic acne	No abnormalities

[a]Adolescent males may have nodular testes as a result of adrenal rest tumor

hypothalamus or pituitary is not known. This inhibition is reversible by suppression of the adrenal hormone production by glucocorticoid treatment.

Following gonadarche, in a majority of successfully treated patients, the milestones of further development of secondary sex characteristics in general appear to be normal,[66,69] although a somewhat delayed sequence of pubertal events was present in girls.[66]

B. Menstrual Disorders

Many patients with treated classic CAH have regular menses after menarche.[67,68,81] However, expected age at menarche of treated CAH patients from various clinics suggests that menarche was significantly delayed, especially when those patients who were not menstruating after 16 years of age were included. Menarche was not observed in untreated patients, only in patients who had received suppressive glucocorticoid treatment.[66–69,82,83]

Menstrual irregularity and secondary amenorrhea with or without hirsutism are not uncommon complications in postmenarchal girls[5,68,69,82,84,85] These menstrual abnormalities have been found frequently in patients with inadequately controlled disease (TABLE 4).[66,67,69,81,82,85] Several studies subsequently reported menarche or the normalization of the menstrual cycle following adequate suppression of adrenal sex steroids with long-acting and more potent glucocorticoid treatment.[82,85,86] Delayed menarche or even primary amenorrhea may result from poor treatment or overtreatment. In poorly treated patients, the mechanism for delayed menarche may be interference by adrenal sex steroids in the cyclicity of the hypothalamic-pituitary-ovarian axis.[66,67] The delayed menarche in patients who are overtreated may be related to the delay in bone age and general maturation known to occur with excessive glucocorticoid treatment.[66]

Many treated women have had successful pregnancies with the delivery of a normal, healthy, full-term infant.[67,87,88] A recent study reports successful pregnancy outcomes in four women with classic CAH (1 simple virilizing and 3 salt wasting).[89] All four glucocorticoid-treated mothers delivered unaffected and non-virilized females. Additionally, a retrospective survey of fertility rates in a large group of women affected with 21-hydroxylase deficiency showed that simple virilizers were more likely than salt wasters to become pregnant and carry the pregnancy to term.[90] Adequacy of glucocorticoid therapy is probably an important variable with respect to fertility outcome.[91] Among all patients questioned, only 50% reported that the vaginal introitus was adequate for intercourse; 5% reported homosexual preference, and 38% had no sexual experience. Based on these data, it seems prudent to perform early surgical correction of clitoromegaly but to delay vaginoplasty until adolescence (when the patient can be expected to assume responsibility for vaginal dilatation and strict adherence to medical therapy).

The clinical observation of gonadal function as described earlier clearly suggests that excess adrenal sex steroid production is the major contributing factor to gonadal dysfunction, menstrual disorders, anovulation, and infertility in girls with classic CAH. The generally accepted theory is that the excessive adrenal androgens may disrupt gonadotropin secretion, leading ultimately to hypogonadism.[69,72,79,83]

C. Male Reproductive Function

Several long-term studies indicate that in a majority of successfully treated male patients with CAH, pubertal development, normal testicular function, and normal spermatogenesis and fertility occur.[5,68,69,92–94] However, complications of small testes and aspermia have been reported in some patients with inadequately controlled disease.[5,68,80,95] In contrast to this observation, some investigators have reported normal testicular maturation and normal spermatogenesis and fertility in patients who had never received glucocorticoid treatment[5,78,93,96,97] or in those whose glucocorticoid therapy was discontinued for several years.[5,9] Thus, male patients with CAH and excessive adrenal androgens may have either normal gonadal function or hypogonadism. The factors resulting in such a disparity in puberty among patients with the same disorder are not known. Some patients with normal gonadal function may have nonclassic rather than classic CAH (see later). Hormonal studies in untreated classic patients with normal sexual maturation have shown either normal or increased gonadotropin production[98] or concentrations and follicle-stimulating hormone excretion.[5,93,98] Of great interest is that in these male patients, excess adrenal sex steroids or their precursor steroids did not seem to affect gonadotropin secretion. Adrenal androgen levels in untreated boys with normal gonadal function did not appear to be lower than those patients with gonadal dysfunction in poor control.[5,68,95] This suggests that adrenal androgens alone have no effect on gonadotropin secretion via a negative feedback mechanism in male patients.

Another frequently reported complication in postpubertal boys with inadequate control of CAH is hyperplastic nodular testes. Almost all patients with such complications were found to have adenomatous adrenal rests within the testicular tissue, as indicated by the presence of specific 11β-hydroxylated steroids in the blood from gonadal veins.[99] These tumors have been reported to be ACTH dependent and to regress following adequate steroid therapy.[100–106]

VI. GENETICS

Studies of families carrying 21-hydroxylase deficiency have demonstrated that the disease locus is situated in the HLA major histocompatibility com-

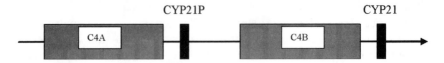

FIGURE 4. Diagram of *CYP21* region on chromosome 6p21.3. *CYP21P*, 21-hydroxylase pseudogene; *C4A* and *C4B*, genes encoding fourth component of serum complement. The arrow indicates the direction of transcription.

plex on the short arm of the sixth chromosome.[107,108] Both classic and non-classic 21-hydroxylase deficiency are transmitted as recessive traits. Characteristic combinations of HLA alleles, or HLA haplotypes, are associated with different forms of 21-hydroxylase deficiency. The genotype for classic 21-hydroxylase deficiency results from the presence of two severely affected alleles and nonclassic 21-hydroxylase deficiency results from the presence of either two mild 21-hydroxylase deficiency alleles or one severe and one mild allele.[109]

Based on estimates of its frequency among Ashkenazi Jews (3%) and all ethnic whites (individuals of mainly European descent) (1%),[46] it is apparent that nonclassic 21-hydroxylase deficiency is among the most frequent human autosomal recessive disorders. Molecular genetic studies have demonstrated that the gene encoding the cytochrome P_{450} enzyme specific for 21-hydroxylation (P450c21) is located in the HLA complex between the genes encoding the transplantation antigens, HLA-B and HLA-DR. This gene, *CYP21*, and an inactive homolog or pseudogene, *CYP21P*, are immediately adjacent to the *C4B* and *C4A* genes encoding the fourth component of serum complement.[110,111] (FIG. 4) The protein-encoding sequence of *CYP21P* is 98% homologous to that of *CYP21*. The high degree of homology permits two types of mutation causing recombination events:

    (1) unequal crossing over during meiosis that results in complementary deletions/duplications of *CYP21*(112, 113), and

    (2) non-correspondences between the pseudogene and the coding gene that, if transferred by gene conversion, result in deleterious mutations.[114]

Approximately 25% of classic 21-hydroxylase deficiency alleles result from deletions of *CYP21*.[115–117] The remaining three-quarters of classic alleles are caused by smaller mutations in *CYP21*, some of which are *de novo* point mutations resulting in amino acid substitutions[118–121] that significantly disrupt synthesis of the protein. Nonclassic 21-OHD is associated with conservative (or mild) amino acid substitutions in highly conserved portions of the gene encoding the active 21-hydroxylase.[122–124]

In studies evaluating the phenotype-genotype relationship, there is generally a good correlation between the severity of the clinical disease and the discrete mutations observed.[118,125] Recent studies, however, have demonstrated that there is often a divergence in phenotypes within mutation-identical groups, the reason for which requires further investigation.[126,127]

VII. EPIDEMIOLOGY

Screening studies indicate that the worldwide incidence of classic 21-OHD is 1:14,199 live births,[128] of which approximately 75% are salt wasters. The frequency of nonclassic 21-OHD is considerably higher; based on population genetic studies this allelic variant occurs in 1:100 persons in the general white population and in higher frequency among selected ethnic groups, most notably Ashkenazi Jews.[46]

VIII. DIAGNOSIS

Congenital adrenal hyperplasia must be suspected in infants born with ambiguous genitalia. The physician is obliged to make the diagnosis as quickly as possible, to initiate therapy, and to arrest the effects of the enzyme disorders. The diagnosis and a rational decision of sex assignment must rely on the determination of genetic sex, the hormonal determination of the specific deficient enzyme, and an assessment of the patient's potential for future sexual activity and fertility. Physicians are urged to recognize the physical findings of ambiguous genitalia characteristic of congenital adrenal hyperplasia in newborns and to refer such cases to appropriate clinics for full endocrine evaluation.

As indicated in TABLE 1, each form of congenital adrenal hyperplasia has its own unique hormonal profile, consisting of elevated levels of precursors and elevated or diminished levels of adrenal steroid products.[20,21] Traditionally, laboratory tests have measured the urinary excretion of adrenal hormones or their urinary metabolites (e.g., 17-ketosteroids). Collection of 24 h urine excretion may be difficult, however, and the results in neonates may often be misleading.[21] The development of simple and reliable radioimmunoassays for circulating serum levels of adrenal steroids is a significant advance in the laboratory diagnostic technique.[20] The direct serum measurement of accumulated precursors and oversecreted adrenal steroids, such as 17-hydroxyprogesterone, Δ4-androstenedione, and dehydroepiandrosterone is now possible, and more exact hormonal profiles of the different forms of congenital adrenal hyperplasia have been established (TABLE 1).

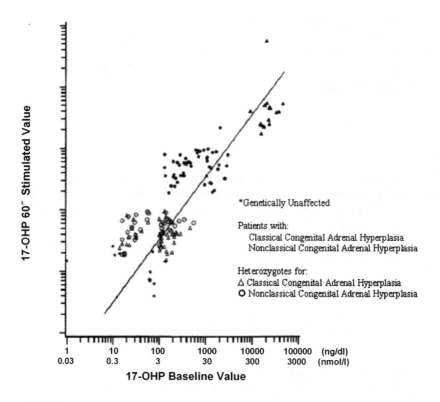

FIGURE 5. Nomogram relating baseline to ACTH-stimulated serum concentrations of 17-hydroxyprogesterone (17-OHP). The scales are logarithmic. A regression line for all data points is shown.

A. Hormonal Standards for Genotyping 21-Hydroxylase Deficiency

In our experience, the best diagnostic hormonal test for 21-hydroxylase deficiency has proven to be an ACTH (Cortrosyn, 0.25 mg) stimulation test measuring the serum concentration of 17-OHP at 0 and 60 minutes after intravenous bolus ACTH administration.[131] The nomogram (FIG. 5) provides hormonal standards for assignment of the 21-hydroxylase genotype, that is, patients whose hormonal values fall on the regression line within a defined group are assigned to this group. Because of the diurnal variation in 17-OHP, an early morning serum concentration of 17-OHP may be useful as a screening test for genotyping 21-OHD. In addition, early morning salivary 17-OHP has proven to be an excellent screening test for the nonclassic form.[132] ACTH stimulation, however, remains the most definitive diagnostic test.[59,132,133] It is important to note that the ACTH stimulation test should not be performed during the initial 24 hours of life as samples from this period are typically elevated in all infants and may yield false-positive results.

Diagnosis of 21-hydroxylase deficiency can also be made by microfilter paper radioimmunoassay for 17-hydroxyprogesterone; this has been useful as a rapid screening test for congenital adrenal hyperplasia in newborns.[19] This convenient test requires only 20 μL blood, obtained by heel prick and blotted on microfilter paper, to provide a reliable diagnostic measurement of 17-hydroxyprogesterone, a cortisol precursor that accumulates in elevated concentrations in 21-hydroxylase deficiency. The simplicity of the test and the ease of transporting microfilter paper specimens through the mail has facilitated the implementation of many congenital adrenal hyperplasia newborn screening programs in the United States and worldwide.

B. Prenatal Diagnosis and Treatment

Prenatal diagnosis and treatment of 21-hydroxylase deficiency has been utilized for over 15 years and is appropriate in families where a previous family member has been affected.[134] Dexamethasone (20 μg/kg/day in 3 divided doses) is administered to the pregnant mother before the 9th week of gestation, or ideally before the 7th week, blind to the sex or affected status of the fetus. This suppresses excess adrenal androgen secretion and prevents virilization should the fetus be an affected female. As the urogenital sinus formation begins at approximately the ninth week of gestation,[135] prenatal treatment must begin as soon as the pregnancy is confirmed in order to prevent virilization of external genitalia in the affected female. Dexamethasone is used because it crosses the placenta, crossing from the maternal to the fetal circulation.

Prenatal diagnosis by DNA analysis[136,137] requires chorionic villus sampling in approximately the 9th week of gestation. Amniotic fluid cells obtained by amniocentesis in the 16th–20th week of gestation may also be used for DNA analysis. If the fetus is determined to be a male upon karyotype or an unaffected female upon DNA analysis, treatment is discontinued. Otherwise, treatment is continued to term. This is the first instance of an inborn metabolic disorder to be successfully treated prenatally. The largest human studies have found that dexamethasone administered in proper doses at or before the 9th week of gestation is effective in reducing virilization in the genetic female so that genitoplasty was not needed in the majority of cases (FIG. 6).[138–140]

Since prenatal treatment became available, the majority of studies have proven it to be effective and safe for both mother and child, provided patients and physicians adhere to the recommended therapeutic protocol.[140] Some results from animal studies, in which excess glucocorticoid dosages were used, suggest there are maternal complications of glucocorticoid treatment.[141]

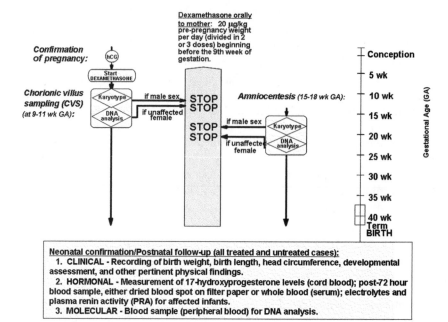

FIGURE 6. Algorithm depicting prenatal management of pregnancy in families at risk for a fetus affected with 21-hydroxylase deficiency. (From Mercado et al.,[142] with permission.)

However, results from one of the largest studies in humans, indicate there are no enduring maternal complications (i.e., edema, striae, excessive weight gain, spontaneous abortion).[140] In fact, all maternal complications disappeared after delivery and all mothers contacted (save three, who did not desire another child) stated that they would repeat their care with dexamethasone if they were pregnant again.

IX. TREATMENT

In ambiguous genitalia caused by congenital adrenal hyperplasia, appropriate surgical repair may be made once a sex assignment has been made based on a reliable diagnosis of the underlying enzyme disorder. In female pseudohermaphroditism caused by 21-hydroxylase deficiency, the aim of surgical repair should be to remove the redundant erectile tissue, preserve the sexually sensitive glans clitoris, and provide a normal vaginal orifice that functions adequately for menstruation, intromission, and delivery.[142] Because of the normal internal genitalia in these patients, normal puberty, fertility, and childbearing are possible when there is early therapeutic intervention.

The aim of endocrine therapy is to replace the deficient hormones. In 21-hydroxylase deficiencies, replacing cortisol both corrects the deficiency in cortisol secretion and suppresses ACTH overproduction. Proper replacement prevents excessive stimulation of the androgen pathway preventing further virilization and allowing normal growth and a normal onset of puberty.

Better understanding of the role of the renin-angiotensin system in congenital adrenal hyperplasia has made better therapeutic control of this condition possible. In addition to hypothalamic-pituitary regulation of adrenal steroidogenesis, the renin-angiotensin system exerts a primary influence on the adrenal secretion of aldosterone. The juxtaglomerular apparatus of the kidney secretes the enzyme renin in response to the state of electrolyte balance and plasma volume. Renin initiates a series of reactions that produce angiotensin II, a potent stimulator of aldosterone secretion.[143]

Although aldosterone levels are not deficient in the simple virilizing form of 21-hydroxylase deficiency, plasma renin activity is commonly elevated in the simple virilizing as well as in the salt-wasting forms.[144] Despite elevated plasma renin activity, it has not been customary to supplement conventional glucocorticoid replacement therapy with the administration of salt-retaining steroids in simple virilizing 21-hydroxylase deficiency. However, Rosler *et al.* have demonstrated that adding salt-retaining hormone to glucocorticoid therapy in patients with classic simple virilizing CAH with elevated plasma renin activity in fact improves the hormonal control of the disease.[145] When plasma renin activity was normalized by the addition of 9α-fludrocortisone acetate, a salt-retaining steroid, the ACTH level also fell and excessive androgen secretion decreased. The addition of salt-retaining steroids to the therapeutic regimen often made possible a decrease in the glucocorticoid dosage. Normalization of plasma renin activity also resulted in improved statural growth.

Steroid radioimmunoassay methods have been an asset not only for the initial diagnosis of congenital adrenal hyperplasia, but also for improved monitoring of hormonal control once therapy has been instituted. Studies indicate that serum 17-hydroxyprogesterone and androstenedione levels provide the most sensitive index of biochemical control. In girls and prepubertal boys (but not in newborn and pubertal boys), the serum testosterone level is also a useful index.[20] The combined determination of plasma renin activity, 17-hydroxyprogesterone, and serum androgens, as well as the clinical assessment of growth and pubertal development, must all be considered in adjusting the dosage of glucocorticoid and salt-retaining steroid. Recently, 3α-androstenediol (3AG) has been proposed as a useful serum metabolic marker of integrated adrenal androgen secretion in CAH patients. However, whether serum 3AG determinations would be useful for therapeutic monitoring of CAH requires further long-term study.[146] Both in our clinic and in others,

combinations of hydrocortisone and 9α-fludrocortisone acetate have proven
to be highly effective treatment modalities.[147] Monitoring of plasma renin
activity is also a useful index of hormonal control in other forms of congenital adrenal hyperplasia.

X. CONCLUSION

Abnormalities of sexual differentiation and development or severe salt-wasting (associated with 21-hydroxylase), are clinical hallmarks of congenital adrenal hyperplasia. The pathophysiology can be traced to discrete, inherited defects in the genes encoding enzymes for adrenal steroidogenesis. Treatment of CAH is targeted to replace the hormones that are produced in insufficient quantity. With proper hormone replacement therapy, normal and healthy development may often be expected. Radioimmunoassay of serum and urinary steroid levels permit reliable diagnosis of the various forms of congenital adrenal hyperplasia. Prenatal diagnosis and therapy are possible in 21-hydroxylase deficiency.

The most common form of CAH, 21-hydroxylase deficiency, has served as a prototype for examination of the molecular genetic basis of phenotypic diversity. Similar studies in other enzymatic defects are now in progress.

REFERENCES

1. DE CRECCHIO, L. 1865. Sopra un caso di apparenzi virili in una donna. Morgagni 7: 154–188.
2. GANONG, W. 1963. The central nervous system and the synthesis and release of adrenocorticotrophic hormone. In Advances in Neuroendocrinology. A. Nalbandov, Ed.: 92. University of Illinois Press. Urbana.
3. GUILLEMIN, R. & A. SCHALLY. 1963. Recent advances in the chemistry of neuroendocrine mediators originating in the central nervous system. In Advances in Neuroendocrinology. A. Nalbandov, Ed.: 314. University of Illinois Press. Urbana.
4. WILKINS, L. 1962. Adrenal disorders. II. Congenital virilizing adrenal hyperplasia. Arch. Dis. Child 37: 231.
5. PRADER, A., M. ZACHMANN & R. ILLIG. 1977. Normal spermatogenesis in adult males with congenital adrenal hyperplasia after discontinuation of therapy. In Congenital Adrenal Hyperplasia. P. Lee, L. Platnick, A. Kowarski & C. Migeo, Eds.: 397. University Park Press. Baltimore.
6. SIMARD, J., E. RHEAUME, F. MEBARKI, et al. 1995. Molecular basis of human 3 beta-hydroxysteroid dehydrogenase deficiency. J. Steroid Biochem. Mol. Biol. 53: 127–138.
7. MOISAN, A., M. RICKETTS, V. TARDY, et al. 1999. New insight into the molecular basis of 3beta-hydroxysteroid dehydrogenase deficiency: identification of eight mutations in the HSD3B2 gene eleven patients from seven new families

and comparison of the functional properties of twenty-five mutant enzymes. J. Clin. Endocrinol. Metab. **84:** 4410–4425.

8. ZERAH, M., E. RHEAUME, P. MANI, *et al.* 1994. No evidence of mutations in the genes for type I and type II 3 beta-hydroxysteroid dehydrogenase (3 beta HSD) in nonclassical 3 beta HSD deficiency. J. Clin. Endocrinol. Metab. **79:** 1811–1817.

9. TAJIMA, T., Y. NISHI, A. TAKASE, *et al.* 1997. No genetic mutation in type II 3 beta-hydroxysteroid dehydrogenase gene in patients with biochemical evidence of enzyme deficiency. Horm. Res. **47:** 49–53.

10. YANASE, T., E. SIMPSON & M. WATERMAN. 1991. 17 alpha-hydroxylase/17,20-lyase deficiency: from clinical investigation to molecular definition. Endocrin. Rev. **12:** 91–108.

11. LIN, D., T. SUGAWARA, J.F. STRAUSS 3rd, *et al.* 1995. Role of steroidogenic acute regulatory protein in adrenal and gonadal steroidogenesis. Science **267:** 1821–1831.

12. BOSE, H., T. SUGAWARA, J.F. STRAUSS 3rd & W. MILLER. 1996. The pathophysiology and genetics of congenital lipoid adrenal hyperplasia. International Congenital Lipoid Adrenal Hyperplasia Consortium. N. Engl. J. Med. **335:** 1870–1878.

13. STOCCO, D. & B. CLARK. 1997. The role of the steroidogenic acute regulatory protein in steroidogenesis. Steroids **62:** 29–36.

14. LEVINE, L.S., M.I. NEW, P. PITT & R.E. PETERSON. 1972. Androgen production in boys with sexual precocity and congenital adrenal hyperplasia. Metabolism **21:** 457–464.

15. LIPPE, B., F.S. LA, N. LAVIN, *et al.* 1974. Serum 17-alpha-hydroxyprogesterone, progesterone, estradiol, and testosterone in the diagnosis and management of congenital adrenal hyperplasia. J. Pediatr. **85:** 782–787.

16. JANNE, O., J. PERHEENTUPA, L. VIINIKKA & R. VIHKO. 1975. Plasma pregnenolone, progesterone, 17-hydroxyprogesterone, testosterone and 5alpha-dihydrotestosterone in different types of congenital adrenal hyperplasia. Clin. Endocrinol. (Oxf) **4:** 39–48.

17. SOLOMON, I., E. SCHOEN, L. DONELAN & D. BRANDT-ERICHSEN. 1975. Blood testosterone values in patients with congenital virilizing adrenal hyperplasia. J. Clin. Endocrinol. Metab. **40:** 355–362.

18. HUGHES, I. & J. WINTER. 1976. The application of a serum 17OH-progesterone radioimmunoassay to the diagnosis and management of congenital adrenal hyperplasia. J. Pediatr. **88:** 766–773.

19. PANG, S., J. HOTCHKISS, A.L. DRASH, *et al.* 1977. Microfilter paper method for 17-hydroxyprogesterone radioimmunassay. J. Clin. Endocrinol. Metab. **45:** 1003–1008.

20. KORTH-SCHUTZ, S., R. VIRDIS, P. SAENGER, *et al.* 1978. Serum androgens as a continuing index of adequacy of treatment of congenital adrenal hyperplasia. J. Clin. Endocrinol. Metab. **46:** 452–458.

21. PANG, S., L.S. LEVINE, D.M. CHOW, *et al.* 1979. Serum androgen concentrations in neonates and young infants with congenital adrenal hyperplasia due to 21-hydroxylase deficiency. Clin. Endocrinol. (Oxf) **11:** 575–584.

22. BONGIOVANNI, A.M., W.R. EBERLEIN & J. CARA. 1954. Studies on metabolism of adrenal steroids in adrenogenital syndrome. J. Clin. Endocrinol. Metab. **14:** 409.

23. BUTLER, G.C. & G.F. MARRIAN. 1937. The isolation of pregnane-3,17,20-triol from the urine of women showing the adrenogenital syndrome. J. Biol. Chem. **119:** 565.

24. GHIZZONI, L., G. MASTORAKOS, A. VOTTERO, *et al.* 1996. Spontaneous cortisol and growth hormone secretion interactions in patients with nonclassic 21-hydroxylase deficiency (NCCAH) and control children. J. Clin. Endocrinol. Metab. **81:** 482–487.

25. GHIZZONI, L., G. MASTORAKOS, M. STREET, *et al.* 1997. Spontaneous thyrotropin and cortisol secretion interactions in patients with nonclassical 21-hydroxylase deficiency and control children. J. Clin. Endocrinol. Metab. **82:** 3677–3683.

26. NEW, M. & L. LEVINE. 1981. Adrenal hyperplasia in intersex states. *In* Pediatric and Adolescent Endocrinology. Z. Laron & P. Tikva, Eds., Vol. **8:** 51. S. Karger. Basel.

27. KLEIN, R. 1960. Evidence for and evidence against the existence of a salt-losing hormone. J. Pediatr. **57:** 452.

28. KOWARSKI, A., J. FINKELSTEIN, J. SPAULDING, *et al.* 1965. Aldosterone secretion rate in congenital adrenal hyperplasia. A discussion of the theories on the pathogenesis of the salt-losing form of the syndrome. J. Clin. Invest. **44:** 1505.

29. KUHNLE, U., M. LAND & S. ULICK. 1986. Evidence for the secretion of an anti-mineralocorticoid in congenital adrenal hyperplasia. J. Clin. Endocrinol. Metab. **62:** 934–940.

30. STONER, E., J. DIMARTINO-NARDI, U. KUHNLE, *et al.* 1986. Is salt-wasting in congenital adrenal hyperplasia due to the same gene as the fasciculata defect? Clin. Endocrinol. (Oxf) **24:** 9–20.

31. LUETSCHER, J.A. 1956. Studies of aldosterone in relation to water and electrolyte balance in man. Recent Prog. Horm. Res. **12:** 175.

32. SPEISER, P.W., L. AGDERE, H. UESHIBA, *et al.* 1991. Aldosterone synthesis in salt-wasting congenital adrenal hyperplasia with complete absence of adrenal 21-hydroxylase. N. Engl. J. Med. **324:** 145–149.

33. VERKAUF, B. & H.J. JONES. 1970. Masculinization of the female genitalia in congenital adrenal hyperplasia: relationship to the salt losing variety of the disease. South Med. .J **63:** 634–638.

34. JONES, H. & G. JONES. 1954. The gynecological aspects of adrenal hyperplasia and allied disorders. Am. J. Obstet. Gynecol. **68:** 1330.

35. JEFFERIES, W., W. WEIR, D. WEIR & R. PROUTY. 1958. The use of cortisone and related steroids in infertility. Fertil. Steril. **9:** 145.

36. DECOURT, M.J., M.F. JAYLE & E. BAULIEU. 1957. Virilisme cliniquement tardif avec excretion de pregnanetriol et insuffisance de la production du cortisol. Ann. Endocrinol. (Paris) **18:** 416.

37. FRASIER, S., I. THORNEYCROFT, B. WEISS & R. HORTON. 1975. Letter: Elevated amniotic fluid concentration of 17 alpha-hydroxyprogesterone in congenital adrenal hyperplasia. J. Pediatr. **86:** 310–312.

38. LEVINE, L.S., B. DUPONT, F. LORENZEN, *et al.* 1980. Cryptic 21-hydroxylase deficiency in families of patients with classical congenital adrenal hyperplasia. J. Clin. Endocrinol. Metab. **51:** 1316–1324.

39. KOHN, B., L.S. LEVINE, M.S. POLLACK, *et al.* 1982. Late-onset steroid 21-hydroxylase deficiency: a variant of classical congenital adrenal hyperplasia. J. Clin. Endocrinol. Metab. **55:** 817–827.

40. ROSENWAKS, Z., P.A. LEE, G.S. JONES, *et al.* 1979. An attenuated form of congenital virilizing adrenal hyperplasia. J. Clin. Endocrinol. Metab. **49:** 335.
41. POLLACK, M.S., L.S. LEVINE, G.J. O'NEILL, *et al.* 1981. HLA linkage and B14, DR1. BfS haplotype assocation with the genes for late onset and cryptic 21-hydroxylase deficiency. Am. J. Hum. Genet. **33**.
42. LARON, Z., M.S. POLLACK, R. ZAMIR, *et al.* 1980. Late-onset 21-hydroxylase deficiency and HLA in the Ashkenazi population: a new allele at the 21-hydroxylase locus. Hum. Immunol. **1:** 55–66.
43. LEVINE, L.S., B. DUPONT, F. LORENZEN, *et al.* 1981. Genetic and hormonal characterization of cryptic 21-hydroxylase deficiency. J. Clin. Endocrinol. Metab. **53:** 1193–1198.
44. BLANKSTEIN, J., C. FAIMAN, F.I. REUES, *et al.* 1980. Adult-onset familial adrenal 21-hydroxylase deficiency. Am. J. Med. **68:** 441.
45. MIGEON, C.J., Z. ROSENWAKS, P.A. LEE, *et al.* 1980. The attenuated form of congenital adrenal hyperplasia as an allelic form of 21-hydroxylase deficiency. J. Clin. Endocrinol. Metab. **51:** 647.
46. SPEISER, P.W., B. DUPONT, P. RUBINSTEIN, *et al.* 1985. High frequency of nonclassical steroid 21-hydroxylase deficiency. Am. J. Hum. Genet. **37:** 650–667.
47. DUMIC, M., L. BRKLJACIC, P.W. SPEISER, *et al.* 1990. An update on the frequency of nonclassical deficiency of adrenal 21-hydroxylase in the Yugoslav population. Acta Endocrinol. **122:** 703–710.
48. TEMECK, J.W., S.Y. PANG, C. NELSON & M.I. NEW. 1987. Genetic defects of steroidogenesis in premature pubarche. J. Clin. Endocrinol. Metab. **64:** 609–617.
49. HAWKINS, L., F. CHASALOW & S. BLETHEN. 1992. The role of adrenocorticotropin testing in evaluating girls with premature adrenarche and hirsutism/oligomenorrhea. J. Clin. Endocrinol. Metab. **74:** 248–253.
50. NEW, M.I., J.M. GERTNER, P.W. SPEISER & P. DEL BALZO. 1991. Growth and final height in congenital adrenal hyperplasia (classical 21-hydroxylase deficiency) and in nonclassical 21-hydroxylase deficiency. *In* Growth Disorders: The State of the Art. L. Cavallo, J.C. Job & M.I. New, Eds. Vol. **81:** 105–110. Raven Press. New York City.
51. LUCKY, A., R. ROSENFIELD, J. MCGUIRE, *et al.* 1986. Adrenal androgen hyperresponsiveness to adrenocorticotropin in women with acne and/or hirsutism: adrenal enzyme defects and exaggerated adrenarche. J. Clin. Endocrinol. Metab. **62:** 840–848.
52. ROSE, L., S. NEWMARK, J. STRAUSS & P. POCHI. 1976. Adrenocortical hydroxylase deficiencies in acne vulgaris. J. Invest. Dermatol. **66:** 324–326.
53. ODRISCOLL, J. & D. ANDERSON. 1993. Untreated congenital adrenal hyperplasia. J. Royal Soc. Med. **86:** 229.
54. PANG, S.Y., A.J. LERNER, E. STONER, *et al.* 1985. Late-onset adrenal steroid 3 beta-hydroxysteroid dehydrogenase deficiency. I. A cause of hirsutism in pubertal and postpubertal women. J. Clin. Endocrinol. Metab. **60:** 428–439.
55. CHILD, D., D. BU'LOCK & D. ANDERSON. 1980. Adrenal steroidogenesis in hirsute women. Clin. Endocrinol. (Oxf) **12:** 595–601.
56. GIBSON, M., R. LACKRITZ, I. SCHIFF & D. TULCHINSKY. 1980. Abnormal adrenal responses to adrenocorticotropic hormone in hyperandrogenic women. Fertil. Steril. **33:** 43–48.
57. LOBO, R. & U. GOEBELSMANN. 1980. Adult manifestation of congenital adrenal hyperplasia due to incomplete 21-hydroxylase deficiency mimicking polycystic ovarian disease. Am . J. Obstet. Gynecol. **138:** 720–726.

58. CHROUSOS, G., D. LORIAUX, D. MANN & G.J. CUTLER. 1982. Late-onset 21-hydroxylase deficiency is an allelic variant of congenital adrenal hyperplasia characterized by attenuated clinical expression and different HLA haplotype associations. Horm. Res. **16:** 193–200.
59. KUTTENN, F., P. COUILLIN, F. GIRARD, et al. 1985. Late-onset adrenal hyperplasia in hirsutism. N. Engl. J. Med. **313:** 224–231.
60. CHROUSOS, G.P., D.L. LORIAUX, R.J. SHERINES & G.B. CUTLER. 1981. Unilateral testicular enlargement resulting from inapparent 21-hydroxylase deficiency. J. Urol. **126:** 127.
61. WISCHUSEN, J., H.W.G. BAKER & B. HUDSON. 1981. Reversible male infertility due to congenital adrenal hyperplasia. Clin. Endocrinol. **14:** 571.
62. BONACCORSI, A.C., I. ADLER & J.G. FIGUEIREDO. 1987. Male infertility due to congenital adrenal hyperplasia: testicular biopsy findings, hormonal evaluation, and therapeutic results in three patients. Fertil. Steril. **47:** 664–670.
63. AUGARTAN, A., R. WEISSENBERG, C. PARIENTE & J. SACK. 1991. Reversible male infertility in late onset congenital adrenal hyperplasia. J. Endocrinol. Invest. **14:** 237–240.
64. MOKSHAGUNDAM, S. & M. SURKS. 1993. Congenital adrenal hyperplasia diagnosed in a man during workup for bilateral adrenal masses. Arch. Intern. Med. **153:** 1389–1391.
65. JARESCH, S., E. KORNELY, H. KLEY & R. SCHLAGHECKE. 1992. Adrenal incidentaloma and patients with homozygous or heterozygous congenital adrenal hyperplasia. J. Clin. Endocrinol. Metab. **74:** 685–689.
66. JONES, H. & B. VERKAUF. 1971. Congenital adrenal hyperplasia: age at menarche and related events at puberty. Am. J. Obstet. Gynecol. **109:** 292.
67. KLINGENSMITH, G., S. GARCIA, H. JONES, et al. 1977. Glucocorticoid treatment of girls with congenital adrenal hyperplasia: effects on height, sexual maturation, and fertility. J. Pediatr. **90:** 996–1004.
68. PANG, S. et al. 1977. Growth and sexual maturation and elevated progesterone levels in women treated for congenital virilizing 21-hydroxylase deficiency. In Congenital Adrenal Hyperplasia. P. Lee et al., Eds. : 233–246. University Park Press. Baltimore.
69. GHALI, I., M. DAVID & L. DAVID. 1977. Linear growth and pubertal development in treated congenital adrenal hyperplasia due to 21-hydroxylase deficiency. Clin. Endocrinol. (Oxf) **6:** 425–436.
70. REITER, E., M. GRUMBACH, S. KAPLAN & F. CONTE. 1975. The response of pituitary gonadotropes to synthetic LRF in children with glucocorticoid-treated congenital adrenal hyperplasia: lack of effect of intrauterine and neonatal androgen excess. J. Clin. Endocrinol. Metab. **40:** 318–325.
71. KIRKLAND, J., R. KIRKLAND, L. LIBRIK & G. CLAYTON. 1974. Serum gonadotropin levels in female adolescents with congenital adrenal hyperplasia. J. Pediatr. **84:** 411–414.
72. WENTZ, A., S. GARCIA, G. KLINGENSMITH, et al. 1977. Hypothalamic maturation in congenital adrenal hyperplasia. In Congenital Adrenal Hyperplasia. P. Lee, L. Plotnick, A. Kowarski & C. Migeon, Eds.: 379. University Park Press. Baltimore.
73. LEVIN, J., E. CARMINA & R. LOBO. 1991. Is the inappropriate gonadotropin secretion of patients with polycystic ovary syndrome similar to that of patients with adult-onset congenital adrenal hyperplasia? Fertil. Steril. **56:** 635–640.

74. PESCOVITZ, O., F. COMITE, F. CASSORLA, *et al.* 1984. True precocious puberty complicating congenital adrenal hyperplasia: treatment with a luteinizing hormone-releasing hormone analog. J. Clin. Endocrinol. Metab. **58:** 857–861.
75. DACOU-VOUTETAKIS, C. & N. KARIDIS. 1993. Congenital adrenal hyperplasia complicated by central precocious puberty: treatment with LHRH-agonist analogue. Ann. N.Y. Acad. Sci. **687:** 250–254.
76. SOLIMAN, A.T., M. AL LAMKI, I. AL SALMI & M. ASFOUR. 1997. Congenital adrenal hyperplasia complicated by central precocious puberty: linear growth during infancy and treatment with gonadotropin-releasing hormone analog. Metabolism **46:** 513–517.
77. QUINTOS, J., M. VOGIATZI, M. HARBISON & M. NEW. 1999. Growth hormone and depot leuprolide therapy for short stature in children with congenital adrenal hyperplasia. 81st Annual Meeting of The Endocrine Society. San Diego, CA.
78. WILKINS, L., J. CRIGLER, S. SILVERMAN, *et al.* 1952. Further studies on the treatment of congenital adrenal hyperplasia with cortisone. II. The effects of cortisone on sexual and somatic development, with an hypothesis concerning the mechanism of feminization. J. Clin. Endocrinol. Metab. **12:** 277.
79. KLINGENSMITH, G., A. WENTZ, W. MEYER & C. MIGEON. 1976. Gonadotropin output in congenital adrenal hyperplasia. J. Clin. Endocrinol. Metab. **43:** 933.
80. KIESSLIN, G. & G. SCHWARZ. 1966. Zur genese des hypogonadismus beim kongenitalen adrenogenitalen syndrome. Arch. Klin. Dermatol. **228:** 684.
81. KIRKLAND, R., B. KEENAN & G. CLAYTON. 1977. Long-term follow-up of patients with congenital adrenal hyperplasia in Houston. *In* Congenital Adrenal Hyperplasia P. Lee, L. Plotnick, A. Kowarski & C. Migeon, Eds.: 273. University Park Press. Baltimore.
82. RICHARDS, G., M. GRUMBACH, S. KAPLAN & F. CONTE. 1978. The effect of long acting glucocorticoids on menstrual abnormalities in patients with virilizing congenital adrenal hyperplasia. J. Clin. Endocrinol. Metab. **47:** 1208–1215.
83. RICHARDS, G., D. STYNE, F. CONTE, *et al.* 1977. Plasma sex steroids and gonadotropins in pubertal girls with congenital adrenal hyperplasia: relationship to menstrual disorders. *In* Congenital Adrenal Hyperplasia. P. Lee, L. Plotnick, A. Kowarski & C. Migeon, Eds.: 233. University Park Press. Baltimore.
84. GRAYZEL, E. 1974. Postpubertal adrenogenital syndrome. Treatable cause of infertility. N. Y. State J. Med. **74:** 1038–1039.
85. GRANOFF, A. 1981. Treatment of menstrual irregularities with dexamethasone in congenital adrenal hyperplasia. J. Adolesc. Health Care **2:** 23–27.
86. ROSENFIELD, R., S. BICKEL & A. RAZDAN. 1980. Amenorrhea related to progestin excess in congenital adrenal hyperplasia. Obstet. Gynecol. **56:** 208–215.
87. RIDDICK, D. & C. HAMMOND. 1975. Adrenal virilism due to 21-hydroxylase deficiency in the postmenarchial female. Obstet. Gynecol. **45:** 21–24.
88. MORI, M. 1970. Congenital adreogenital syndrome and successful pregnancy: report of a case. J. Obstet. Gynecol. **35:** 394.
89. LO, J., V. SCHWITZGEBEL, J. TYRRELL, *et al.* 1999. Normal female infants born of mothers with classic congenital adrenal hyperplasia due to 21-hydroxylase deficiency. J. Clin. Endocrinol. Metab. **84:** 930–936.
90. MULAIKAL, R.M., C.J. MIGEON & J.A. ROCK. 1987. Fertility rates in female patients with congenital adrenal hyperplasia due to 21-hydroxylase deficiency. N. Engl. J. Med. **316:** 178–182.

91. PREMAWARDHANA, L., I. HUGHES, G. READ & M. SCANLON. 1997. Longer term outcome in females with congenital adrenal hyperplasia (CAH): the Cardiff experience. Clin. Endocrinol. (Oxf) **46:** 327–332.

92. STEWART, J. 1960. A fertile male with untreated congenital adrenal hyperplasia. Acta Endocrinol. (Suppl.) **51:** 661.

93. URBAN, M, P. LEE & C. MIGEON. 1978. Adult height and fertility in men with congenital virilizing adrenal hyperplasia. N. Engl. J. Med. **299:** 1392.

94. VALENTINO, R., S. SAVASTANO, A. TOMMASELLI, et al. 1997. Success of glucocorticoid replacement therapy on fertility in two adult males with 21-CAH homozygote classic form. J. Endocrinol. Invest. **20:** 690–694.

95. MOLITOR, J., B. CHERTOW & B. FARISS. 1973. Long-term follow-up of a patient with congenital adrenal hyperplasia and failure of testicular development. Fertil. Steril. **24:** 319.

96. BAHNER, F. & G. SCHWARZ. 1961. Congenitale nebennierenrinden hyperplasie beim mann mit normaler keimdrusenfunktion und fertilitat. Acta Endocrinol. **38:** 236.

97. WILKINS, L. 1965. The Diagnosis and Treatment of Endocrine Disorders. Charles C. Thomas. Springfield, IL, pp. 368–381.

98. RAITI, S., N. MACLAREN & F. AKESODE. 1977. Gonadotropin-adrenal--testicular axis in males with congenital adrenal hyperplasia and idiopathic sexual precocity. In Congenital Adrenal Hyperplasia. P. Lee, L. Plotnick, A. Kowarski & C. Migeon, Eds.: 403. University Park Press. Baltimore.

99. BLUMBERG-TICK, J., P. BOUDOU, K. NAHOUL & G. SCHAISON. 1991. Testicular tumors in congenital adrenal hyperplasia: steroid measurements from adrenal and spermatic veins. J. Clin. Endocrinol. Metab. **73:** 1129–1133.

100. SCHOEN, E., V. DIRAIMONDO & O. DOMINGUEZ. 1961. Bilateral testicular tumors complicating congenital adrenocortical hyperplasia. J. Clin. Endocrinol. Metab. **21:** 518.

101. MILLER, E. & H. MURRAY. 1962. Congenital adrenocortical hyperplasia: case previously reported as "bilateral interstitial cell tumor of the testicle". J. Clin. Endocrinol. Metab. **22:** 655.

102. GLENN, J. & W. BOYCE. 1963. Adrenogenitalism with testicular adrenal rests simulating interstitial cell tumor. J. Urol. **89:** 456.

103. RADFAR, N., F. BARTTER, R. EASLEY, et al. 1977. Evidence for endogenous LH suppression in a man with bilateral testicular tumors and congenital adrenal hyperplasia. J. Clin. Endocrinol. Metab. **45:** 1194–1204.

104. SRIKANTH, M., B. WEST, M. ISHITANI, et al. 1992. Benign testicular tumors in children with congenital adrenal hyperplasia. J. Pediatr. Surg. **27:** 639–641.

105. RUTGERS, J., R. YOUNG & R. SCULLY. 1988. The testicular "tumor" of the adrenogenital syndrome. A report of six cases and review of the literature on testicular masses in patients with adrenocortical disorders. Am. J. Surg. Pathol. **12:** 503–513.

106. CHAKRABORTY, J., R. FRANCO-SAENZ & K. KROPP. 1983. Electron microscopic study of testicular tumor in congenital adrenal hyperplasia. Hum. Pathol. **14:** 151–157.

107. DUPONT, B., S.E. OBERFIELD, E.M. SMITHWICK, et al. 1977. Close genetic linkage between HLA and congenital adrenal hyperplasia (21-hydroxylase deficiency). Lancet **2:** 1309–1312.

108. LEVINE, L.S., M. ZACHMANN & M.I. NEW, *et al.* 1978. Genetic mapping of the 21-hydroxylase-deficiency gene within the HLA linkage group. N. Engl. J. Med. **299:** 911–915.

109. SPEISER, P. & M. NEW. 1987. Genotype and hormonal phenotype in nonclassical 21-hydroxylase deficiency. J. Clin. Endocrinol. Metab. **64:** 86–91.

110. WHITE, P.C., D. GROSSBERGER, B.J. ONUFER, *et al.* 1985. Two genes encoding steroid 21-hydroxylase are located near the genes encoding the fourth component of complement in man. Proc. Natl. Acad. Sc.i USA **82:** 1089–1093.

111. CARROLL, M.C., R.D. CAMPBELL & R.R. PORTER. 1985. The mapping of 21-hydroxylase genes adjacent to complement component C4 genes in HLA, the major histocompatibility complex in man. Proc. Natl. Acad. Sci. USA **82:** 521–525.

112. HIGASHI, Y., H. YOSHIOKA, M. YAMANE, *et al.* 1986. Complete nucleotide sequence of two steroid 21-hydroxylase genes tandemly arranged in human chromosome: a pseudogene and a genuine gene. Proc. Natl. Acad. Sci USA **83:** 2841–2845.

113. WHITE, P.C., M.I. NEW & B. DUPONT. 1986. Structure of the human steroid 21-hydroxylase genes. Proc. Natl. Acad. Sci. USA **83:** 5111–5115.

114. TUSIE-LUNA, M. & P. WHITE. 1995. Gene conversions and unequal crossovers between CYP21 (steroid 21-hydroxylase gene) and CYP21P involve different mechanisms. Proc. Natl. Acad. Sci. USA **92:** 10796–10800.

115. WERKMEISTER, J.W., M.I. NEW, B. DUPONT & P.C. WHITE. 1986. Frequent deletion and duplication of the steroid 21-hydroxylase genes. Am. J. Hum. Genet. **39:** 461–469.

116. WHITE, P.C., A. VITEK, B. DUPONT & M.I. NEW. 1988. Characterization of frequent deletions causing steroid 21-hydroxylase deficiency. Proc. Natl. Acad. Sci. USA **85:** 4436–4440.

117. RUMSBY, G., M. CARROLL, R. PORTER, *et al.* 1986. Deletion of the steroid 21-hydroxylase and complement C4 genes in congenital adrenal hyperplasia. J. Med. Genet. **23:** 204–209.

118. WEDELL, A., E.M. RITZEN, S.B. HAGLUND & H. LUTHMAN. 1992. Steroid 21-hydroxylase deficiency: three additional mutated alleles and establishment of phenotype-genotype relationships of common mutations. Proc. Natl. Acad. Sci. USA **89:** 7232–7236.

119. RODRIGUES, N.R., I. DUNHAM & C.Y. YU. 1987. Molecular characterization of the HLA-linked steroid 21-hydroxylase B gene from an individual with congenital adrenal hyperplasia. EMBO J. **6:** 1653–1661.

120. OWERBACH, D., A. BALLARD & M. DRAZNIN. 1992. Salt-wasting congenital adrenal hyperplasia: detection and characterization of mutations in the steroid 21-hydroxylase gene, CYP21, using the polymerase chain reaction. J. Clin. Endocrinol. Metab. **74:** 553–558.

121. TAJIMA, T., K. FUJIEDA & Y. FUJII-KURIYAMA. 1993. De novo mutation causes steroid 21-hydroxylase deficiency in one family of HLA-identical affected and unaffected siblings. J. Clin. Endocrinol. Metab. **77:** 86–89.

122. SPEISER, P.W., M.I. NEW & P.C. WHITE. 1988. Molecular genetic analysis of nonclassic steroid 21-hydroxylase deficiency associated with HLA-B14,DR1. N. Engl. J. Med. **319:** 19–23.

123. TUSIE-LUNA, M.T., P.W. SPEISER, M. DUMIC, *et al.* 1991. A mutation (Pro-30 to Leu) in CYP21 represents a potential nonclassic steroid 21-hydroxylase deficiency allele. Mol. Endocrinol. **5:** 685–692.

124. OWERBACH, D., L. SHERMAN, A.L. BALLARD & R. AZZIZ. 1992. Pro-453 to ser mutation in CYP21 is associated with nonclassic steroid 21-hydroxylase deficiency. Mol. Endocrinol. **6:** 1211–1215.
125. SPEISER, P.W., J. DUPONT, D. ZHU, *et al.* 1992. Disease expression and molecular genotype in congenital adrenal hyperplasia due to 21-hydroxylase deficiency. J. Clin. Invest. **90:** 584–595.
126. WILSON, R.C., A.B. MERCADO, K.C. CHENG & M.I. NEW. 1995. Steroid 21-hydroxylase deficiency: genotype may not predict phenotype. J. Clin. Endocrinol. Metab. **80:** 2322–2329.
127. KRONE, N., A. BRAUN, A. ROSCHER, *et al.* 2000. Predicting phenotype in steroid 21-hydroxylase deficiency? Comprehensive genotyping in 155 unrelated, well defined patients from southern Germany. J. Clin. Endocrinol. Metab. **85:** 1059–1065.
128. PANG, S.Y., M.A. WALLACE, L. HOFMAN, *et al.* 1988. Worldwide experience in newborn screening for classical congenital adrenal hyperplasia due to 21-hydroxylase deficiency. Pediatrics **81:** 866–874.
129. ZACHMANN, M., D. TASSINARI & A. PRADER. 1983. Clinical and biochemical variability of congenital adrenal hyperplasia due to 11beta-hydroxylase deficiency. J. Endocrinol. Metab. **56:** 222–229.
130. ROSLER, A., E. LEIBERMAN & T. COHEN. 1992. High frequency of congenital adrenal hyperplasia (classic 11 beta-hydroxylase deficiency) among Jews from Morocco. Am . J. Med. Genet. **42:** 827–834.
131. NEW, M., F. LORENZEN, A. LERNER, *et al.* 1983. Genotyping steroid 21-hydroxylase deficiency: hormonal reference data. J. Clin. Endocrinol. Metab. **57:** 320–326.
132. ZERAH, M., S.Y. PANG, M.I. NEW. 1987. Morning salivary 17-hydroxyprogesterone is a useful screening test for nonclassical 21-hydroxylase deficiency. J. Clin. Endocrinol. Metab. **65:** 227–232.
133. KUTTEN, F. 1986. Late-onset adrenal hyperplasia (letter). N. Engl. J. Med. **314:** 450.
134. SPEISER, P.W., N. LAFORGIA, K. KATO, *et al.* 1990. First trimester prenatal treatment and molecular genetic diagnosis of congenital adrenal hyperplasia (21-hydroxylase deficiency). J. Clin. Endocrinol. Metab. **70:** 838–848.
135. JOSSO, N. 2001. Anatomy and endocrinology of fetal sex differentiation. In Endocrinology. L. DeGroot and J. Jameson, Eds.: 1947–1954. W.B. Saunders Company. Philadelphia, PA.
136. WILSON, R.C. *et al.* 1995. Rapid DNA analysis by allele-specific PCR for detection of mutations in the steroid 21-hydroxylase gene. J. Clin. Endocrinol. Metab. **80**(5): 1635–1640.
137. WHITE, P.C. & M.I. NEW. 1988. Molecular genetics of congenital adrenal hyperplasia. Baillieres Clin. Endocrinol. Metab. **2**(4): 941–965.
138. FOREST, M. H. BETUEL & M. DAVID. 1989. Prenatal treatment in congenital adrenal hyperplasia due to 21-hydroxylase deficiency: up-date 88 of the French multicentric study. Endocr. Res. **15**(1-2): 277–301.
139. LAJIC, S., A. WEDELL, T. BUI, *et al.* 1998. Long-term somatic follow-up of prenatally treated children with congenital adrenal hyperplasia. J. Clin. Endocrinol. Metab. **83:** 3872–3880.
140. NEW, M.I. *et al.* 2001. Extensive personal experience: prenatal diagnosis for congenital adrenal hyperplasia in 532 pregnancies. J. Clin. Endocrinol. Metab. **86**(12): 5651–5657.

141. SECKL, J.R. & W.L. MILLER. 1997. How safe is long-term prenatal glucocorti-coid treatment? JAMA **277**(13): 1077–1079.
142. MERCADO, A.B., R.C. WILSON, K.C. CHENG, *et al.* 1995. Extensive personal experience: Prenatal treatment and diagnosis of congenital adrenal hyperpla-sia owing to steroid 21-hydroxylase deficiency. J. Clin. Endocrinol. Metab. **80:** 2014–2020.
143. LARAGH, J. 1971. Aldosteronism in man: factors controlling secretion of the hormone. *In* The Human Adrenal Cortex. N. Christy, Ed.: 483. Harper and Row. New York.
144. BARTTER, F. 1977. Adrenogenital syndromes from physiology to chemistry. *In* Congenital Adrenal Hyperplasia. P. Lee, L.P. Plotnick, A. Kowaraski & C. Migeon, Eds.: 9. University Park Press. Baltimore.
145. ROSLER, A., L.S. LEVINE, B. SCHNEIDER, *et al.* 1977. The interrelationship of sodium balance, plasma renin activity and ACTH in congenital adrenal hyper-plasia. J. Clin. Endocrinol. Metab. **45:** 500–512.
146. PANG, S., M. MACGILLIVRAY, M. WANG, *et al.* 1991. 3 alpha-androstanediol glucuronide in virilizing congenital adrenal hyperplasia: a useful serum meta-bolic marker of integrated adrenal androgen secretion. J. Clin. Endocrinol. Metab. **73:** 166–174.
147. WINTER, J. 1980. Current approaches to the treatment of congenital adrenal hyperplasia [editorial]. J. Pediatr. **97:** 81–82.

Genetic Causes of Mental Retardation

HUGO W. MOSER, MD

Director, Neurogenetics Research Center Kennedy Krieger Institute, University Professor of Neurology and Pediatrics, Johns Hopkins University School of Medicine, Baltimore, Maryland 21205, USA

ABSTRACT: Mental retardation has been categorized into severe mental retardation where genetics plays a very important role and mild mental retardation, in which genetics in some instances plays a role but in which cultural factors also matter a great deal. The pathogenetic, clinical and behavioral characteristics of genetically determined disorders associated with mental retardation differ greatly—as exemplified by two genetic disorders that have been clarified recently, namely Rett syndrome and the Williams syndrome. In the work-up of the developmentally disabled child, previous studies have shown that genetic studies are of have great importance and high yield. Early biochemical diagnosis in newborn screening has tremendous potential and has been strongly supported by NICHD— the PKU story being so much part of what NICHD has done. We must gain a better understanding of structure/function relationships, which becomes more and more possible with neuroimaging. A better understanding of neural plasticity can lead to correction by early intervention.

KEYWORDS: Rett syndrome; Williams syndrome; mental retardation; neural plasticity

There are a great many controversies surrounding the definition of mental retardation. There is a social definition, an administrator's definition, an educational definition, and also an etiological definition. Mental retardation has been categorized into severe mental retardation where genetics plays a very important role and mild mental retardation, in which genetics in some instances plays a role but in which cultural factors also matter a great deal (FIG. 1).

Back in 1995, we created a list of the most common causes for mental retardation (FIG. 2). The frequency and degree of severity with which mental retardation occurs are also included. However, with the advent of the genome project at the last count 8,737 genetic abnormalities have been identified, and

Address for correspondence: Hugo W. Moser, MD, Director, Neurogenetics Research Center, Kennedy Krieger Institute, 707 North Broadway, Baltimore, MD 21205, USA. Voice: 443-923-2750.

moser@kennedykrieger.org

Ann. N.Y. Acad. Sci. 1038: 44–48 (2004). © 2004 New York Academy of Sciences.
doi: 10.1196/annals.1315.010

Two Group Approach to Mental Retardation

- **Mild mental retardation:**
  - IQ 50-70
  - Prevalence up to 2-3%, varies with method ascertainment
  - Sociocultural factors prominent
- **Severe mental retardation:**
  - IQ < 50
  - Prevalence between 03-0.4% in most surveys
  - Biologic cause in most instances

FIGURE 1. Definition of mental retardation.

10 most common genetic causes of MR

Cause	Incidence per thousand	Mental Retardation (4 = most severe)	
		Frequency	Severity
Down Syndrome	1.3	4	2-4
47 XXX or XXY	1	2	2
Klinefelter Syndrome	0.8	1	1
Fragile – X	0.6	4	2-3
Neurofibromatosis	0.3	1	1
Congen. Hypothyroid	0.25	4	4
Acyl-CoA dehydrogenase deficiency	0.17	1	1
Duchenne Musc. Dystr.	0.15	2	2
Trisomy 15	0.15	4	4
Trisomy 13	0.13	4	4

Moser, Mental Retardation and Development Disabilities Research Reviews, 1995

FIGURE 2. Common genetic causes of mental retardation.

mental retardation is a feature in 492 of them. It is interesting to note the large proportion due to X-linked mental retardation. Why this is the case is a very important issue, which is under investigation.

The pathogenetic, clinical and behavioral characteristics of genetically determined disorders associated with mental retardation differ greatly. This is exemplified by two genetic disorders that have been clarified recently, namely Rett syndrome and the Williams syndrome.

The main features of Rett syndrome are listed in FIGURE 3. Recognition of this syndrome was based upon the astute clinical observation of Dr. Andreas Rett in 1963 and of Bengt Hagberg and associates in 1983, who realized that this set of symptoms frequently co-occurred in girls with the characteristic stereotypic hand movements providing a clinical alert of key importance. Patients with Classical Rett syndrome would be classified as having a profound level of mental retardation, but with behavioral characteristics that bear some resemblance to autism. This pioneering clinical delineation of a "new" syndrome, quickly led to the awareness that this condition is relatively common world-wide and through an intense international research effort it was shown to be due to a defect in methyl-CpG-binding protein 2 (MECP2) that is normally involved in transcriptional silencing and involves the expression patterns of many neuronal genes, with the formation of synapses being severely affected. A mouse model of Rett syndrome has been developed. The clinical manifestations in the mouse model vary with the nature of the MECP2 abnormality. It is of interest that some produce a mouse analogue of the hand movement pattern in the human disorder. It is also of interest that certain MECP2

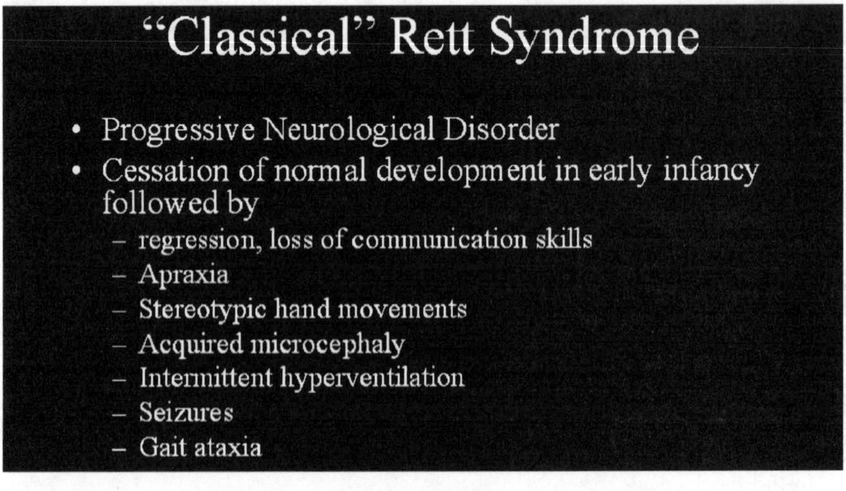

> ## "Classical" Rett Syndrome
>
> - Progressive Neurological Disorder
> - Cessation of normal development in early infancy followed by
>   - regression, loss of communication skills
>   - Apraxia
>   - Stereotypic hand movements
>   - Acquired microcephaly
>   - Intermittent hyperventilation
>   - Seizures
>   - Gait ataxia

FIGURE 3. Classical features in Rett syndrome.

mutations lead to milder syndromes, and in males may be associated with profound mental retardation but not the other features of classical Rett syndrome.

Williams syndrome presents with a totally different and characteristic cognitive profile with peaks and valleys of abilities. The patients retain complex expressive abilities, but spatial cognition is profoundly impaired and there are characteristic abnormalities in auditory processing, including hyperacusis. Curiously some patients have exceptional musical ability. Considerable progress has been made in clarifying the pathogenesis of Williams syndrome. There is an overall reduction in cerebral volume, but a relative preservation of the anterior frontal lobes and of the auditory regions (Herschl's gyrus). The underlying defect appears to involve the protein kinases LIMK-1 and 2 that regulate cofilin phosphorylation and actin dynamics. LIMK1 knockout mice show impaired dendritic spine morphology and synapse formation and impaired fear responses and spatial learning.

Rett syndrome and Williams both are causes of mental retardation, and both affect the structure of dendritic spines and synaptic function, as do many other disorders associated with mental retardation, such as Down syndrome. Yet, the nature of the cognitive and behavioral deficits and the cytoarchitectural alterations and genetic defects differ profoundly.

Walsh and Ross have clarified the pathogenesis of disorders of neuronal migration which can cause varying degrees of mental retardation with specific patterns.

Dr. Michael Johnston has emphasized that many genetic disorders that are associated with severe mental retardation, such as neurofibromatosis 1, Rett syndrome, Fragile-X syndrome, the Coffin-Lowry syndrome and the Rubinstein-Taybe syndrome, involve intracellular signaling pathways that alter long-term potentiation and are activity dependent. These pathways are crucial for learning, and defects in these pathways would be expected to play a significant role in the pathogenesis of various forms of severe mental retardation. They may also be of great significance in the understanding of mild mental retardation and contribute to the development of strategies for its prevention. The central principle here is that these pathways are plastic, that is, they can be shaped and molded by experience. The extent to which this happens diminishes with age. Exciting work on the environmental factors associated with developmental disability are in progress, and there is the possibility that, as we understand the plasticity in early childhood, we can clarify the connection between environmental deprivation and biological development. Dr. Craig Ramie is trying to isolate factors that play a role in the interaction between mother and child, an interaction that provides crucial developmental stimuli. Many children who lack them suffer from so-called mild mental retardation.

In the work-up of the developmentally disabled child (see FIGURE 4), previous studies have shown that genetic studies are of have great importance

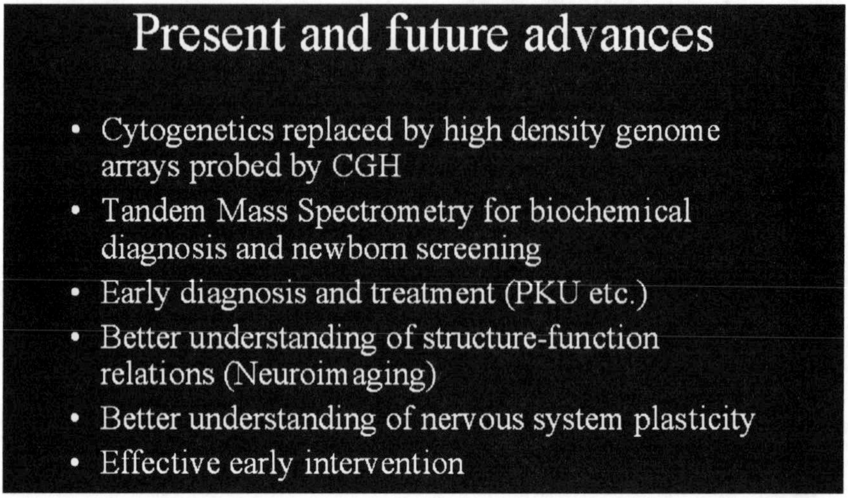

Present and future advances

- Cytogenetics replaced by high density genome arrays probed by CGH
- Tandem Mass Spectrometry for biochemical diagnosis and newborn screening
- Early diagnosis and treatment (PKU etc.)
- Better understanding of structure-function relations (Neuroimaging)
- Better understanding of nervous system plasticity
- Effective early intervention

FIGURE 4. Advances in understanding mental retardation.

and high yield. It is expected that probably in the next five years or so, high-density genome probes will replace cytogenetics. Early biochemical diagnosis in newborn screening has tremendous potential and has been strongly supported by NICHD. We all know, and emphasize the importance of early diagnosis and treatment, the PKU story being so much part of what NICHD has done. For the future, we must gain a better understanding of structure/function relationships, which becomes more and more possible with neuroimaging. A better understanding of neural plasticity, which has been highlighted by Dr. Johnston, can lead to correction by early intervention.

REFERENCES

JOHNSTON, M.V., L. ALEMI, & K.H. HARUM. 2003. Learning, memory, and transcription factors. Pediatr. Res. **53:** 369–374.

LENHOFF, H.M., P.P. WANG, F. GREENBERG & U. BELLUGI. 1997. Williams syndrome and the brain. Sci. Am. **69:** 68–73.

MCCABE, L.L. & R.B. MCCABE. 2002. Newborn screening as a model for population screening. Mol. Genet. Metab. **75:** 299–307.

SHAHBAZIAN, M.D. & H.Y. ZOGHBI. 2002. Rett syndrome and MeCP2: linking epigenetics and neuronal function. Am. J. Hum. Genet. **71:** 1259–1272.

WALSH, C.A. 1999. Genetic malformations of the human cerebral cortex. Neuron **23:** 19–29.

Future Vaccine Development at NICHD

JOHN B. ROBBINS, MD[a] AND RACHEL SCHNEERSON, MD[b]

[a]Chief, Laboratory of Developmental and Molecular Immunity, [b]Chief, Section on Bacterial Disease, Pathogenesis and Immunity, Laboratory of Developmental and Molecular Immunity, NICHD, NIH, Bethesda, Maryland 20892, USA

ABSTRACT: Using published data and the results of our studies, we hypothesized that a critical level of serum IgG antibodies to the surface structures of invasive pathogens (capsular polysaccharides of *Haemophilus influenzae* type b, pneumococcus, meningococcus, *Salmonella typhi*, *Escherichia coli*, and *Staphylococcus aureus*, the O-specific polysaccharide LPS domain of the LPS of *Shigella*, non-typhoidal *Salmonella*, and *E. coli*, and the capsular polypeptide of *Bacillus anthraces*) confer immunity to these pathogens. Covalent attachment to a protein increases their immunogenicity and bestows T-cell properties to these antigens. We have also shown that a critical level of serum IgG antibodies to pertussis toxin alone induces immunity on both an individual and on a community basis (herd immunity) to Bordetella pertussis. It is likely that all the above conjugates and pertussis toxoid will be incorporated into vaccines for routine infant immunization.

KEYWORDS: capsular polysaccharide; O-specific polysaccharide; serum IgG; capsular polypeptide; pertussis toxin

HAEMOPHILUS

The work on *Haemophilus* type b vaccines started in New York City in 1968 and was entirely supported by the Child Health Institute. Dr. Schneerson and I moved here in 1970. The vaccine, which was recognized by the World Health Organization in 1987 is now routinely administered to children in most developed countries. It has virtually eliminated this cause of bacterial

John B. Robbins and Rachel Schneerson: Lasker Award, Clinical Medical Research, 1996

Address for correspondence: John B. Robbins, MD, Laboratory of Developmental and Molecular Immunity, NICHD, NIH, Building 6, Room 436, Bethesda, MD 20892, USA. Voice: 301-496-0850.

robbinsj@nichd.nih.gov; schneerr@mail.nih.gov

Ann. N.Y. Acad. Sci. 1038: 49–59 (2004). © 2004 New York Academy of Sciences.
doi: 10.1196/annals.1315.011

meningitis in all countries that practice routine immunization with the vaccine. It eliminated the major cause of acquired mental retardation in the United States and many other countries. What did we learn from it? How could this be applied to other symptoms?

This all goes back to 1930, when two investigators published a paper about the relationship between the prevalence of bactericidal antibodies in the serum of individuals and the incidence of disease. They showed that in newborns, who are born with bactericidal antibody, the antibody disappears as the parent-derived globulin is metabolized. However, it reappears during adult life. The incidence of disease is highest during this period when the antibodies have disappeared and the adult levels have not been reached. This showed us that we have to make a vaccine that would protect infants and children but that we did not have to worry about the vaccine-induced immunity in adult life because the stimulus for these antibodies was not the organism but crossreacting nonpathogenic bacteria. *Haemophilus influenzae* has six polysaccharides, but only one, type b, is responsible for most systemic infections. *In vitro* systems showed that only the type b organism is virulent, and this allowed us to predict that if we prevented the type b organisms by vaccinating with the type b vaccine, the other organisms would not emerge because they are not virulent.

The polysaccharide itself failed to induce protective levels of antibody in infants and young children, the age group for which the disease had highest incidence. We used a method that had been first described in the 1920s at the Rockefeller University, by which we bound the polysaccharide to a protein. The polysaccharide alone is a good immunogen in adults but fails to immunize the very age group in which the disease occurs. However, when bound to a protein, the polysaccharide is a much better immunogen than when given alone, incidentally the best we have seen. It does induce protective levels of antibody in the infant age group. As you know, it is now licensed and highly successful.

The principle developed by the study was immediately applicable to other polysaccharides of capsulated pathogens. We were surprised to discover that the polysaccharide did not exert particular activity in the blood but actually on the epithelial surface of the respiratory tract, so that children immunized with the conjugate did not get colonized with the type b organisms. The polysaccharide inhibited colonization, and this effect was not in evidence for noncapsulated organisms or other capsulated pathogens that had different polysaccharides. This means that vaccination that induced antibody would not only protect but would interrupt transmission. In all countries where the vaccine is used, the phenomenon of herd immunity has occurred because the organism is no longer a transmitted in the infant and young child age group. Since *H. influenzae* type b is a pathogen in humans only, it is conceivable we could eradicate the organism from the planet, as well as the other capsulated pathogens.

TYPHOID

Vaccines prevent disease. Therefore the study of the disease symptoms is not useful for developing a vaccine, because if you have a vaccine you do not have a disease. So we looked at the early steps in how vaccines might act and we noticed that there was a great similarity between the immunity to hemophilus influenza and to enterics. We do not have vaccines for most enteric infections, as you know. We asked ourselves whether the incidence of the diseases is age-related. This essential virulence factors are surface polysaccharides, and most individuals have natural antibodies to the surface polysaccharides which are not induced by the organism. When we went to look at enterics, exactly the same features were observed. *Salmonella*, the cause of typhoid fever is a capsulated organism. The capsule is called Vi. As you know, the existing typhoid vaccines are limited because they cannot be used for routine immunization of infants and children. We reported that if you attach the Vi to a medically useful protein, to form a conjugate, the efficacy of such a vaccine in two-to-five-year-old children is over 90%. This study was conducted in Vietnam, which has the highest incidence of typhoid fever. The vaccine is thus highly effective, and follow-through shows that the efficacy lasts for at least 2.5 years. We are now looking at a new vaccine for typhoid fever, which we think can be administered routinely to infants and children.

SHIGELLOSIS

The other enterics do not have capsules. They have a lipopolysaccharide that has three domains. Lipid A attaches to the outer membrane, the source of symptoms of this molecule; there is a region that does not appear to participate in immunity; and the outermost region of this LPS called the O-specific polysaccharide, which acts as a capsule. It is possible to purify this O-specific polysaccharide. The first disease we addressed is shigellosis, because shigellosis is probably a major cause of stunted growth throughout the world. If you look at diarrhea and dysentery and its effect on weight, you can see that diarrhea, just watery diarrhea, has an effect on weight that is not statistically significant three years later. However, if there is dysentery, with fever, cramps, mucus, then three years later, there is stunted growth. Thus, children who suffer several attacks of dysentery, most caused by shigella, have stunted growth. They lose four or five months of growth with each infection because it causes a diffuse inflammation of the intestine, which interferes with absorption.

Shigellosis is a serious disease. There is a common misconception about intestinal infection that the intestinal immunity mediated by the locally secreted IgA is protective. There is no evidence for that at all. But shigellosis is not reported before the age of 6 months, and the only thing that could account for that is IgG antibodies. In the Israeli defense forces, who suffer a high incidence of shigellosis during the summer months, we were able to show that those who did not have IgG anti-LPS antibody were susceptible to shigellosis, whereas those who did did not get shigellosis. On the basis of these results, one can predict that a vaccine has to induce IgG anti-LPS. We made conjugates of the two common shigella polysaccharides and we looked at the pre-injection and post-injection levels and compared them with pre-illness and convalescent levels. Our conjugates induce as least much antibody as does infection with *Shigella sonnei*. Pre-injection levels of these antibodies are not induced by *S. sonnei* but by cross-reacting organisms. In a clinical trial in three companies in which the incidence of disease is unusually high (that is why the study could be done with so few recruits), subjects were given either conjugate *S. sonnei* vaccine or an orally administered strain of *Shigella flexneri*. The efficacy of the vaccine was about 75 percent. One company was of particular interest because some of the troops got the disease within the first two weeks of immunization because they were infected at the time they were immunized. Although the efficacy is lower, the vaccine was still effective, showing that this vaccine could be administered during an epidemic with benefit to the recipients.

We observed an age-related development of antibodies to the O-specific polysaccharide of *S. sonnei* and *S. flexneri*. The younger an individual, the lower the antibody levels. We are now in the middle of a study, conceived mostly by Dr. Schneerson, my colleague for many years, to see if our conjugates will prevent shigellosis in infants. We should know the answer within a year or two.

SYNTHETIC IMMUNOGENS

Another approach is to synthesize these carbohydrates. The materials we prepare from bacteria are heterogeneous, but they can also be synthesized. In a really extraordinary piece of work by our associates at the NIH, a synthetic polysaccharide of *Shigella dysenteriae* was prepared which was as long as 16 units, the second largest synthetic polysaccharide ever made. This is a bacterial polysaccharide; we have no enzymes—this is just hard chemistry. It was attached to a protein at its reducing end. This material was injected into mice, and the results have been very useful. When one looks at the number of saccharide units per protein (the density of the saccharide on the protein), i.e., the length of the saccharide and the density on the carrier protein, one finds that there is an optimum level of both saccharide size and density for producing antibodies. We have interpreted this to mean that there is a useful compromise between the interaction of this conjugate vaccine with B cells to stimulate antibodies and with T cells to stimulate the accelerated development that T cell immunity brings. The advantage of these conjugates is that one can obtain an accurate molecular picture of them. An analysis of these conjugates gives the distribution of the saccharides on the protein, representing for the first time an unambiguous picture of the structure of these proteins. We believe that we will now no longer need to rely upon animal testing but can have physical chemical measurements to predict the behavior of such conjugates.

E. COLI O157

One of the most important E. coli serotypes is O157. It is similar to Shigella dysenteriae because it has the same toxin, and the infection gives the same general picture. If a conjugate is made, bactericidal antibodies are induced in adults, and the vaccines are safe. In our studies, there were no reactions in the adults, and they synthesized a high level of bacterial antibody. We think the same results can be obtained in children, and this will be written up soon. However, we believe that the most important aspect of this program is to see if we can induce antibodies in cows or cattle to kill an inoculum of O157 and eliminate carriage of this organism, which causes no symptoms in cattle. Studies using these conjugated vaccines in cattle are under way

ANTHRAX

The information we obtained from these studies was applied to anthrax. We now have a vaccine for anthrax. It is composed of the binding protein of anthrax toxin, which is called a protective antigen. It is the only component in the vaccine. However, the organism also makes a capsule, which is a virulence factor. But antibodies against the capsule have not been studied because the capsule is composed of polygamma d acid, and d amino acid polymers are not immunogenic. But the polymer can be coupled to a protein to form a conjugate. In this case we used synthetic polymers, which were shown to be more immunogenic than the natural material and easier to work with. This was largely done by Joanna Kubler-Kielb in our laboratory. You can now make an anthrax vaccine that induces activity against the anthrax. One could conceivably improve the actions of vaccine by adding additional components.

STAPHYLOCOCCUS AUREUS

We are also attempting to make a vaccine for opportunistic pathogens; the most common and serious opportunistic pathogen is staphylococcus. This organism is the main cause of disease in patients on renal dialysis—it is a major cause of morbidity in this group—3.5 percent of patients on renal dialysis get a staph infection at least once a year. The vaccine was shown to be effective for about 10 months and the effectiveness was shown to be related to the level of antibody. We and our colleagues have shown that reinjection of the patients brings the antibody levels back to the level that is associated with efficacy. Thus, we now believe that we can make a vaccine against staphylococcus that will protect the most debilitated of patients. It should work better and for long periods in patients who are immunologically intact, such as those being fitted with prostheses or intracardiac devices and who are, as a consequence, subject to a high incidence of staph infection.

REFERENCES

Hypothesis: Serum IgG antibodies are both essential and sufficient to confer protection against infectious disease

ROBBINS, J.B., R. SCHNEERSON & S.C. SZU. 1995. Perspective: Hypothesis: Serum IgG antibody is sufficient to confer protection against infectious diseases by inactivating the inoculum. J. Infect. Dis. **171:** 1387–1398.

ROBBINS, J.B., R. SCHNEERSON, P. ANDERSON & D.H. SMITH. 1996. Prevention of systemic infections, especially meningitis, caused by *Haemophilus influenzae* type b: impact on public health and implications for other polysaccharide-based vaccines. JAMA **276:** 1181–1185.

ROBBINS, J.B., R. SCHNEERSON, S.C. SZU, *et al.* 1998. Standardization may suffice for licensure of conjugate vaccines. Dev. Biol. Stand. **95:** 161–167.

Haemophilus influenzae type b

RODRIGUES, L.P., R. SCHNEERSON & J.B. ROBBINS. 1971. Immunity to *Haemophilus influenzae* type b. I. The isolation, and some physicochemical, serologic, and biologic properties of the capsular polysaccharide of *Haemophilus influenzae* type b. J. Immunol. **107:** 1071–1080.

SCHNEERSON, R., L.P. RODRIGUES, J.C. PARKE, JR. & J.B. ROBBINS. 1971. Immunity to disease caused by *Haemophilus influenzae* type b. II. Specificity and some biologic characteristics of "natural," infection-acquired, and immunization-induced antibodies to the capsular polysaccharide of *Haemophilus influenzae* type b. J. Immunol. **107:** 1081–1089.

SCHNEERSON, R. & J.B. ROBBINS. 1971. Age-related susceptibility to *Haemophilus influenzae* type b disease in rabbits. Infect. Immun. **4:** 397–401.

SCHNEERSON, R., M. BRADSHAW, J.K. WHISNANT, *et al.* 1971. An *Escherichia coli* antigen cross-reactive with the capsular polysaccharide of *Haemophilus influenzae* type b: occurrence among known serotypes, and immunochemical and biologic properties of *E. coli* antisera towards *H. influenzae* type b. J. Immunol. **108:** 1551–1562.

PARKE, J.C., JR., R. SCHNEERSON & J.B. ROBBINS. 1972. The attack rate, incidence, racial distribution and case fatality rate of *Haemophilus influenzae* type b meningitis in Mecklenburg County, North Carolina. J. Pediatr. **81:** 765–769.

ROBBINS, J.B., R.L. MYEROWITZ, J.K. WHISNANT, *et al.* 1972. Enteric bacteria cross-reactive with *N. meningitidis* groups A and C and *Diplococcus pneumoniae* types I and III. Infect. Immun. **6:** 651–656.

ROBBINS, J.B., J.K. WHISNANT, R. SCHNEERSON & J.C. PARKE, JR. 1973. Quantitative measurement of the "natural" and immunization-induced *Haemophilus influenzae* type b capsular polysaccharide antibodies. Pediatr. Res. **7**(3): 103–110.

SCHNEERSON, R. & J.B. ROBBINS. 1975. Induction of serum *Haemophilus influenzae* type b capsular antibodies in adult volunteers fed cross-reacting *Escherichia coli* 075:K100:H5. N. Engl. J. Med. **292:** 1093–1096.

PARKE, J.C., JR, R. SCHNEERSON, J.B. ROBBINS & J.J. SCHLESSELMAN. 1977. Interim report of a controlled field trial of immunization with capsular polysaccharides of *Haemophilus influenzae* type b and group C *Neisseria meningitidis* in Mecklenburg County, North Carolina (March 1974–March 1976). J. Infect. Dis. **136:** S51–S56.

SCHNEERSON, R., O. BARRERA, A. SUTTON & J.B. ROBBINS. 1980. Preparation, characterization and immunogenicity of *Haemophilus influenzae* type b polysaccharide-protein conjugates. J. Exp. Med. **152:** 361–376.

SUTTON, A., R. SCHNEERSON, S. KENDALL-MORRIS & J.B. ROBBINS. 1982. Differential complement resistance mediates virulence of *Haemophilus influenzae* type b. Infect. Immun. **35:** 95–104.

TARR, P.I., S.W. HOSEA, E.J. BROWN, *et al.* 1982. The requirerment of specific anti-capsular IgG for killing of *Haemophilus influenzae* by the alternative pathway of complement activation. J. Immunol. **128:** 1772–1775.

CHU, C., R. SCHNEERSON, J.B. ROBBINS & S.C. RASTOGI. 1983. Further studies on immunogenicity of *Haemophilus influenzae* type b and pneumococcal 6A polysaccharide-protein conjugates. Infect. Immun. **40:** 245–256.

EGAN, W., R. SCHNEERSON, K.E. WERNER & G. ZON. 1982. Structural studies and chemistry of bacterial capsular polysacchawrides isolated from *Haemophilus influenzae* types a,b,c amd f: NMR spectroscopic identification and chemical modification of endgroups and the nature of based-catalyzed hydrolytic depolymeriation. J. Am. Chem. Soc. **104:** 2898–2910.

SCHNEERSON, R., J.B. ROBBINS, J.C. PARKE, Jr., *et al.* 1986. Quantitative and qualitative analyses of serum antibodies elicited in adults by *Haemophilus influenzae* type b and pneumococcus type 6A capsular polysaccharide-tetanus toxoid conjugates. Infect. Immun. **52:** 519–528.

CLAESSON, B.A., R. SCHNEERSON, B. TROLLFORS, *et al.* 1999. Duration of serum antibodies elicited by *Haemophilus influenzae* type b capsular polysaccharide alone or conjugated to tetanus toxoid in 18- to 23-month old children. J. Pediatr. **116:** 929–931.

PARKE, J.C., JR., R. SCHNEERSON, C. REIMER, *et al.* Clinical and immunologic responses to *Haemophilus influenzae* type b tetanus toxoid conjugate vaccine in infants injected 3,5,7 and 18 months of age. J. Pediatr. **118:** 84–190.

CLAESSON, B.A., B. TROLLFORS, P.W. ANDERSON, *et al.* 1996. Serum antibodies in six-year-old children vaccinated in infancy with a *Haemophilus influenzae* type b-tetanus toxoid conjugate vaccine. Pediatr. Infect. Dis. J. **15**(2): 170–172.

Streptococcus pneumoniae (pneumococcus)

SZU, S.C., C-J. LEE, J.C. PARKE, JR, *et al.* 1982. Cross-immunogenicity of pneumo-coccal group 9 capsular polysaccharides in adult volunteers. Infect. Immun. **35:** 777–782.

ROBBINS, J.B., R. AUSTRIAN, C-J. LEE, *et al.* 1983. Consideration for formulating the second generation pneumococcal vaccine with emphasis on the cross-reactive types within groups. J. Infect. Dis. **148:** 1136–1159.

SZU, S.C., G. ZON, R. SCHNEERSON & J.B. ROBBINS. 1986. Characterization of the depolymerization of bacterial polysaccharides induced by ultrasonic irradia-tion. Carbohydr. Res. **152:** 7–20.

SZU, S.C., R. SCHNEERSON & J.B. ROBBINS. 1986. Rabbit antibodies to the cell wall polysaccharide of *Streptococcus pneumoniae* fail to protect mice from lethal infection with encapsulated pneumococci. Infect. Immun. **54:** 448-455.

FATTOM, A., W.F. VANN, S.C. SZU, *et al.* 1988. Synthesis and physiochemical and immunological characterization of pneumococcus type 12F polysaccharide-diphtheria toxoid conjugates. Infect. Immun. **56:** 2292–2298.

SCHNEERSON, R., L. LEVI, J.B. ROBBINS, *et al.* 1992. Synthesis of a conjugate vac-cine composed of pneumococcus type 14 capsular polysaccharide bound to pertussis toxin. Infect. Immun. **60:** 3528–3532.

Neisseria meningitidis (meningococcus)

VANN, W.F., T.-Y. LIU & J.B. ROBBINS. 1976. *Bacillus pumilus* polysaccharide cross-reactive with meningococcal group A polysaccharide. Infect. Immun. 13654–13662.

WONG, K.H., O. BARRERA, A. SUTTON, *et al.* 1977. Standardization and control of meningococcal vaccines, group A and group C polysaccharides. J. Biol. Stand. 5(3): 197–215.

DEVI, S.J.N., J.B. ROBBINS & R. SCHNEERSON. 1991. Antibodies to poly[(2→8)-alpha-N-acetylneuraminic acid] and poly[(2→9)-alpha-N-acetylneuraminic acid] are elicited by immunization of mice with *Escherichia coli* K92 conju-gates: potential vaccines for groups B and C meningococci and *E. coli* K1. Proc. Natl. Acad. Sci. USA **88:** 7175–7179.

ROBBINS, J.B., D.W. TOWNE, E.C. GOTSCHLICH & R. SCHNEERSON. 1997. "Love's labours lost:" failure to implement mass vaccination against group A menin-gococcal meningitis in sub-Saharan Africa. Lancet **350:** 880–882.

ROBBINS, J.B., R. SCHNEERSON & E.C. GOTSCHLICH. 2000. A rebuttal: epidemic and endemic meningococcal meningitis in sub-Saharan Africa can be pre-vented now by routine immunization with group A meningococcal capsular polysaccharide vaccine. Pediatr. Infect. Dis. J. **19:** 945–953.

ROBBINS, J.B., R. SCHNEERSON, E.C. GOTSCHLICH, *et al.* 2003. Meningococcal meningitis in sub-Saharan Africa: the case for mass and routine vaccination with available polysaccharide vaccines. Bull. WHO **81:** 745–750.

Salmonella typhi (typhoid fever)

ROBBINS, J.D. & J.B. ROBBINS. 1984. Re-examination of the immunopathogenic role of the capsular polysaccharide (Vi antigen) of *Salmonella typhi*. J. Infect. Dis. **150:** 436–449.

ACHARYA, I.L., C.U. LOWE, R. THAPA, *et al.* 1987. Prevention of typhoid fever in Nepal with the Vi capsular polysaccharide of *Salmonella typhi*: a preliminary report one year after immunization. N. Engl. J. Med. **317:** 1101–1104.

KLUGMAN, K.P., I.T. GILBERTSON, H.J. KOORNHOF, *et al.*, Vaccine Advisory Committee. 1987. Protective activity of Vi capsular polysaccharide vaccine against typhoid fever. Lancet **ii:** 1165–1169.

SZU, S.C., A.L. STONE, J.D. ROBBINS, *et al.* 1987. Vi capsular polysaccharide-protein conjugates for prevention of typhoid fever. Preparation, characterization, and immunogenicity in laboratory animals. J. Exp. Med. **166:** 1510–1524.

KOSSACZKA, Z., F-YC. LIN, V.A. HO, *et al.* 1999. Safety and immunogenicity of Vi conjugate vaccines for typhoid fever in adults, teenagers and 2- to 4-year-old children in Vietnam. Infect. Immun. **67:** 5806–5810.

LIN, F-YC., V.A. HO, P.V. BAY, *et al.* 2002. The epidemiology of typhoid fever in the Dong Thap Province, MeKong Delta region of Vietnam. Am. J. Trop. Med. Hyg. **62:** 644–648.

LIN, F-YC., V.A. HO, H.B. KHIEM, *et al.* 2001. The efficacy of a *Salmonella typhi* Vi conjugate vaccine in two-to-five-year-old children. N. Engl. J. Med. **344:** 1263–1269.

LANH, M.N., F-Y.C. LIN, P.V. BAY, *et al.* 2003. Persistence of antibodies and efficacy against typhoid fever 28–46 months following Vi conjugate vaccine (Vi-*r*EPA) in 2 to 5 years-old children. N. Engl. J. Med. **349:** 1390–1391.

KONADU, E., J. SHILOACH, D.A. BRYLA, *et al.* 1996. Synthesis, characterization and immunological properties in mice of conjugates composed of detoxified lipopolysaccharide of *Salmonella paratyphi* A bound to tetanus toxoid, with emphasis on the role of O-acetyls. Infect. Immun. **64:** 2709–2715.

KONADU, E.Y., F-YC. LIN, V.A. HO, *et al.* 2000. Phase 1 and phase 2 studies of *Salmonella enterica* serovar *paratyphi* A O-specific polysaccharide-tetanus toxoid conjugates in adults, teenagers and 2-to-4-year-old children in Vietnam. Infect. Immun. **68:** 1529–1534.

Shigellosis

ROBBINS, J.B., C. CHU, D.C. WATSON, *et al.* 1991. O-specific side-chain toxin-protein conjugates as parenteral vaccines for the prevention of *Shigellosis* and related diseases. Rev. Infect. Dis. **13:** S362–S365.

CHU, C., B. LIU, D. WATSON, *et al.* 1991. Preparation, characterization and immunogenicity of conjugates composed of O-specific polysaccharide of *Shigella dysenteriae* type 1 (Shiga's bacillus) bound to tetanus toxoid. Infect. Immun. **59:** 4450–4458.

ROBBINS, J.B., C. CHU & R. SCHNEERSON. 1992. Hypothesis for vaccine development: protective immunity to enteric diseases caused by nontyphoidal *Salmonellae* and *Shigellae* may be conferred by serum IgG antibodies to the O-specific polysaccharide of their lipopolysaccharides. Clin. Infect. Dis. **15:** 346–361.

COHEN, D., S. ASHKENAZI, M.S. GREEN, *et al.* 1997. Double-blind vaccine-controlled randomized efficacy trial of an investigational *Shigella sonnei* conjugate vaccine in young adults. Lancet **349:** 155–159.

ASHKENAZI, S., J.H. PASSWELL, E. HARLEV, *et al.*, and The Israel Pediatric *Shigella* Study Group. 1999. Safety and immunogenicity of *Shigella sonnei* and *Shi*-

gella flexneri 2a O-specific polysaccharide conjugates in children. J. Infect. Dis. **179:** 1565–1568.

POZSGAY, V., C. CHU, L. PANNELL, *et al.* 1999. Protein conjugates of synthetic saccharides elicit higher levels of serum IgG lipopolysaccharide antibodies in mice than do those of the O-specific polysaccharide from *Shigella dysenteriae* type 1. Proc. Natl. Acad. Sci. USA **96:** 5194–5197.

PAVLIAKOVA, D., J.S. MONCRIEF, D.M. LYERLY, *et al.* 2000. *Clostridium difficile* recombinant toxin A repeating units as a carrier protein for conjugate vaccines: studies of pneumococcal type 14, *Escherichia coli* K1, and *Shigella flexneri* type 2a polysaccharides in mice. Infect. Immun. **68:** 2161–2166.

PASSWELL, J.H., S. ASHKENAZI, E. HARLEV, *et al.*, and the Israel *Shigella* Study Group, C. CHU, J. SHILOACH, J.B. ROBBINS & R. SCHNEERSON. 2003. Safety and immunogenicity of *Shigella sonnei*-CRM9 and *Shigella flexneri* type 2a-rEPA$_{\text{succ}}$ conjugates in 1 to 4-year-old children. Pediatr. Infect. Dis. J. **22:** 701–706.

Escherichia coli O157

KONADU, E.Y., J.B. ROBBINS, J. SHILOACH, *et al.* 1994. Preparation, characterization and immunological properties in mice of *Escherichia coli* O157 O-specific polysaccharide-protein conjugate vaccines. Infect. Immun. **62:** 5048–5054.

KONADU, E.Y., J.C. PARKE, JR., H.T. TRAN, *et al.* 1998. Investigational vaccine for *Escherichia coli* O157: Phase 1 study of O157 O-specific polysaccharide-*Pseudomonas aeruginosa* recombinant exoprotein A (rEPA) conjugates in adults. J. Infect. Dis. **177:** 383–387.

Anthrax

RAMIREZ, D.M., S. LEPPLA, R. SCHNEERSON & J. SHILOACH. 2002. Production, recovery and immunogenicity of the protective antigen from a recombinant strain of *Bacillus anthracis*. J. Ind. Microbiol. Biotech. **28:** 232–238.

SCHNEERSON, R., J. KUBLER-KIELB, T-Y. LIU, *et al.* 2003. Poly(γ-D-glutamic acid protein) conjugates induce IgG antibodies in mice to the capsule of *Bacillus anthracis*. Proc. Natl. Acad. Sci. USA **100:** 8945–8950.

Staphylococcus aureus

KARAKAWA, W.W., J.M. FOURNIER, W.F. VANN, *et al.* 1985. Methods for the serological typing of the capsular polysaccharides of *Staphylococcus aureus*. J. Clin. Microbiol. **22:** 445–447.

SOMPOLINKSKY, O., Z. SAMRA, W.W. KARAKWAWA, *et al.* 1988. Encapsulation and capsular types in isolates of *Staphylococcus aureus* from different sources in relation to phage types. J. Clin. Microbiol. **22:** 828–834.

KARAKAWA, W.W., A. SUTTON, R. SCHNEERSON, *et al.* 1988. Capsular antibodies induce type-specific phagocytosis of capsulated *Staphylococcus aureus* by human polymorphonuclear leukocytes. Infect. Immun. **56:** 1090–1095.

FATTOM, A., R. SCHNEERSON, D.C. WATSON, *et al.* 1993. Laboratory and clinical evaluation of conjugate vaccines composed of *Staphylococcus aureus* type 5 and type 8 capsular polysaccharides bound to *Pseudomonas aeruginosa* recombinant exoprotein A. Infect. Immun. **610:** 1023–1032.

WELCH, P.G., A. FATTOM, J. MOORE, JR., *et al.* 1996. Safety and immunogenicity of *Staphylococcus aureus* type 5 capsular polysaccharide-*Pseudomonas aeruginosa* recombinant exoprotein A conjugate vaccine in patients on hemodialysis. J. Am. Soc. Nephrol. **7:** 247–253.

SHINEFIELD, H., S. BLACK, A.I. FATTOM, *et al.* 2002. Use of a *Staphylococcus aureus* conjugate vaccine in patients receiving hemodialysis. N. Engl. J. Med. **346:** 491–496.

Study of Translational Control of Eukaryotic Gene Expression Using Yeast

ALAN G. HINNEBUSCH, PHD, KATSURA ASANO, PHD,
DEANNE S. OLSEN, PHD, LON PHAN, PHD, KLAUS H. NIELSEN, PHD,
AND LEOŠ VALÁŠEK, PHD

*Laboratory of Gene Regulation and Development, National Institute of
Child Health and Human Development, National Institutes of Health,
Bethesda, Maryland 20892, USA*

ABSTRACT: Eukaryotic cells respond to starvation by decreasing the rate
of general protein synthesis while inducing translation of specific mRNAs
encoding transcription factors GCN4 (yeast) or ATF4 (humans). Both responses are elicited by phosphorylation of translation initiation factor 2
(eIF2) and the attendant inhibition of its nucleotide exchange factor
eIF2B—decreasing the binding to 40S ribosomes of methionyl initiator
tRNA in the ternary complex (TC) with eIF2 and GTP. The reduction in
TC levels enables scanning ribosomes to bypass the start codons of upstream open reading frames in the *GCN4* mRNA leader and initiate translation at the authentic *GCN4* start codon. We exploited the fact that *GCN4*
translation is a sensitive reporter of defects in TC recruitment to identify
the catalytic and regulatory subunits of eIF2B. More recently, we implicated the C-terminal domain of eIF1A in 40S-binding of TC *in vivo*. Interestingly, we found that TC resides in a multifactor complex (MFC) with eIF3,
eIF1, and the GTPase-activating protein for eIF2, known as eIF5. Our biochemical and genetic analyses indicate that physical interactions between
MFC componens enhance TC binding to 40S subunits and are required for
wild-type translational control of *GCN4*. MFC integrity and eIF3 function
also contribute to post-assembly steps in the initiation pathway that impact
GCN4 expression. Thus, apart from its critical role in the starvation response, *GCN4* regulation is a valuable tool for dissecting the contributions
of multiple translation factors in the eukaryotic initiation pathway.

KEYWORDS: translation; regulation; GCN4; initiation factor; ribosome;
protein kinase

Address for correspondence: Alan G. Hinnebusch, PhD, Chief, Laboratory of Gene Regulation and Development, Head, Section on Nutrient control of Gene Regulation, Division of Intramural Research, NICHD, NIH, Bldg. 18T, Rm. 106, Bethesda, MD 20892. Voice: 301-496-4480;
fax: 301-496-6828.

ahinnebusch@nih.gov

Ann. N.Y. Acad. Sci. 1038: 60–74 (2004). © 2004 New York Academy of Sciences.
doi: 10.1196/annals.1315.012

INTRODUCTION

A translational control mechanism conserved throughout the eukaryotic kingdom mediates a broad alteration in gene expression in response to nutrient starvation or stress. This regulatory response involves four protein kinases that phosphorylate the alpha subunit of translation initiation factor 2 (eIF2α) in response to amino acid starvation (GCN2), unfolded proteins (PERK), virus infection (PKR), or hemin limitation (HRI). Phosphorylation of eIF2 reduces its function by inhibiting the recycling of inactive GDP-bound eIF2 to the active GTP-bound state by the guanine nucleotide exchange factor (GEF) eIF2B. Consequently, general protein synthesis declines with attendant reductions in cell growth and division. In parallel, sequence-specific transcription factors are induced at the translational level that, in turn, stimulate the transcription of numerous genes that enable cells to ameliorate stress or starvation conditions (FIG. 1A).[1,2]

Because of the powerful genetic tools available, we have been dissecting this conserved regulatory mechanism in the yeast *Saccharomyces cerevisiae*, where it is known as the General Amino Acid Control. Indeed, the eIF2α kinase GCN2 was first discovered in this yeast by its role in the induction of amino acid biosynthetic genes under the control of transcriptional activator GCN4. When yeast cells are starved for any amino acid, the uncharged tRNAs that accumulate bind to a regulatory domain in GCN2 and activate its eIF2α kinase function. This leads to increased translation of *GCN4* mRNA, and the GCN4 thus produced activates the transcription of some 500 genes of diverse function, including nearly all amino acid and vitamin biosynthetic enzymes. The elevated levels of biosynthetic enzymes allows for increased amino acid production, high-level tRNA charging, and a restoration of optimal translation rates in the cell.[2,3]

Regulatory mutants incapable of this response, called general control noninducible (Gcn⁻) mutants, are sensitive to multiple amino acid analogs, including 3-aminotriazole (3-AT) that inhibits histidine biosynthesis, because the amino acid biosynthetic enzymes cannot be induced by GCN4 in such mutants. By screening for this Gcn⁻ phenotype, we and others identified mutants with defects in *GCN4* translational induction which lack the kinase GCN2 or one of its positive effectors, or that contain amino acid changes in eIF2 or eIF2B. Biochemical analyses of these mutants has helped to elucidate the molecular mechanisms of translation initiation and the control of gene expression by eIF2α phosphorylation.[2]

The conventional view of the translation initiation pathway (FIG. 1B) commences with the binding of initiator methionyl-tRNA (Met-tRNA$_i^{Met}$) to the 40S ribosome to form the 43S initiation complex. The Met-tRNA$_i^{Met}$ is transferred to the 40S subunit in a ternary complex (TC) with eIF2 and GTP, and this reaction is stimulated by the eIF3 complex, eIF1 and eIF1A. The 43S complex then binds to the capped 5′ end of the mRNA with the help of the

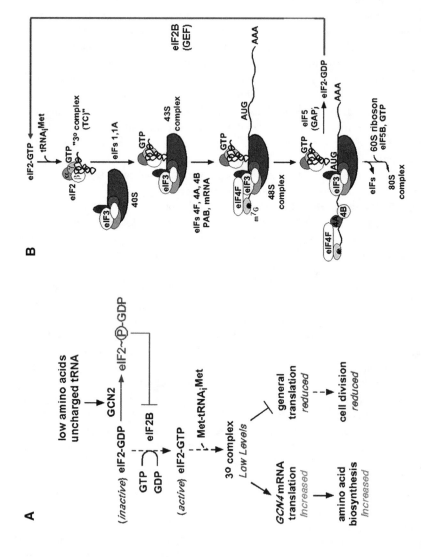

FIGURE 1. Translational control via eIF2α phosphorylation and the translation initiation pathway.

mRNA-binding, eIF4 group of factors (to form the 48S complex), and scans the mRNA leader for an AUG triplet to serve as the initiation codon. On base-pairing between the anticodon of Met-tRNA$_i^{Met}$ and the AUG triplet, the GTP bound to the TC is hydrolyzed in a reaction stimulated by the GTPase activating protein (GAP), eIF5. The 60S ribosomal subunit then joins to form an 80S complex capable of protein synthesis. The eIF2-GDP released in this reaction must be recycled by eIF2B to eIF2-GTP to re-form the TC for sub-sequent rounds of initiation. This exchange reaction is down-regulated by phosphorylation of eIF2α by GCN2 in starved cells because phosphorylated eIF2-GDP is a competitive inhibitor, rather than a substrate, for eIF2B (re-viewed in Hinnebusch[4])). As indicated above, the consequent reduction in TC formation reduces general translation but specifically stimulates transla-tion of *GCN4* mRNA (FIG. 1A).

The paradoxical induction of *GCN4* translation in response to eIF2 phos-phorylation is determined by four short open-reading-frames (ORFs) of only 2-3 codons in length present in the leader of *GCN4* mRNA leader. Only the first and fourth of these upstream ORFs (uORFs 1 and 4) are sufficient for translational control (FIG. 2A). In non-starved cells, scanning ribosomes se-lect the first AUG, translate uORF1 and resume scanning downstream. Be-cause eIF2B activity is high and the TC is abundant, all of the scanning 40S ribosomes re-bind TC before reaching uORF4, and following translation of uORF4 are ejected from the mRNA by signals surrounding the uORF4 stop. Hence, no GCN4 protein is produced (FIG. 2A, *left*). (Note that specialized sequences exist at the uORF1 stop codon that permit most ribosomes to re-main attached to the mRNA and resume scanning after terminating uORF1 translation.)[2]

In starved cells, GCN2 phosphorylates eIF2α to reduce eIF2B activity and thereby lower the abundance of TC in the cell. While there remains a suffi-cient amount of TC to permit translation of uORF1, it takes much longer to "recharge" the reinitiating 40S ribosomes scanning downstream from uORF1 with the TC. This delay in TC recruitment enables about 50% of the 40S sub-units to bypass uORF4, rebind TC in the uORF4-*GCN4* interval, and reini-tiate at *GCN4* instead (FIG. 2A, *right*). Thus, a reduction in the level of TC induces *GCN4* translation by allowing a fraction of ribosomes to scan past the inhibitory uORF4 and select the *GCN4* start codon for reinitiation.[2]

The fact that *GCN4* expression (and that of its target genes) is induced whenever TC levels drop in the cell, allowed us to identify genetically all of the subunits of the exchange factor eIF2B and to assign them with catalytic or regulatory functions. Mutants lacking GCN2 cannot induce *GCN4* trans-lation under starvation conditions and thus exhibit constitutively low levels of histidine biosynthetic enzymes and the attendant sensitivity to 3AT that signifies a Gcn⁻ phenotype (FIG. 2B, *left*). We identified temperature-sensitive lethal mutations in the four essential subunits of eIF2B that reduce the level of eIF2-GTP and TC formation and thereby induce *GCN4* transla-

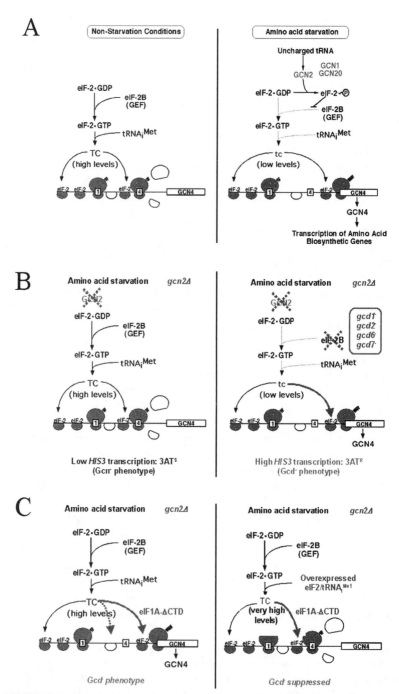

FIGURE 2. Translational control of *GCN4* is an *in vivo* indicator of defects in TC formation or recruitment.

tion in the absence of GCN2. This produces a general control derepressed (Gcd⁻) phenotype, which occurs whenever a delay in TC recruitment allows ribosomes to bypass uORF4 and translate the *GCN4* ORF (Fig. 2B, *right*).[2]

We also identified regulatory mutations in the α, β, and δ subunits of eIF2B that exhibit a Gcn⁻ phenotype. In such mutants, no GCN4 is produced even though eIF2α phosphorylation occurs when GCN2 is activated by starvation. Our biochemical analysis showed that these mutations allow eIF2B to accept phosphorylated eIF2-GDP as a substrate, rather than being inhibited by it. Furthermore, we showed that these three eIF2B subunits can exist as a stable subcomplex that binds eIF2α in a manner stimulated by phosphorylation, and that the Gcn⁻ mutations in the eIF2B subunits weaken this interaction. The remaining two eIF2B subunits (γ and ε) form a subcomplex that harbors the GEF activity but is insensitive to phosphorylation of eIF2. Thus, we concluded that the regulatory subunits "sense" the phosphate group on eIF2α and their physical interaction with phosphorylated eIF2 leads to an allosteric inhibition of the GEF function lodged in the γ and ε subunits of eIF2B.[5]

THE C-TERMINAL DOMAIN OF eIF1A PROMOTES TC RECRUITMENT TO 40S RIBOSOMES *IN VIVO*

In cell-free translation systems, the eIFs -1, -1A and -3 promote binding of TC to the 40S subunit (Fig. 1B), but their relative importance for this reaction *in vivo* is unknown. We reasoned that mutations in these factors that impede TC recruitment in living cells should mimic eIF2α phosphorylation and derepress *GCN4* translation in a *gcn2* background (Fig. 2C, *left*). This prediction was borne out for a particular C-terminal truncation of eIF1A, as discussed next.

A schematic representation of the eIF1A polypeptide (encoded by the *TIF11* gene) is shown in Figure 3A. The OB-fold domain of eIF1A is related to the bacterial initiation factor IF1. Because eIF2 is not found in bacteria, we reasoned that the eukaryotic-specific C-terminal domain (CTD) of eIF1A might mediate a functional interaction with eIF2 that would be instrumental in TC recruitment. In accordance with this prediction, deletions of the eIF1A CTD reduced the growth rate of cells and caused a significant depletion of polyribosomes, a hallmark of reduced translation initiation rates (Figs. 3A,B). Importantly, the largest truncation of *TIF11* we examined (*Δ108–153*) suppressed the 3AT^s phenotype of the *gcn2Δ* mutation, indicating constitutive derepression of *GCN4* translation (the Gcd⁻ phenotype) (Fig. 3C, data encircled by dotted red lines [color appears in online version]). Furthermore, this Gcd⁻ phenotype was suppressed by co-overexpressing the macromolecular components of TC (three subunits of eIF2 and tRNA$_i$^{Met}) from the four cognate genes carried on a high-copy plasmid (Fig. 3C).[6]

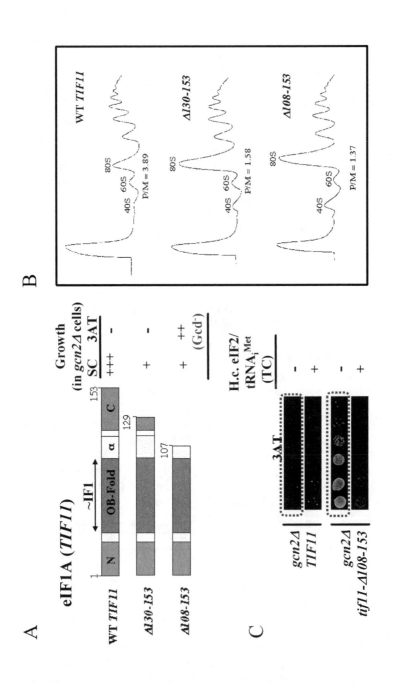

FIGURE 3. Truncation of the eIF1A CTD impairs translation initiation and confers a Gcd⁻ phenotype suppressible by TC overexpression.

To explain these results, we propose that the *Δ108–153* deletion in the eIF1A CTD delays the rebinding of TC to the 40S subunits scanning downstream from uORF1 in the *GCN4* mRNA leader. This allows a fraction of scanning 40S subunits to bypass uORF4, rebind the TC in the uORF4-*GCN4* interval, and reinitiate at *GCN4*, even though TC levels are at maximal levels due to the absence of GCN2 and eIF2α phosphorylation. Thus, *GCN4* translation is constitutively induced, producing the Gcd⁻ phenotype (FIG. 2C, *left*). When TC is overexpressed, the defect in TC binding to 40S subunits is suppressed by mass-action and all reinitiating ribosomes now rebind the TC before reaching uORF4. Hence, the constitutive repression of *GCN4* mRNA characteristic of *gcn2Δ* cells is restored and the Gcd⁻ phenotype of *tif11-Δ108-153* is suppressed (Fig. 2C, *right*). We recently obtained biochemical evidence that TC binding to 40S ribosomes is reduced in *tif11-Δ108–153* cells (Christie Fekete and A.G.H., unpublished observations) using a newly developed method for *in vivo* cross-linking of 43S complexes in living cells.[7] Together, our results provide the first evidence implicating eIF1A in TC recruitment *in vivo*.

FORMATION OF A MULTIFACTOR COMPLEX CONTAINING eIF1, eIF3, eIF5 AND THE TC IS REQUIRED FOR OPTIMAL RATES OF TRANSLATION INITIATION *IN VIVO*

The roles of eIF1 and the eIF3 complex in TC binding are at once more complex and interesting. We found that these factors reside with the TC itself, and with the GAP eIF5, in a multifactor complex (MFC) that can exist free of 40S ribosomes. We affinity-purified this complex by attaching the FLAG epitope to eIF5 and identified the copurifying proteins (by immunoblot analysis) as the three subunits of eIF2, the five core subunits of eIF3 (a to e), and eIF1 (FIG. 4A).[8] We have used various protein-protein interaction assays to map the domains in each polypeptide of the MFC that mediates its interactions with other MFC components. Unexpectedly, we found that the CTD of the GAP eIF5 bridges eIF2 and eIF3 by interacting simultaneously with eIF2β and the N-terminal domain (NTD) of NIP1/eIF3c (FIG. 4B). The NIP1-NTD and eIF5-CTD also interact with eIF1.[8–10] Consistent with these findings, co-sedimentation of the native MFC components in a high molecular-weight nonribosomal complex was disrupted by a cluster of point mutations in the eIF5-CTD (encoded by *tif5-7A*) (FIG. 3C). We showed that the *tif5-7A* mutation weakens the binary interactions of the isolated eIF5-CTD with eIF2β and NIP1-NTD, respectively. Importantly, the *tif5-7A* mutation impairs growth and reduces polysome abundance *in vivo*, and these phenotypes can be partially suppressed by overexpressing the components of TC.[8,9] These findings indicate that the linkage of eIF5 to other factors in the MFC, particularly the TC, is required for optimal rates of translation initiation *in vivo*.

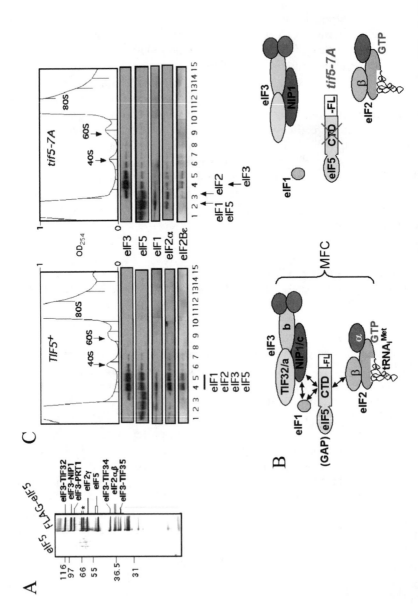

FIGURE 4. Integrity of the multifactor complex (MFC), containing eIF3, eIF5, eIF1, and TC, is dependent on the CTD of eIF5.

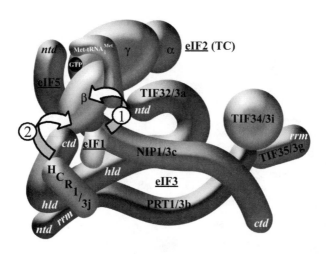

FIGURE 5. A 3D model of the MFC and interactions linking eIF3 to eIF2 involving the NIP1-NTD via eIF5 (1) and the TIF32-CTD (2).

INDEPENDENT CONTACTS BETWEEN eIF2 AND eIF3 IN THE MFC ENHANCE TC RECRUITMENT *IN VIVO*

We hypothesized that physical linkage of the various eIFs in the MFC would allow for their cooperative binding to the 40S ribosome, enhancing the rate of 43S complex formation. To test this model, we compared the binding of radiolabeled Met-tRNA$_i$^{Met} to 40S ribosomes in cell-free extracts prepared from *TIF5* and *tif5-7A* strains. We observed reduced Met-tRNA$_i$^{Met} to 40S subunits in the mutant extract that could be rescued with purified, recombinant eIF5. This result supports the notion that MFC integrity promotes recruitment of the TC to the 40S ribosome.[11]

In contrast to the *in vitro* data just described, we did not observe a reduction in TC binding to 40S subunits in cross-linked *tif5-7A* mutant cells. This finding suggested that there are additional interactions that stabilize the MFC that must be disrupted simultaneously with the *tif5-7A* mutation to diminish TC recruitment *in vivo*. In the course of affinity-purifying and characterizing the MFC subcomplexes formed by truncated forms of the TIF32/a subunit of eIF3, we discovered that deletion of C-terminal residues 791–964 (*TIF32-Δ6*) results in dissociation of eIF2 without loss of eIF5, eIF1, or eIF3 subunits from the MFC. Furthermore, a TIF32 fragment containing these C-terminal residues formed a specific complex with eIF2 (and no other MFC components) when expressed *in vivo*. Thus, the TIF32-CTD interacts directly with eIF2. In a similar way, we found that TIF32 residues 642–791 harbor an additional eIF1 binding site in eIF3. The identification of these new contacts

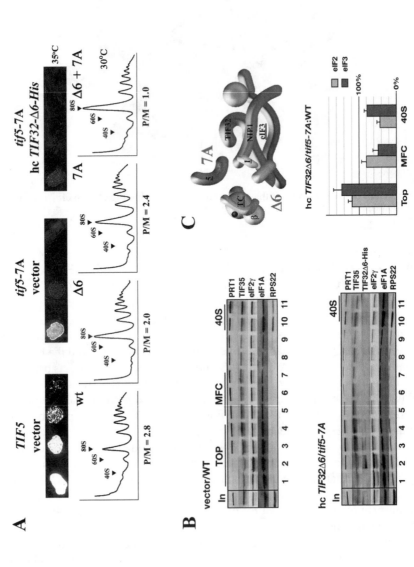

FIGURE 6. Two independent contacts linking eIF2 and eIF3 in the MFC make additive contributions to TC recruitment and translation initiation.

linking eIF3 to eIF2 and eIF1 necessitated the development of a 3D model of the MFC (shown in FIG. 5) which encompasses the network of interactions linking the TIF32-CTD and NIP1-NTD with eIF1, eIF2 and eIF5.[12]

The *TIF32-Δ6* allele does not support cell viability, demonstrating that the TIF32-CTD carries out an essential function, and it confers a dominant slow-growth (Slg⁻) phenotype when expressed in cells harboring wild-type *TIF32*. This phenotype results from competition of the truncated TIF32-Δ6 protein with native TIF32 for interaction with other eIF3 subunits, thus reducing the concentrations of wild-type eIF3 and MFC. Importantly, this Slg⁻ phenotype is partially suppressed by overexpressing the TC (as was observed for *tif5-7A*), and overexpressing *TIF32-Δ6* exacerbates the cell-growth defect and depletion of polysomes in *tif5-7A* cells (FIG. 6A). These genetic data suggest that the independent contacts between eIF3 and eIF2 mediated by the eIF2β/eIF5/NIP1-NTD interactions (disrupted by *tif5-7A*) and the eIF2β/TIF32-CTD interaction (disrupted by *TIF32-Δ6*) have additive effects on 43S complex assembly.

To test this last hypothesis, we used formaldehyde treatment of living yeast cells to cross-link 43S complexes *in vivo*. Analysis of the eIFs bound to free 40S subunits recovered from these cells revealed a 60% reduction in the amounts of 40S-bound eIF2 and eIF3 in *tif5-7A* cells overexpressing *TIF32-Δ6* compared to wild-type cells (FIG. 6B-C). We also observed wild-type amounts of 40S-bound factors in *tif5-7A* single mutants (data not shown).[7] These results provide the first direct evidence that eIF2-eIF3 contacts in the MFC enhance TC recruitment and 43S complex assembly *in vivo*.

To our surprise, the *tif5-7A* cells overexpressing *TIF32-Δ6* did not exhibit the Gcd⁻ phenotype that would be expected from a delay in TC binding to reinitiating 40S ribosomes on *GCN4* mRNA. To account for this unexpected finding, we propose that disrupting the MFC impairs an additional step in the pathway downstream from 43S assembly, and that this secondary defect compensates for the delay in TC recruitment, thereby preventing ribosomes from bypassing uORF4 and reinitiating at *GCN4*. The *tif5-7A* mutation may retard the rate of scanning from uORF1 to uORF4, or delay GTP hydrolysis at the uORF4 start codon by the proportion of 40S ribosomes that succeeded in rebinding TC before reaching uORF4. Either defect would produce a roadblock that delays passage of all re-scanning 40S subunits past uORF4 and thereby compensate for the reduced rate of TC binding produced by overexpressing *TIF32-Δ6*. Consistent with this explanation, we found that *tif5-7A* alone produces a Gcn⁻ phenotype, which is suppressed by overexpression of *TIF32-Δ6*[7]. Hence, these two mutations have opposing, compensatory effects on *GCN4* translation. More recently, we isolated point mutations in the TIF32-CTD that produce a strong Gcd⁻ phenotype that can be suppressed by overexpression of the TC (Laxminaryana Burela and A.G.H, unpublished observations). Thus, it now seems clear that contact between eIF2 and eIF3 in the MFC mediated by the TIF32-CTD stimulates TC recruitment *in vivo*.

THE eIF3 HAS A CRITICAL FUNCTION DOWNSTREAM
OF 48S COMPLEX ASSEMBLY

In addition to its function in 43S assembly, our analysis of the *prt1-1* mutation in the b subunit of eIF3 provides strong evidence that eIF3 has an essential function at a post-assembly step in the pathway. Although heat-treated extracts from this mutant exhibit virtually no binding of Met-tRNA$_i^{Met}$ or mRNA to 40S subunits,[10] heat-treating *prt1-1* mutant cells leads to an accumulation of eIF2 and other MFC components on 40S subunits and no reduction in mRNA recruitment. Consistent with this last finding, the temperature-sensitive phenotype of *prt1-1* cells is not suppressed by overexpressing the TC, and the mutation has a Gcn⁻ phenotype rather than a Gcd⁻ phenotype.[7] The Gcn⁻ phenotype would be consistent with a defect in scanning or GTP hydrolysis at uORF4, as described above for the *tif5-7A* mutation.

We can reconcile the discrepant effects of the *prt1-1* mutation observed *in vitro* and *in vivo* with a simple kinetic model of the initiation pathway. The first steps involve assembly of 43S and 48S complexes, wherein TC binds to the 40S ribosome and mRNA joins this assembly. The *prt1-1* mutation reduces the rates of both assembly reactions *in vitro*, whereas 43S/48S complexes were found to accumulate *in vivo*. This discrepancy can be explained by proposing that the *prt1-1* mutation has an even stronger effect on the post-assembly steps of scanning or GTP hydrolysis that convert 48S to 80S complexes. Hence, the mutation leads to a net accumulation of 48S complexes *in vivo*. *In vitro*, the conversion of 48S to 80S complexes was prevented by inclusion of non-hydrolyzable GTP in the assays; thus, only the assembly reactions were being monitored in these experiments. It is also possible that 43S/48S complexes are more thermolabile *in vitro* than *in vivo*, so that the assembly defects produced by *prt1-1* are relatively more severe *in vitro*.

CONCLUSIONS

- The experiments summarized above have allowed us to achieve the following new insights into the mechanism of translation initiation and the translational control of *GCN4* mRNA.

- The CTD of eIF1A promotes binding of the eIF2-GTP/ Met-tRNA$_i^{Met}$ ternary complex (TC) to the 40S ribosome *in vivo*.

- The TC resides with eIF1, eIF3, and eIF5 in multifactor complex (MFC) that can exist free of 40S ribosomes.

- The integrity of the MFC is required for optimal rates of translation initiation *in vivo* and for TC binding to 40S subunits *in vitro*.

- The independent contacts linking eIF2 to eIF3 in the MFC via the eIF2β/eIF5/NIP1-NTD interactions and the eIF2β/TIF32-CTD interaction have additive stimulatory effects on TC binding to the 40S ribosome *in vivo*.

- Disruption of the MFC by the *tif5-7A* mutation in the eIF5-CTD, or mutational inactivation of PRT1/eIF3b subunit by *prt1-1*, impairs scanning or GTP hydrolysis as the rate-limiting defect *in vivo*, suppressing the Gcd⁻ phenotype that would be expected from the defects in TC recruitment produced by these mutations observable *in vitro*.

- The MFC and eIF1A participate in the reinitiation mechanism that underlies the gene-specific translational control of *GCN4* mRNA via eIF2α phosphorylation by GCN2.

- *GCN4* translational control is a sensitive *in vivo* reporter that can be used to identify molecular interactions involving eIFs -2B, -1, -1A, -3 and -5 that contribute to formation of the TC or its recruitment to the 40S ribosome.

REFERENCES

1. HARDING, H.P., I. NOVOA, Y. ZHANG, *et al.* 2000. Regulated translation initiation controls stress-induced gene expression in mammalian cells. Mol. Cell **6:** 1099–1108.
2. HINNEBUSCH, A.G. 1996. Translational control of GCN4: gene-specific regulation by phosphorylation of eIF2. *In* Translational Control. J.W.B. Hershey, M. B. Mathews & N. Sonenberg, Eds.: 199–244. Cold Spring Harbor Laboratory Press. Cold Spring Harbor, NY.
3. NATARAJAN, K., M.R. MEYER, B.M. JACKSON, *et al.* 2001. Transcriptional profiling shows that Gcn4p is a master regulator of gene expression during amino acid starvation in yeast. Mol. Cell Biol . **21:** 4347–4368.
4. HINNEBUSCH, A.G. 2000. Mechanism and regulation of initiator methionyl-tRNA binding to ribosomes. *In* Translational Control of Gene Expression. N. Sonenberg, J.W.B. Hershey & M.B. Mathews, Eds.: 185–243. Cold Spring Harbor Laboratory Press, Cold Spring Harbor, NY.
5. PAVITT, G.D., K.V.A. RAMAIAH, S.R. KIMBALL & A.G. HINNEBUSCH. 1998. eIF2 independently binds two distinct eIF2B subcomplexes that catalyze and regulate guanine-nucleotide exchange. Genes Dev. **12:** 514–526.
6. OLSEN, D.S., E.M. SAVNER, A. MATHEW, *et al.* 2003. Domains of eIF1A that mediate binding to eIF2, eIF3 and eIF5B and promote ternary complex recruitment in vivo. EMBO J. **22:** 193–204.
7. NIELSEN, K.H., B. SZAMECZ, L. VALASEK, *et al.* 2004. Functions of eIF3 downstream of 48S assembly impact AUG recognition and GCN4 translational control. EMBO J. **23:** 1166–1177.

8. ASANO, K., J. CLAYTON, A. SHALE & A.G. HINNEBUSCH. 2000. A multifactor complex of eukaryotic initiation factors eIF1, eIF2, eIF3, eIF5, and initiator tRNA^{Met} is an important translation initiation intermediate in vivo. Genes Dev. **14:** 2534–2546.
9. ASANO, K., T. KRISHNAMOORTHY, L. PHAN, et al. 1999. Conserved bipartite motifs in yeast eIF5 and eIF2Be, GTPase-activating and GDP-GTP exchange factors in translation initiation, mediate binding to their common substrate eIF2. EMBO J. **18:** 1673–1688.
10. PHAN, L., X. ZHANG, K. ASANO, et al. 1998. Identification of a translation initiation factor 3 (eIF3) core complex, conserved in yeast and mammals, that interacts with eIF5. Mol . Cell Biol. **18:** 4935–4946.
11. ASANO, K., A. SHALEV, L. PHAN, et al. 2001. Multiple roles for the carboxyl terminal domain of eIF5 in translation initiation complex assembly and GTPase activation. EMBO J. **20:** 2326–2337.
12. VALÁŠEK, L., K.H. NIELSEN & A.G. HINNEBUSCH. 2002. Direct eIF2-eIF3 contact in the multifactor complex is important for translation initiation in vivo. EMBO J. **21:** 5886–5898.

The Formins

Connecting Embryonic Pattern Formation and Hypofertility in the Mouse

PHILIP LEDER, MD

Harvard Medical School, Boston, Massachusetts 02115, USA

KEYWORDS: formin; fertility; spindle body; chromosome

The major interest in our laboratory is understanding the genetic basis for cancer. In that work, we have used the technologies that have been developed to produce transgenic mice, knockout mice, and many variations on that theme, which are powerful in understanding a systemic disease such as cancer.

I decided to focus on a problem that was encountered in our laboratory a number of years ago, which proved to be so interesting, so perplexing, and I must say so difficult, that we could not give it up. It served as the basis for theses of a number of graduate students in addition to teaching us something very interesting, but was far from revealing all its secrets. The problem began with the observation made by our animal technician, who showed me a litter of mice that were formed by crossing two transgenic animals bearing the transgene at exactly the same locus. One appeared to have something very wrong with its limbs: its feet were on backwards, it would seem, but the defect was really in the number of bony elements that form both the fore and hind limbs. This is an autosomal recessive disorder that was caused by the introduction of transgenes, producing an essential mutation resulting in this phenotype. In addition, there was a low penetrance (0, 12, 15%) of either unilateral or bilateral renal aplasia.

Lasker Award, Basic Medical Research, 1987

Address for correspondence: Philip Leder, MD, Harvard Medical School, 77 Avenue Louis Pasteur, Boston, MA 02115. Voice: 617-432-7667; fax: 617-432-7944.

leder@rascal.med.harvard.edu

Ann. N.Y. Acad. Sci. 1038: 75–79 (2004). © 2004 New York Academy of Sciences.
doi: 10.1196/annals.1315.013

THE *formin* GENE

We were able to isolate the gene causing the renal aplasia. The gene was called *formin* because we thought at the time that it had something to do with the formation of the limb, but obviously it has something to do with the formation of the kidney. All these years later, it is still not absolutely certain that the *formin* gene is responsible for this phenotype. Nonetheless, the gene has proved to be very interesting. It is expressed in a limited number of organ systems, among them the ectodermal ridge, which is important in formation in the limbs and also the kidney; expression in the kidney is very clear and pronounced.

We wanted to know what these formins do at the molecular level. We realized that, although this gene is definitely expressed and can be picked up by RNA hybridization, the accumulation of protein was so low that we could never really find it within the cell; perhaps either the level of protein production or its stability was low. I gave a graduate student the task of looking every month as succeeding chapters of the human genome or mouse genome were produced, the idea being that when we had a very closely homologous hit, we would attempt to understand the function of that protein as a possible clue as to the function of formin. A number of formin-related proteins or formin family members have since been discovered in many organisms. Eventually we came up with a hit in the human and mouse genomes. Each of these formins would be relatively large proteins, something in the order of 1,500 amino acids in length, each carrying two highly conserved formin homology regions. The first is proline-rich, and the second, FH2, is thought to be a protein interaction domain, the general nature of which is not clear.

PHENOTYPE OF *formin-2* KNOCKOUT MICE

We decided to take a classical approach to understanding the function of the *formin-2* gene, namely to knock it out. We picked the proline-rich region, and created in it a large deletion, which produced an in-frame termination mutation so the protein produced as a result of this mutation should be null, i.e., it should have no function, and we then crossed heterozygotes to see what kind of a phenotype it had.

Those of you who work with knockout mice know that there are two terrible results of this type of work: one is a dead embryo and nothing to work with; the other is no phenotype. We had one of those results (we reasoned that it is impossible to have both). The *formin-2* phenotype is as follows: the adult is normal in appearance and behavior (we did extensive behavioral tests on these animals because the *formin-2* gene is expressed in the central nervous system). Our examination and that of experts showed that the morphology of the central nervous system was essentially normal. We looked at the offspring to see if they were dying *in utero*, but found the expected ratio indicating that the homozygous offspring were surviving to produce the appropriate genotype.

The graduate student who was involved decided to go further with the analysis and looked at the second generation animals that were homozygous. Expecting to find the same normal litter, he instead found that there were either no live offspring or very, very few in each litter, maybe one or two. There was obviously some defect in the next generation. We asked ourselves whether the fault lay with the male or the female parent. We mated homozygous males with wild-type females and their litter size was normal. Evidently the reproductive tract of the male was normal. However, when we mated females with wild-type males, we found maternal infertility, a very interesting phenotype. The offspring of the homozygous females were very abnormal embryos.

We tested the function of the endocrine axis and the birth apparatus by taking wild-type fertilized oocytes and transplanting them into homozygous females, which yielded a normal litter. We concluded, therefore, that the hypothalamic/pituitary/adrenal axis was intact and the uterus is functioning normally. We then tested the function of the ovary, which produced some rather interesting results. The homozygous female ovary produces normal numbers of ova, and the ova and the ovary appear to be normal. But when we ablated the indigenous ovary and replaced it with a normal wild-type ovary, normal reproductive function was restored in these animals. We realized, therefore, that the problem was in the ovary; the *formin-2* gene is a maternal effect gene, and it produces largely defective ova.

ROLE OF *formin-2* IN CHROMOSOMAL SEGREGATION

A study done *in vivo* and *in vitro* showed that, after fertilization of the ova, the mutants rarely formed a polar body—oocytes from mutant mothers failed to form polar bodies in a timely fashion. We analyzed the chromosomal content of fertilized zygotes from mutant mothers. Very often they were nearly triploid or occasionally pentaploid, suggesting that there was a failure to segregate the spindle bodies in meiosis I and possibly meiosis II. The polyploidy could obviously account for the embryonic abnormalities we observed. Evidently the fundamental defect lay in the ability of the spindle body to migrate to a polar location on the cortex of the oocyte, leading to the conclusion that *formin* plays some role in this process by guiding the spindle body to the cortex where it could form a polar body. The failure to form that polar body results in polyploidy and the failure to segregate the chromosomes. This can happen in meiosis 1. But since we are finding cells, it probably also happens in some aspect of meiosis 2 as well.

We know from this analysis that *formin, formin-2* in this case, is required for spindle positioning and that affected mice display a maternal effect phenotype in the offspring of a homozygous female and that failure to locate the spindle body, that is to move it to the cortex, leads to failure of fertilization. This fits to some extent with the role that formin-related proteins appear to play in yeast and *Drosophila* and in the organization of the skeleton, although there is no evidence for that as yet.

PROSPECTS FOR GENE THERAPY

We can introduce messenger RNA corresponding to a formin cDNA into these ova and restore the ratio of normal ploidy in these organisms, indicating that this disease or disorder is subject to a form of gene therapy. If there were a difficulty in segregating the spindle body, it could be rescued by the introduction of the messenger RNA corresponding to the gene and the defect could therefore be reversed. We have no direct evidence yet that the human gene is involved in this process and whether it might account for human infertility. But there are reports in the literature suggesting that arrest of human oocyte development during meiosis 1 is a heritable disorder. It remains for us to find out whether these women who have hypofertility syndromes and aneuploidy in their oocytes carry a mutation in the human version of the *formin* gene. If that were found to be the case, one would hope it could be reversed by this gene therapy approach.

ACKNOWLEDGMENTS

The work that I describe here, though as I said not on the main track of the research that we do, has been carried on by a number of generations of graduate students, not ordinary graduate students, but MD/PhD graduate students, who are part of an extraordinary program that has produced a group of wonderful scientists. I know there is at least one graduate of the program in the audience; one of the leaders in this endeavor was Ben Leader, who is a graduate student of mine. He assures the audience that although he is related to me phonetically, he is not related genetically.

REFERENCES

LEADER, B. & P. LEDER. 2000. Formin 2, a novel formin homology protein of the cappucino subfamily, is highly expressed in the developing and adult central nervous system. Mech. Dev. **93:** 221--231.

LEADER, B. , H. LIM, M.J. CARABATSOS, *et al.* 2002. *Formin*-2, polyploidy, hypofertility, and the positioning of the meiotic spindle in mouse oocytes. Nature
Cell Biol. **4:** 921–928.

WOYCHIK, R.P., R.L. MAAS, R. ZELLER, *et al.* 1990. The formins of proteins
deduced from the alternative transcripts of the limb deformity gene. Nature
346: 858–853.

Results of a Search for the Mechanisms of Steroid Receptor Regulation of Gene Expression

BERT W. O'MALLEY, MD

Professor and Chairman, Department of Molecular and Cellular Biology, Baylor College of Medicine, Houston, Texas 77030, USA

ABSTRACT: This publication provides a brief summary of a presentation given at the NICHD Anniversary Symposium that was designed to describe the research progress of the O'Malley laboratory over the past 30 years of its NICHD funding. It highlights a few of the lab's major discoveries during the course of the pursuit of its long-standing goal to define the molecular pathway for steroid hormone action. The key discovery that set the scientific tone for the lab over the ensuing few decades began with the discovery that steroid hormones induced the nuclear production of specific mRNAs for ovalbumin and avidin in the chick oviduct. This completed the pathway from receptor to specific proteins and indicated that steroid receptors were transcription factors. More recently the lab discovered the first coactivators (e.g., SRC-1) for steroid hormone receptors and has subsequently elucidated the many and diverse roles of nuclear coactivators in transcription reactions and in cell signaling.

KEYWORDS: steroid receptors; coactivators; transcription; hormone action

I have been attempting to define the pathway of steroid hormone action since 1963, the year I went to the NIH. Elwood Jensen had previously published his discovery that hormones bound to a novel "receptor" in target cells. Our lab group set out to describe how the hormone-receptor complex functioned. In 1972, we reported that steroid hormones could induce a rise in the messenger RNA levels for ovalbumin and this induction preceded new synthesis of ovalbumin protein[1,2] (FIG. 1). This experiment was the first demonstration that a steroid hormone (estrogen) could induce the synthesis of a specific mRNA in animal cells. From the kinetics and concentrations of the mRNA, we correctly predicted that this was a transcriptional effect—and

Address for correspondence: Bert W. O'Malley, Department of Molecular and Cellular Biology, Baylor College of Medicine, One Baylor Plaza, Houston, TX.
berto@bcm.tmc.edu

Ann. N.Y. Acad. Sci. 1038: 80–87 (2004). © 2004 New York Academy of Sciences.
doi: 10.1196/annals.1315.014

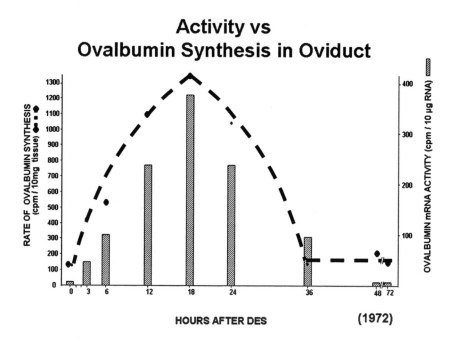

FIGURE 1. Illustration of our 1972 experiment[1,2] showing the effect of DES (diethylstilbestrol) on the rate of ovalbumin protein synthesis (*dashed lines*) and levels of ovalbumin mRNA (*bars*) during 48 hours after administration of the hormone to immature chicks. The coincidence of the curves implies cause and effect.

that the steroids were acting effectively at the point of gene expression into mRNA. Consequently, we realized that the receptor was a transcription factor; this information allowed us to close the loop on the pathway of steroid hormone action from hormone to functional protein.

In the next 20 years our laboratory published various advances, including the purification of the progesterone receptor and its subunit structure, the structural mechanism by which an agonist or antagonist activates the ligand binding domain of a receptor, the fact that receptors could be activated by ligand-independent mechanisms, etc. (see ref. 3). It was not until 1995, however, that we found not just another missing pathway ingredient but something that is probably as important as the receptor itself in the biology, physiology, and pathology of steroid hormone function: "coactivators." During this time, many other things had happened: much work had been done on the TATA box promoter of genes, hormone response elements were discovered, and data that predicted adaptors for DNA-transcription factors were published. When we first started our search for coactivators, we had no idea they might have the diverse functions we ultimately discovered in them. In

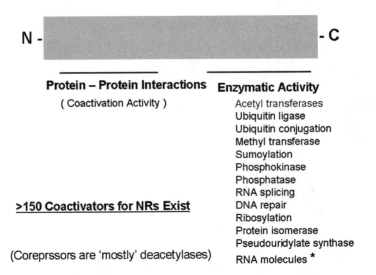

N - ... **- C**

Protein – Protein Interactions
(Coactivation Activity)

Enzymatic Activity
Acetyl transferases
Ubiquitin ligase
Ubiquitin conjugation
Methyl transferase
Sumoylation
Phosphokinase
Phosphatase
RNA splicing

>150 Coactivators for NRs Exist

DNA repair
Ribosylation
Protein isomerase
Pseudouridylate synthase

(Coreprssors are 'mostly' deacetylases)

RNA molecules *

FIGURE 2. An illustration of the general structural design of nuclear receptor coactivator proteins. The coactivators usually have one of more protein-protein interaction domains which are important for their coactivator activity on transcription. They also usually have a domain that either contains inherent enzymatic activity or binds a protein with enzyme activity. A list of the common activities noted in various different coactivators is shown on the left of the diagram.

1995, we published the first cloning of a steroid receptor coactivator-1 (SRC-1) in *Science*.[3] Our prediction at that time was that coactivators were power boosters for transcription. From other studies we could show that virtually all the potency of the receptor was due to the coactivators.

Our research revealed that the steroid receptor was actually a "locator protein" designed to search the nuclear DNA, to find the promoters of target genes and to bind to them and then to recruit coactivators; the rest of the specific functions of transcription were then carried out by the coactivators. One particular coactivator family, the SRC-1 family, has three members. They have binding domains for receptors and usually contain an acetylase enzyme activity. This general structure is recapitulated in the multitude of now known coactivators, of which there are >150 in number. There are >15 different enzyme activities known to be present in different coactivators (FIG. 2). We knocked out a number of coactivator genes in mice and found that each phenotype was different and not overlapping, and although there is some ability for one coactivator to compensate for the loss of another, they carry out different functions within tissues.[4,5] Thus, an SRC-1 knockout results in steroid resistance, an SRC-2 knockout (Chambon lab) contains reproductive organ defects, and an SRC-3 knockout results in small mice with steroid-hormone and growth-hormone resistance.

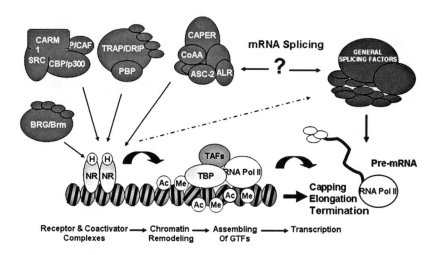

*Caper-α is an ER coactivator and is also found in the splicesome (SRp54) (SB)

FIGURE 3. This represents a hypothetical schematic diagram of the sequence of different coactivator multi-protein complexes that are sequentially recruited to a promoter undergoing hormone stimulation. Shown in a hypothetical sequence are the BRG/Brm complex (chromatin remodeling), followed by the SRC-CBP complex (histone modification), followed by the TRAP/DRIP complex (initiation/elongation of transcription), followed by the CAPER/CoAA complex (alternative RNA splicing), etc. The different complexes are recruited sequentially by the nuclear receptor/hormone complex (NR-H), and the information from each of the recruited complexes is transmitted to the general transcription factors (TBP/TAFs) and in turn to the RNA polymerase at the TATA box promoter.

We also found that the coactivators bind to have effects on metabolism. SRC-1 affects, to a large degree, insulin sensitivity and carbohydrate metabolism; SRC-2, lipid; and SRC-3, anabolic functions.[6] The coactivators are thus a kind of "master gene." They can conscript groups of DNA binding transcription factors and coordinately upregulate them to produce the desired metabolic functions. The coactivators do not bind to the receptor one by one at the promoter, but rather, they exist in large functional complexes which bind sequentially to the activated receptor. These high molecular weight complexes exchange in a regulated sequence to carry out the individual functions required for turning a gene on and, indeed, eventually turning it off because the last complex they recruit is one that contains ubiquitinylation enzymes to degrade the transcription initiation complex (FIG. 3).

The diversity of coactivator activities was further described by us a couple of years ago, when we considered that there might be other functions of steroid receptor coactivators. They certainly are regulators of the amount of RNA made during transcription. However, we have ~30,000 genes to produce ~120,000 proteins, which means that there is extensive alternative mRNA splicing occurring in the nucleus. We wondered whether steroid hormones, while changing the quantity of mRNA product, could in certain instances, also qualitatively change the gene product. Our experiments confirmed our suspicion.[7] In one of the first experiments we undertook to investigate this issue, we used the reporter gene CD44, a highly spliceable gene, which we linked to a progesterone-responsive promoter. Progesterone changed the ratio of the reaction RNA splice products, an effect that was receptor-dependent and cell type–specific and had nothing to do with the rate of transcription. The mechanism underlying the change in gene product again involves coactivators. For example, we demonstrated that by changing the ratio of coactivators, splicing can be changed over ~fourfold or more in the cell. Not all coactivators have that capacity, but we have defined a subset of about eight that do.

So, current evidence suggests that induction of transcription by hormones (or other agents) involves a sequential recruitment of a series of diverse but critical multi-protein coactivator complexes to the gene by the hormone receptor bound to the hormone-response element in the promoter. In turn, these complexes provide a series of reactions required for induction of gene transcription, and include chromatin remodeling, histone modification, initiation and elongation by RNA polymerase, alternative RNA splicing, and finally ubiquitination and turnover of the complexes themselves. (FIG. 3).

We felt that understanding the nature of the intracellular proteins that form a complex with coactivators might lead us to discover other unsuspected coactivator functions in the cell. As an example, we isolated complexes containing SRC-1, SRC-2, and SRC-3 and analyzed the proteins present in these complexes by mass spectrometry. We showed that SRC-3/AIB1 is a substrate for a number of different kinases and that it is a highly phosphorylated protein with about eight different phosphorylation sites.[8,9] The question thus arose as to whether the various signaling pathways were changing the activity of SRC-3 so that different transcription factors recognized different sites of phosphorylation and formed preferential complexes with the coactivator. In other words, could environmental factors signal to the genome via coactivators whose activity was regulated by the membrane receptor initiated signaling pathways?

Consequently, we mutated six of the individual phosphorylation sites. We concluded from these experiments that SRC-3 function depends on precise phosphorylation sites, which have differential effects on different transcription factors. We have gone on to show that certain mutations prevent the appropriate formation of receptor/coactivator complexes on the nuclear DNA. Thus, the phosphorylation sites act as a type of "phospho-code."[9] Coactivators act as sensors of the local cellular environment, directing transcription in one direction or another, depending on what is happening at the membrane or outside the cell.

Finally, in breast tissue SRC-3 is a major coactivator for steroids. The estrogen receptor uses SRC- 3 to turn on growth genes. For example, when we deleted the SRC-3 gene, mice became resistant to carcinogens or oncogenic viruses.[10] In separate studies, Miles Brown has recently shown that if one overexpresses SRC-3 in transgenic mice, 70% of the animals develop breast tumors by 10 months. Also, this gene is frequently amplified in breast cancers, and is overexpressed in a majority of breast cancers. Thus, this coactivator molecule is also an oncogene and tends to be overproduced in cancers. SRC-3 is being detected in many different cancers now, especially those of the endocrine pathway, but it has been detected in other types too. Over production of coactivators gives the cell quite a selective growth advantage. It is just another example of how smart the cancer cell is in terms of using mutations and overexpression patterns of regulatory molecules to its own advantage.

The diversity of the effects of these coactivator molecules derives from the fact that tissue specificity and kinetics are dependent on the levels of the coactivators in the cells. Coactivators are involved in initiation and reinitiation of transcription but also in additional reactions such as mRNA splicing and in the turnover of transcription factors and coactivators. The second coactivator we cloned was an E3 ligase, which was puzzling in view of the fact that one would think that proteolytic enzymes should be kept away from proteins such as transcription factors. But in fact, this turnover mechanism for transcription factors in the nucleus is absolutely necessary for efficient transcrip-

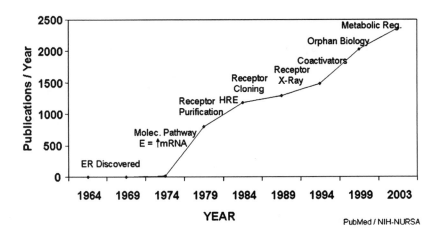

FIGURE 4. This graph contains a plot of the publications/year for all "steroid" receptors over the past 40 years. This graph was taken from the NIDDK/NURSA Web site (<http://www.NURSA.org>); it contains information collated from PubMed.

tion. Also, because of differential quantitative coactivator patterns in different cells, the same ligand with the same receptor will turn a gene on in one cell, and off in another. This is the basic principle involved in selective estrogen receptor modulator drug actions, such as Tamoxifen and Raloxifene.[11] Thus, coactivators are involved in normal growth and tissue function, as well as in the abnormal growth patterns of malignancies. They may even be the dominant familial factor in determining individual phenotypes in humans.

In summary, the field of hormone action and nuclear receptors has grown tremendously over the past four decades, as evidenced by the rate of publications in the field (FIG. 4). Beginning with the discovery of receptors, and the explosive expansion following the description of the molecular pathway for steroid hormone action, the field has continued to expand with each new advance in concept and methodology. It is now bearing fruit in terms of understanding a myriad of metabolic and pathologic processes, and more is sure to come over the next couple of decades.

ACKNOWLEDGMENTS

I am exceedingly grateful for the support for this work from NICHD (HD 07857; HD 08818).

REFERENCES

1. MEANS, A.R., J.P. COMSTOCK, G.C. ROSENFELD & B.W. O'MALLEY. 1972. Ovalbumin messenger RNA of chick oviduct: partial characterization, estrogen dependence and translation *in vitro*. Proc. Natl. Acad. Sci. USA **69:** 1146.
2. CHAN, L., A.R. MEANS & B.W. O'MALLEY. 1973. Rates of induction of specific translatable mRNAs for ovalbumin and avidin by steroid hormones. Proc. Natl. Acad. Sci. USA **70:** 1870.
3. OÑATE, S.A., S.Y. TSAI, M.-J. TSAI & B.W. O'MALLEY. 1995. Sequence and characterization of a coactivator for the steroid hormone receptor superfamily. Science **270:** 1354–1357.
4. XU, J., Y. QUI, F.J. DEMAYO, *et al.* 1998. Partial hormone resistance in mice with disruption of the steroid receptor coactivator 1 (SRC-1) gene. Science **279:** 1922–1925.
5. XU, J., L. LIAO, G. NING, *et al.* 2000. The steroid receptor coactivator SRC-3 (p/CIP/RAC3/AIB1/ACTR/TRAM-1) is required for normal growth, puberty, female reproductive function and mammary gland development. Proc. Natl. Acad. Sci. USA **97:** 6379–6384.
6. PICARD, F., M. GEHIN, J.-S. ANNICOTTE, *et al.* 2002. SRC-1 and TIF2 control energy balance between white and brown adipose tissues. Cell **111:** 931–941.

7. AUBOEUF, D., A. HÖNIG, S.M. BERGET & B.W. O'MALLEY. 2002. Coordinate regulation of transcription and splicing by steroid receptor coregulators. Science **298:** 416–419.

8. WU, R.-C., J. QIN, Y. HASHIMOTO, *et al.* 2002. Regulation of SRC-3 (pCIP/ACTR/AIB-1/RAC-3/TRAM-1) coactivator activity by IkB kinase. Mol. Cell. Biol. **22:** 3549–3561.

9. WU, R.-C., J. QIN, P. YI, , *et al.* 2004. Selective phosphorylations of the SRC-3/AIB1 coactivator integrate genomic responses to multiple cellular signaling pathways. Mol. Cell **15:** 1–20.

10. KUANG, S.-Q., L. LIAO, H. ZHANG, *et al.* 2004. AIB1/SRC-3 deficiency affects insulin-like growth factor I signaling pathway and suppresses *v*-Ha-*ras*-induced breast cancer initiation and progression in mice. Cancer Res. **64:** 1875–1885.

11. SMITH, C.L., Z. NAWAZ & B.W. O'MALLEY. 1997. Coactivator and corepressor regulation of the agonist/antagonist activity of the mixed antiestrogen, 4-hydroxytamoxifen. Mol. Endocrinol. **11:** 657–666.

Developmental Biology of Zebrafish

IGOR B. DAWID, PHD

Chief, Laboratory of Molecular Genetics, Division of Intramural Research, NICHD, National Institutes of Health, Bethesda, Maryland 20892, USA

ABSTRACT: The biology and genetics of zebrafish has become a very popular system in developmental biology especially because of their suitability for genetics and the transparent embryo of this small tropical fish. Studies reported briefly here demonstrate that one can use gene expression in the zebrafish embryo to find new components of important and well-studied developmental mechanisms and signal transduction pathways. The study of zebrafish developmental genetics has proven invaluable in determining many aspects of vertebrate development. Further use of this model organism promises to generate many interesting and useful data.

KEYWORDS: gene expression; zebrafish; genetics; signal transduction; *Sef*; fibroblast growth factor (FGF)

The biology and genetics of zebrafish has become a very popular system in developmental biology for several reasons, chief among them being the suitability for genetics and transparent embryo of this small tropical fish. During the first eight hours of development or so, one can watch the embryonic cells cleave on top of the yolk, followed by epiboly as embryonic cells move down and at the same time establish the anterior-posterior axis. The formation of different organ systems can be followed under the microscope in the ensuing developmental period, offering many opportunities for the study of organogenesis. In this brief article I shall outline approaches to the study of development that have been used in my laboratory and in the laboratories of two of my colleagues in the Laboratory of Molecular Genetics at the NICHD.

Making use of the optical properties of the zebrafish embryos, my group has carried out a screen for genes with developmentally controlled expression patterns.[1] Many different regions, prospective tissues, and organs are highlighted through the expression patterns of a number of genes that one can study in different ways. One of the uses of such a screen is to detect genes

Address for correspondence: Igor B. Dawid, PhD, Chief, Laboratory of Molecular Genetics, Division of Intramural Research, NICHD, NIH, Building 6B, Room 413, Bethesda, MD 20892, USA. Voice: 301-496-4448.

dawidi@mail.nih.gov

Ann. N.Y. Acad. Sci. 1038: 88–93 (2004). © 2004 New York Academy of Sciences.
doi: 10.1196/annals.1315.015

with similar expression patterns that often prove to function within a common pathway. One such example is shown in FIGURE 1, which illustrates the expression of a group of genes that includes two genes of the fibroblast growth factor (FGF) family. FGFs are factors that work in intercellular communication, with important functions in virtually all processes in development as well as in cell proliferation and cell survival. Several human diseases are affected by FGF pathway components, and the signal transduction mechanism of the FGF family is widely studied. We found a new gene that we called similar expression to FGF (*Sef*) because its expression pattern.[2] The first thing we found is that FGF regulates the expression of *Sef*. Overexpression of FGF in the embryo causes more *sef* expression compared with the control, and when one inhibits FGF signaling in half of the embryo, *sef* is turned off, confirming that it is under FGF regulation.

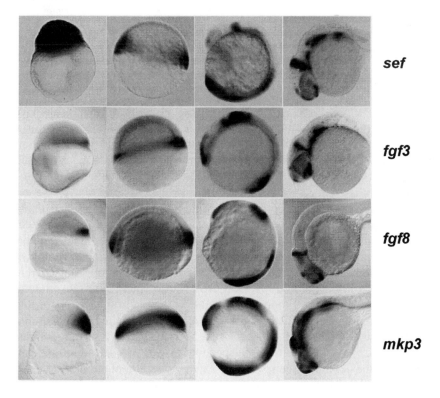

FIGURE 1. Expression patterns at four different stages of development of two genes encoding fibroblast growth factors (FGF) and two other genes with similar patterns. One of these genes, *mkp3* was already known as a feedback inhibitor of FGF signaling, whereas *sef* represents a newly discovered FGF signaling feedback inhibitor.

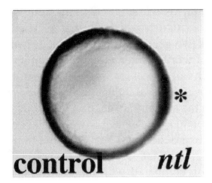 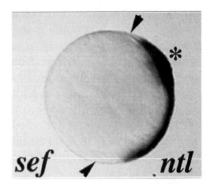

FIGURE 2. Sef inhibits FGF signaling. In the half embryo where Sef is overexpressed, the FGF target gene *ntl* is suppressed.

What does *Sef* itself do? It inhibits FGF signaling. You can see that by monitoring its effect on *ntl*, a well-known target gene of FGF signaling. After injecting *Sef* into half the embryo, the target gene is turned off (FIG. 2). Thus, *Sef* is itself regulated by FGF but it also acts as a negative regulator of FGF signaling. The molecule is a transmembrane protein, which, as we have shown, can bind to the FGF receptor, which is itself a well-known transmembrane protein. This interaction may well be the mechanism by which *Sef* inhibits FGF signaling. The exact mechanism by which this happens is still under investigation.

These studies demonstrate that one can use gene expression in the zebrafish embryo to find new components of important and well-studied developmental mechanisms and signal transduction pathways. In this particular case, we found a new component of the FGF pathway, which is a negative feedback regulator because its expression is stimulated by FGF signaling but it itself inhibits FGF expression. We have shown that its action is needed in the embryo to limit the FGF pathway from, so to speak, going overboard. Such negative regulatory loops are common in signaling mechanisms and play an important role in the tight control over signaling levels during development.[3]

The work of Ajay Chitnis, an independent investigator in the Laboratory, focuses on the nervous system. A fairly extensive region of the embryo is determined to become the future nervous system. Within this region, however, not all cells become neurons; some become different kinds of cells. Dr. Chitnis is interested in how the number and location of particular types of neurons are determined in the zebrafish embryo and, by extension, in other vertebrate embryos. It is well known that this regulation involves lateral inhibition based on a pathway mediated by Delta/Notch signaling.

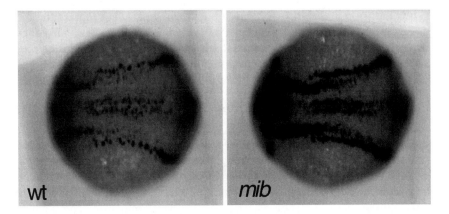

FIGURE 3. The *mindbomb* mutation leads to an excess of neurons, here visualized by staining with a gene that is specific for neuronal precursor cells. (From Itoh *et al.*, 2003.[4])

By looking for mutants in neurogenesis, Chitnis and colleagues found a mutant called *mib* that has too many neurons (FIG. 3). Extensive work has shown that this is because the Delta/Notch signaling pathway is not working properly in the mutant animal. After identifying the molecule that is defective in this mutant, they found that it represents a rather complex protein that represents an E3 ubiquitin ligase.[4] Ubiquitin ligases are key players in a pathway in which a small protein, ubiquitin, is attached to substrate proteins. There are many possible substrates, and the key step is catalyzed by an E3 ligase because it determines substrate specificity. The best-known consequence of ubiquitin modification of proteins is its degradation, but that is not the case here. In this case, the Mindbomb protein ubiquitinates the intracellular domain of Delta and this modification affects trafficking of the Delta protein. Why this mechanism enhances Delta/Notch signaling is still under active investigation. The main point, however, of this simplified presentation is that by using the zebrafish as a genetic organism one can identify new components in a well-studied pathway that is both developmentally and medically of considerable importance.

Dr. Brant Weinstein, another independent investigator in the department, is interested in the vascular development in the zebrafish, specifically how blood vessels form and how they are patterned in this organism. Here, the transparency of the zebrafish is strikingly valuable. One can look in great detail at individual blood cells going through the capillaries of a live animal, a really powerful approach to studying blood vessels. One can also inject fluorescent dyes into these animals and take a set of images and reconstruct them, giving a detailed, beautiful three-dimensional representation of all the blood vessels in the animal at different days of development. These representations can be viewed in various ways and can be rotated and sliced in various planes. Using this approach Dr. Weinstein and his colleagues labeled and identified each vessel, and then put the information into a website which represents an accesible and highly detailed description of this vascular system during development.[5]

When green fluorescent protein (GFP) is expressed in the blood vessels of the zebrafish by a transgene in which GFP is driven by an endothelial cell-specific promoter, the blood vessels of the animal are outlined in great detail. Quite remarkably, one can visualize very fine subcellular projections of endothelial cells in a live larva. This can all be imaged in the living animal to show blood vessels in the process of growing and making new connections or conversely, in the process of severing connections, so that one can obtain a detailed description of their organization and patterning in the process of development.[6]

One can also to use these fluorescent fish, in which the developing blood vessels are easily visualized, as a substrate to look for mutants in which vessel formation is disturbed (FIG. 4). Dr. Weinstein and colleagues have found a number of such mutations by this approach, and they are studying them to great advantage.

In sum, the study of zebrafish developmental genetics has proven invaluable in determining many aspects of vertebrate development. The further use

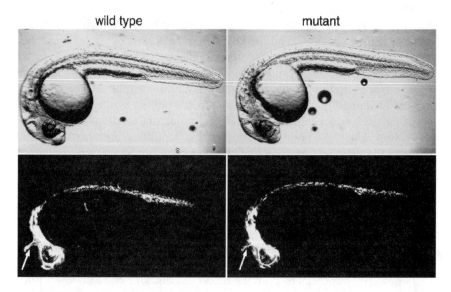

FIGURE 4. Wild type and mutant zebrafish with fluorescent blood vessels. The mutant shows defects in blood vessel formation (B.M. Weinstein, unpublished).

of this model organism promises to continue to generate much interesting and useful information.

ACKNOWLEDGMENTS

I thank Ajay Chitnis and Brant Weinstein for providing information and photographs.

REFERENCES

1. KUDOH, T., M. TSANG, N.A. HUKRIEDE, et al. 2001. A gene expression screen in zebrafish embryogenesis. Genome Res. **11:** 1979–1987.
2. TSANG, M., R. FRIESEL, T. KUDOH & I.B. DAWID. 2002. Identification of Sef, a novel modulator of FGF signalling. Nature Cell Biol. **4:** 165–169.
3. TSANG, M. & I.B. DAWID. 2004. Promotion and attenuation of FGF signaling through the Ras-MAPK pathway. Science STKE 2004, pe17.
4. ITOH, M., C.H. KIM, G. PALARDY, et al. 2003. Mind bomb is a ubiquitin ligase that is essential for efficient activation of Notch signaling by Delta. Dev. Cell **4:** 67–82.
5. ISOGAI, S., M. HORIGUCHI & B.M. WEINSTEIN. 2001. The vascular anatomy of the developing zebrafish: an atlas of embryonic and early larval development. Dev. Biol. **230:** 278–301.
6. ISOGAI, S., N.D. LAWSON, S. TORREALDAY, et al. 2003. Angiogenic vascular network formation in the developing vertebrate trunk. Development **130:** 5281–5290.

Developmental Genetics of *Drosophila*

EDWARD B. LEWIS, PHD†

Thomas Hunt Morgan Professor of Biology, California Institute of Technology, Pasadena, California 91125, USA

ABSTRACT: *Drosophila melanogaster* is one of the most valuable organisms in biological research, particularly in the areas of genetics and developmental biology. *Drosophila* has been used as a model organism in research for almost a century. The organism is easy to breed and has a short life cycle, making it ideal for the study of genetic mutations. The importance to human health and development lies in the homology of *Drosophila* genes to those in man, e.g., the homeobox gene complex.

KEYWORDS: *Drosophila*; history of genetics; development; homeobox genes

My interest in *Drosophila* started about 65 years ago, when I was in high school. I have been working ever since with this organism, which, at first, seemed to be the prime example of a good organism for genetic purposes and, after many years of work, one of the best organisms for studying development as well.

It all started with Bateson, who wrote a book in which he gave examples of transformations that he called examples of homeosis. His definition was very broad: something that has been transformed into the likeness of something else. The term refers to the fact that you will see one structure being turned into a homologous structure. That is the origin of homeo. A Danish professor, W. Johannsen, gave us the term gene and Bateson also invented the term genetics. Homeosis or homeotic transformation of, for example, one of the thoracic segments is not a duplication, but rather a conversion into the likeness of the normal segment that bears the mammary glands. Bateson compiled literally hundreds of examples of this. One was a wasp that had the tip

†Deceased. Please see *In Memoriam*, this volume.

Nobel Prize in Medicine, 1995; Lasker Award, Basic Medical Research, 1991

Address for correspondence: James A. Kennison, PhD, Head, Section on Drosophila Gene Regulation, Laboratory of Molecular Genetics, Division of Intramural Research, NICHD, NIH, Building 6B, Room 331, 6 Center Drive, Bethesda, MD 20892-2785.

jim_kennison@nih.gov

Ann. N.Y. Acad. Sci. 1038: 94–97 (2004). © 2004 New York Academy of Sciences.
doi: 10.1196/annals.1315.016

of the antenna on one side converted to the tip of one of its legs. We have a mutation that was found by one of our graduate students in 1948, which he called *antennapedia*, a rather nice transformation of the antenna to leg. Not everyone appreciates the pleasure of working with these organisms.

The field was very much advanced when Thomas Hunt Morgan at Columbia University discovered the white-eyed fly. The white-eyed flies we have in our stock room at Cal Tech are probably a descendents of the original one. The Nobel website has pictures of them together with an essay on Morgan and his work. The site also shows an animated picture of how inversions behave. Morgan had several famous students: three of them were A.H. Sturtevant, C.B. Bridges, and H.J. Muller. It was Bridges who started developmental genetics because, in 1915, he was able to find the first homeotic mutation in an animal, namely one that converted the second, or third thoracic segments into the second, which produced the spectacular effect of an extra pair of wings—true flies have only one pair of wings. It is very much like the transformation of mammary glands in human beings. One could make the prediction that it might be the same gene if someone would go to the trouble of cloning it, of trying to investigate the nature of the genetic changes involved, because, in many vertebrates, including humans, it is a fairly common trait to have extra mammary glands.

A June 2003 article in *Genetics* on the history of genetic discoveries describes how far Bridges attempted to go in testing a hypothesis. He had the idea that new genes are formed by gene duplication, that one of the duplicates is converted to a new function while the old gene is copied to carry out the old function. He was trying to prove this with genes, many of which he had discovered. Being a geneticist, he found a dominant gene we call *ultrabithorax*. Bridges saved all these mutations. It was in 1938, many years after they had been identified, that he began to study the possibility that these genes would be found in the visible duplicated bands in the salivary gland. He thought he would find here genetic evidence from mutations such as duplicates that would have derived from each other by this process of gene duplication and diversification. Sadly, he failed to prove his hypothesis. Hard as he tried, he did not grow enough flies. He was also ill at the time in 1938 and only a few months later he died at the age of 49, having accomplished unbelievable amount of work mapping all our genes, drawing beautiful maps of the chromosomes, and saving the stock so everybody could write to the Center and get the flies. He and others had come to Cal Tech in 1928 from Columbia where he maintained these flies and, among many other things, he was working on these at Cal Tech when he died.

As early as 1951, we already had a fairly good idea about the function of these genes in terms of how they were affecting development. We subsequently found more genes. To make a long story short, we found a complex, which we called the homeobox complex because the genes involved were all involved in homeotic mutations.

The *Drosophila* life cycle starts with an egg. The egg develops in one day at room temperature. Then the larvae struggle to emerge from the egg. About five days later, the larva has matured; it has developed black hooks, which it uses to burrow into the food, and spiracles for breathing. After pupation, adult tissues gradually replace larval tissues until eyes and wing pads become visible. Nine days after egg harvesting, the adult emerges from the pupa case in less than an hour but the wings have not expanded. It has legs on the first, second, and third segments. The second segment is well developed. The last two segments are solid black in the male. In the adult female, the fifth and sixth abdominal segments lack the solid black pigmentation we saw in the male. As this sequence ends, the life cycle starts over again.

The development of *Drosophila* mirrors to some extent evolution. Thus, we started at the largely undifferentiated worm-like stage, which requires a head segment, resulting in animals such as the earthworm. Next came animals with antennae and pseudolegs, animals that may be the missing link. True legs formed on most of the body segments including the head to produce the trilobites, whose only living relative is the horseshoe crab; next, legs on the head segments turned into mandibles to produce the millipedes or centipedes. Legs gradually disappeared, leaving an eight-legged ancestor and then six-legged insects. Later, winged insects evolved, the first of which probably had three pairs of wings, as some rare fossils would indicate. Insects evolved; the earliest flying insects probably had identical wings in the second and third segments. We next see a true fly. Also in the higher diptera, the eyes greatly enlarged and the wings became considerably reduced in size.

Loss-of-function mutants of the bithorax complex, such as those bearing a double mutant combination of *bithorax* and *post-bithorax*, result in a four-winged fly. This was the best transformation of the third thoracic segment that could be achieved. In this four-winged fly, the third thoracic segment now resembles the second, but the wings on the thorax are significantly smaller than those on the second segment. In summary, the four-winged fly genotype involves partial loss of function of T3-regulatory regions. As a result, T3 transforms toward T2, i.e., a T2-like wing on T3.

Next we discovered that we could make a much-improved four-winged fly by adding the bithorax mutants to the double mutant combination. In these four-winged flies, the third thoracic segment is transformed into a virtually exact replica of the second, as demonstrated by the identity of the wing vein patterns and hair and bristle patterns of the two. This genotype is remarkably constant in expression even though it represents only a partial loss of function of the ultrabithorax complex. The widespread belief that all mutants are variable in expression is incorrect. Another mutant is *bithoraxoid*, in which the first abdominal segment is partially transformed into a thoracic segment. The fourth pair of legs is capable of moving. In some animals that have only one dose of the *bithoraxoid* mutation, a partially wing-like abdominal halter arises on the first abdominal segment.

The first-gain-of function mutant found in the bithorax complex was *ultrabithorax*. It is a dominant X-ray-induced mutation, which results in transformation of the second thoracic segment into the third, just the opposite of the loss-of-function mutants described above. Halters replace the second pair of wings in *ultrabithorax* mutants. At high magnification one can see where the halters of the second thoracic segment (T2) approach those of the third and the thorax proper begins to be greatly reduced. The next gain-of-function mutant is *hyperabdominal*, in which T3 transforms to A2. The result is a four-legged fly. This *hyperabdominal* mutation has been shown by others to involve a single base pair change in a binding site for the Krüpple protein, a transrepressor of one of the genes of the complex. The expression is highly variable so that only a few animals have four legs and no halters. At high magnification it is evident that there are no halters as well as no T3 legs.

In order to deduce the function of the major regulatory regions, special genotypes were constructed. We added to the deficient *p9* phenotype, which counteracts the Ubx^+ domain of the complex except for the portion of the domain that is not activated; such embryos have the trunks restored. Thus, Ubx^+ is able to connect up the tracheal trunks from T3 to A8. We added duplication p10 to p9. This genotype has all of the domain including bxd^+. We now see that bxd^+ has three functions it carries out from A1–A8. It suppresses the ventral pits, potentially suppresses the organs and partially develops the ventral bands. C-4 uses only the wild-type regions. We can infer that $iab-2^+$ completes development of the bands from A2 to A8 and completes the suppression of the organs.

This work has demonstrated that the genes turn on in the same order that they are on the chromosome, which is also true for the human homeobox genes that have exact homologs to the ones being discussed there. So, gradually about 30 years ago we began to understand that we were studying development instead of just studying the genetics of closely linked genes. That is how we finally came around to recognizing that *Drosophila* was after all not such a bad organism in which to study development.

Origins of Growth Factors: NGF and EGF

STANLEY COHEN, PHD

Distinguished Professor, Department of Biochemistry, Vanderbilt University Medical Center, Nashville, Tennessee 37235, USA

ABSTRACT: This presentation describes the events that led to the sequential discoveries of nerve growth factor (NGF) and epidermal growth factor (EGF). Each was isolated during attempts to understand the biochemical basis for unexpected biological observations. The *in vivo* stimulation of the growth of specific nerve fibers following the transplantation of a mouse sarcoma into a chick embryo eventually resulted in the finding of NGF, not only in the transplanted tumor but also in snake venom and in the mouse salivary gland. Unexpectedly, treatment of newborn animals with extracts of the mouse salivary gland resulted not only in enhancement of nerve growth but also in precocious eyelid opening and tooth eruption. The latter observations led to the isolation of both EGF and its tyrosine kinase–active receptor.

KEYWORDS: growth factors; EGF; NGF; EGF receptors

As is often the case, new things are found by accident; growth factors were discovered by accident. The initial experiments were started in the zoology laboratory of Washington University and had nothing to do with growth factors. The investigators were studying the following phenomenon: if one transplants a wing bud from one chicken embryo into another, the limb bud develops and the chicken has extra wings and they are functional. The researchers were trying to determine how the nerves know where to grow into the wing, a question that is still with us. A graduate student looked at the experiment and observed that the wing looked as if it were growing faster and thought that perhaps any rapidly growing tissue would attract nerve fibers. By accident, he picked a transplantable mouse tumor sarcoma 180 and, instead of transplanting a wing bud, he transplanted a piece of the tumor—an embryo will grow anything. He sectioned the embryos at days three and

Nobel Prize in Medicine, 1986; Lasker Award, Basic Medical Research, 1986.
Address for correspondence: Stanley Cohen, PhD, 11306 East Limberlost Road, Tucson, AZ 85749.
stancohen@earthlink.net

Ann. N.Y. Acad. Sci. 1038: 98–102 (2004). © 2004 New York Academy of Sciences.
doi: 10.1196/annals.1315.017

eight and found that the tumor that grew was full of nerve fibers. He concluded that any rapidly growing tissue would "attract" nerve fibers. An Italian physician, Rita Levi-Montalcini, who was working in that lab, repeated the experiments and discovered another phenomenon. She transplanted the sarcoma into an embryo and as before, the tumor grew, and nerve fibers invaded the tumor. However, in addition, many sensory and sympathetic nerve fibers went to tissues other than the tumor, a remarkable phenomenon. She thought something was coming out of the tumor that made nerves grow. To find out what was making these fibers grow, she developed an *in vitro* assay in tissue culture. She took sensory ganglia, put them into a hanging drop culture on a glass slide in a plasma clot either alone or next to a piece of the tumor. Twenty-four hours later, just looking under the microscope, she could see nerve fibers growing out of the sensory ganglia but *only* when placed near the tumor.

I was hired as a postdoc to figure out what was happening. It was a good combination because I did not know any neuro-embryology, and they did not know any biochemistry so we never fought. Biochemists grind and find. I ground up the sarcoma 180 and made an extract and sure enough, the extract made nerves grow in 24 hours. The activity was greater if you grew the tumor in chick embryos. We tried to purify the active component and identify it (in those days, this is now 50 years ago, there were no columns) by ammonium sulfate precipitation. We incubated the preparation with DNAse and RNAse, but nothing happened. We thought it was a protein because the activity was destroyed by proteases. Others suggested that it might be a virus and that we should make sure that the preparation contained no DNA or RNA. A colleague suggested we incubate it with snake venom phosphodiesterase to get rid of any nucleic acids. To our astonishment, next day the culture looked like nothing I had ever seen before.

The phosphodiesterase preparation itself made nerve fibers grow in tissue culture. It was thousands of times more effective than our best tumor extract. However, it had nothing to do with the phosphodiesterase itself but was due to an impurity in the preparation. To find out what the active ingredient was, we obtained dried snake venom (all snakes produce the factor). and we purified a protein with nerve growth activity from the snake venom. If one injects this protein into embryos, it did the same thing as the tumor did: sensory and sympathetic nerves grew all over the embryo, and one could not tell the difference whether one injected the purified snake venom protein or a growing tumor.

Our next question was the possible relationship between nerve fibers and snake venom and tumors—nothing very obvious. However I learned in Biology 101 that snake venom comes from a modified salivary gland in a snake. After growth activity was originally found in tumors of mice, I had spent years grinding up everything in the mouse and nothing worked. Finally after five years, I ground up the salivary gland of the mouse, and there it was. By chance, I had picked the male mouse and to this day that is the best source of natural NGF. A crude extract of salivary gland was as good as the snake venom. It was incredibly potent—instead of milligrams one needed only nanograms to stimulate nerve growth in cultures of sensory ganglia.

If one takes a crude extract of adult male mouse salivary gland and injects it into baby mice every day, after seven days one observes some general growth retardation in the animal, except for the sympathetic nervous system—which is markedly enlarged. Furthermore, teeth erupt earlier and the eyes open earlier in treated mice and rats. When we purified, as best we could, the nerve growth factor from the salivary gland, it made nerves grow but no longer had any effect on the eye opening or tooth eruption. We decided that there must be something else in the crude extract. We knew the nerve growth factor was physiologically important because when we made an antibody in rabbits to the purified nerve factor from the salivary gland, and injected the antibody into newborn mice, almost 90 percent of the sympathetic nerve cells were destroyed. Thus, one can immuno-sympathectamize an animal. Since that time immense of amounts of other work has been done in many laboratories and Nerve Growth Factor (NGF) has been sequenced and cloned.

In 1959, I moved from my postdoc position at Washington University to a job at Vanderbilt. There I switched my research from the nerve growth factor to determining what made eyes open and teeth erupt precociously in newborn animals. There were many ways to slow an animal down but very few ways to speed up a normal process. Thus, the prospect of finding what was accelerating the appearance of teeth and eye opening was intriguing. We used the eye-opening assay; the biological unit of activity was how much one would have to inject every day into the newborn animal to get the eyes to open up at 9 days instead of the normal 14. With that assay and the columns we now had, we isolated a polypeptide peptide that had an eye-opening effect when injected into the animal. Every time we doubled the dose, eyes opened up a day earlier; we could get the eyes of mice to open as early as day 6 instead of day 14. Together with many colleagues, we determined the amino acid sequence of this 53-amino acid protein now know as epidermal growth factor (EGF).

To understand how this molecule made eyes open up, I asked my friends in anatomy why eyes open, but they could not give me a satisfactory answer. So I went back to biology and compared histological sections of the eyes, particularly cross-sections of the eyelid area, of eight-day old rats that had been treated with EGF with those of control animals. It became clear what was happening: eyelids opened up because the epidermis was growing more rapidly and keratinizing. A week later the control animal would look like the experimental animal, confirming that eye-opening was due to epidermal growth. In an *in vitro* experiment, similar to one we did with the nerve growth factor, we looked at the chick embryo cornea and human embryonic skin in three-day organ cultures without and with EGF, and demonstrated a direct growth stimulating effect on epidermal cells. The initial culture experiments were performed during a sabbatical in Rome in the laboratory of Dr. Rita Levi-Montalcini with D. Attordi.

At about this time I sent the compound to Dr. Cuatracasas as a control for insulin that has approximately the same molecular weight as EGF. I believe he was the first to show that EGF stimulated thymidine incorporation into human fibroblasts. However, we called it epidermal growth factor because that is what we saw first. Since human fibroblasts in culture also were stimulated by mouse EGF, we concluded that humans must make a factor that corresponds to mouse EGF. ^{125}I- labeled EGF binds to human fibroblasts in culture in a highly specific manner: each fibroblast has about 50,000 receptors with a dissociation constant of about 10^{-10}. The only way to block the binding is with unlabeled EGF—no other hormone preparation tested had any effect on the binding. This presented a new bioassay method.

The question was where should we look in humans—we could not grind them up. Since I knew that some hormones showed up in urine we tried urine and found something in urine that inhibited the binding of mouse ^{125}I-labeled EGF to human fibroblasts in culture. Using this receptor assay, we could isolate a polypeptide from human urine. When we put the human protein into culture it made the cells grow, and when we injected it into mice, it made their eyes open up. So we called it human EGF. Its amino acid composition was similar, but not identical, to mouse EGF.

In England, Harry Gregory, at a pharmaceutical company, knew there was something called urogastrone in urine that inhibited stomach acid secretion. From 70,000 liters of urine he isolated a polypeptide, determined the sequence, looked in the literature and found that it looked like mouse EGF. There was a 70% sequence identity between our mouse EGF and human urogastrone. They both opened eyes, both made cells grow in culture, and both inhibited acid secretion. (Gregory's method of isolation used the inhibition of histamine-induced acid secretion in a rat as an assay.) We concluded that uragastrone isolated by Gregory and human EGF isolated from urine were identical. We are still waiting for someone to figure out how it inhibits acid secretion, but we were more interested in the growth effects.

EGF makes cells grow and we wanted to find out how it does this. A biochemist such as myself prefers a cell free system to which she/he adds a hormone to stimulate or inhibit a chemical reaction, so that one can begin to unravel what was happening. At that time, the only experiment of that nature was the activation of adenyl cyclase in membranes by glucagon. Here at NIH, a friend of mine, Joe DeLarco, was assaying all their cells for EGF receptors. He discovered a human epidermal tumor cell with millions of EGF receptors, not thousands per cell. I thought that these cells should make it many times easier to isolate a first step in EGF action. He very kindly sent me those cells, human epidermoid carcinoma cells (A431). From these cells one can make membranes that bind to EGF. We prepared membranes from these cells, added ^{32}P-ATP, plus or minus EGF, incubated for a few minutes, and then checked for radioactivity. EGF stimulated the incorporation of ^{32}P-ATP into membranes.

To determine what we were we phosophorylating in membranes, we incubated membranes with ^{32}P-ATP and increasing amounts of EGF and analyzed for ^{32}P-ATP-labeled proteins on SDS gels. A major 170-KD ^{32}P-labeled protein was detected in the EGF-treated membranes. To see whether it might be related to the receptor, we attempted to isolate the receptor by making a Triton extract of the membranes and pouring it through an EGF affinity column and eluting the receptor with either EGF or strong salt. In this manner we isolated the receptor. It indeed was a 170 KD protein with 3 distinctive properties. It bound EGF, had EGF-activated protein kinase activity and was itself phosphorylated.

At this time it had just been discovered that the transforming factor was a protein kinase and that it specifically phosphorylated tyrosine residues. Using amino acid hydrolysis and paper electrophoresis to separate phosphorylated amino acids, we examined our ^{32}P-labeled membrane preparation and found that here, too, tyrosine was phosphorylated. The EGF receptor was the first normal protein found to be a ligand-activated tyrosine kinase.

Since that time thousands of papers on the subject have been published. Both EGF and the EGF receptor have been cloned and their sequences determined. EGF is a member of a family of EGF-like proteins. It was also discovered that the erythroblastosis virus genome contained a sequence that was nearly 90% homologous to part of the EGF receptor. The membrane receptor resides half outside, half inside the cell and is about 1200 amino acids long. The EGF receptor family comprises four members: the original one and three others. EGFR2 is the one that is over expressed in some human breast cancers. As is now well known, it is possible to inhibit some cancers that over express EGF family members with anti-receptor antibodies and specific tyrosine kinase inhibitors. To get to this point, having started with mouse eye opening, I thought was pretty good.

ACKNOWLEDGMENTS

I am most indebted to the students and colleagues who were associated with me over the past fifty years without whom the work I have summarized could not have been accomplished.

Insights into the Biogenesis of Lysosome-Related Organelles from the Study of the Hermansky-Pudlak Syndrome

JUAN S. BONIFACINO, PHD

Cell Biology and Metabolism Branch, National Institute of Child Health and Human Development, National Institutes of Health, Bethesda, Maryland 20892, USA

ABSTRACT: Lysosome-related organelles (LROs) are a family of cell-type-specific organelles that include melanosomes, platelet dense bodies, and cytotoxic T cell granules. The name, LRO, recognizes the fact that all of these organelles contain subsets of lysosomal proteins in addition to cell-type-specific proteins. The recent identification of genetic disorders that cause combined defects in several of these organelles indicates that they share common biogenetic pathways. Studies of one of these disorders, the Hermansky-Pudlak syndrome (HPS), have provided helpful insights into the molecular machinery involved in LRO biogenesis. HPS is a genetically heterogeneous disorder caused by mutations in any of 7 genes in humans and 15 genes in mice. These genes encode subunits of 4 multi-protein complexes named AP-3, BLOC-1, BLOC-2 and BLOC-3, in addition to miscellaneous components of the general protein trafficking machinery. The AP-3 complex is a coat protein involved in vesicle formation and cargo selection in the endosomal-lysosomal system. One of these cargo molecules is the melanosomal enzyme, tyrosinase, the missorting of which may explain the defective melanosomes in AP-3-deficient humans and mice. The function of the BLOC complexes is unknown, although they are thought to mediate either vesicle tethering/fusion or cytoplasmic dispersal of LROs. Further studies of these complexes should contribute to the elucidation of the mechanisms of LRO biogenesis and the pathogenesis of HPS.

KEYWORDS: lysosomes; endosomes; clathrin; pigmentation; sorting signals; melanine

Address for correspondence: Juan S. Bonifacino, PhD, Cell Biology and Metabolism Branch, National Institute of Child Health and Human Development, Building 18T/Room 101, National Institutes of Health, Bethesda, MD 20892, USA. Voice: 301-496-6368; fax: 301-402-0078.
juan@helix.nih.gov

Ann. N.Y. Acad. Sci. 1038: 103–114 (2004). © 2004 New York Academy of Sciences.
doi: 10.1196/annals.1315.018

TABLE 1. Examples of endosomal-lysosomal sorting signals

Protein	Signal
Tyrosine-based sorting signals (YXXØ)	
Transferrin receptor	16-PLSY**TR**FSLA-35-Tm
Lamp-1	Tm-RKRSHA**GYQT**I
TRP2	Tm-RRLRK**GYTP**LMET-11
Dileucine-based sorting signals (D/E/XXLL/I-type)	
TCR-CD3-γ	Tm-8-S**DKQTLL**PN-26
Limp-II	Tm-11-**DERAPLI**RT
Tyrosinase	Tm-8-E**EKQPLL**ME-12

Key amino acid residues of the signals are indicated in bold. Amino acids are in the single letter code. X is any amino acid and Ø an amino acid with a bulky hydrophobic side chain. Numbers correspond to residues that are amino- and carboxy-terminal to the indicated sequences. Tm, transmembrane; TRP2, tyrosinase-related protein 2, TCR-CD3-γ, CD3-γ subunit of the T-cell antigen receptor. See ref. 2 for a comprehensive listing of endosomal-lysosomal sorting signals.

PROTEIN SORTING TO LYSOSOME-RELATED ORGANELLES

Since the early 1990s, my laboratory has worked on the molecular mechanisms by which proteins are targeted to different compartments within the cell, with a particular focus on the organelles that constitute the endosomal-lysosomal system. This system comprises various types of endosomes and lysosomes, as well as a group of cell-type-specific, "lysosome-related organelles" (LROs) including melanosomes, platelet dense bodies, and cytotoxic T cell granules (FIG. 1A).[1] Each of these organelles has a characteristic complement of transmembrane and luminal proteins that are responsible for their cellular functions. A major goal of my laboratory has been to understand how this protein composition is achieved. We now know that proteins are targeted to organelles of the endosomal-lysosomal system by virtue of sorting signals that direct incorporation of the proteins into transport vesicles bound for these organelles. Transmembrane proteins, for example, contain degenerate motifs within their cytosolic tails, which function as sorting signals.[2] Some of these motifs have a critical tyrosine residue and are therefore referred to as "tyrosine-based" sorting signals (TABLE 1). Among the proteins that contain this type of signal are endocytic receptors such as the transferrin receptor, lysosomal membrane proteins such as Lamp-1, and melanosomal proteins such as the tyrosinase-related protein 2 (TRP2). Other motifs share a critical leucine-leucine or leucine-isoleucine pair and are known as "dileucine-based" sorting signals (these signals were first described at the NICHD by François Letourneur and Richard Klausner) (TABLE 1). Dileucine-based sorting signals are found in signaling receptors such as the T cell antigen receptor, lysosomal membrane proteins such as Limp-II, and melanoso-

A

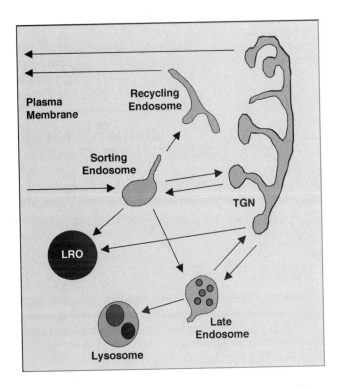

B

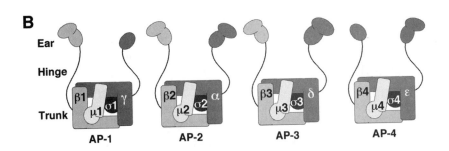

FIGURE 1. Organelles of the endosomal-lysosomal system and adaptor protein complexes. (**A**) Schematic representation of the organelles that make up the endosomal-lysosomal system and the pathways that interconnect them. LRO: lysosome-related organelle. TGN: *trans*-Golgi network. (**B**) Schematic representation of adaptor protein (AP) complexes. The names of the AP subunits are indicated by Greek symbols. The two large subunits of each complex are subdivided into trunk, hinge, and ear domains. Some of the AP subunits occur as two or three isoforms encoded by different genes. One isoform of β3, β3A, is defective in HPS-2.

mal proteins such as tyrosinase. Mutation of either tyrosine-based or dileucine-based signals abrogates transport of all of these transmembrane proteins to endosomes, lysosomes, and/or LROs, and causes their missorting to the plasma membrane. Thus, despite their different structural features, both types of signal mediate sorting to the same set of endosomal-lysosomal organelles. This led to the hypothesis that the same family of recognition proteins must recognize both tyrosine-based and dileucine-based sorting signals.

RECOGNITION OF SORTING SIGNALS BY ADAPTOR PROTEIN COMPLEXES

Work from my laboratory and other laboratories resulted in the identification of four heterotetrameric complexes named AP-1 (γ-β1-μ1-σ1), AP-2 (α-β2-μ2-σ2), AP-3 (δ-β3-μ3-σ3), and AP-4 (ϵ-β4-μ4-σ4) as the recognition molecules for subsets of both tyrosine-based and dileucine-based sorting signals (subunit compositions are indicated in parentheses) (FIG. 1B).[2] Tyrosine-based signals bind to the μ subunits of the four AP complexes, whereas dileucine-based signals bind to the AP-1 γ-σ1 and AP-3 δ-σ3 subunits.[3] The recognition of both types of signal by the same protein complexes explains how they can mediate similar sorting events. AP-2 is associated with the cytosolic face of the plasma membrane and mediates rapid endocytosis from the cell surface, whereas AP-1, AP-3 and AP-4 are localized to the *trans*-Golgi network (TGN) and/or endosomes and mediate intracellular sorting events. AP-1 and AP-2 were known long before we started our work on signal recognition. AP-3 and AP-4, on the other hand, were identified later on in my laboratory and that of Margaret Robinson (University of Cambridge, UK).[4] The biochemical properties of AP-3 and AP-4 determined in our studies were consistent with them playing a role in protein sorting. However, the exact sorting events mediated by these complexes *in vivo* were not immediately obvious.

DEFECTS IN AP-3 ARE A CAUSE OF HERMANSKY-PUDLAK SYNDROME

A breakthrough in the understanding of the physiological role of AP-3 occurred when the Drosophila *garnet* mutant was shown to have defective expression of the AP-3 δ subunit.[5] *Garnet* mutant flies had been first isolated in 1916 by Calvin Bridges (Columbia University) based on their defective pigmentation of the eyes and other organs. We went on to show that mutations in the β3, μ3 and σ3 subunits in Drosophila underlie the pigmentation defect in the *ruby, carmine,* and *orange* mutant flies, respectively.[6,7] These observa-

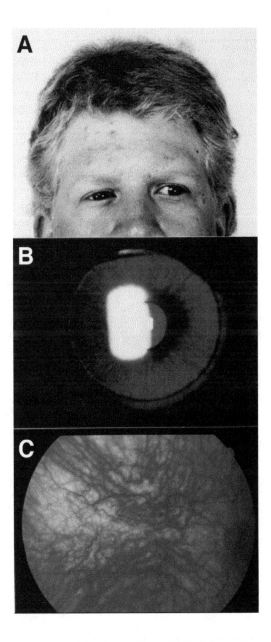

FIGURE 2. Pigmentation defect in a patient with HPS-2. (**A**) Reduced pigmentation of the hair and skin. (**B**) Transillumination of the iris due to decreased melanine content (*red area* [color appears online]). (**C**) Hypopigmentation of the retina (*yellow* [color appears online]). Pictures courtesy of William Gahl (NICHD). Reprinted from ref. 16 with permission.

tions demonstrated that mutations in any of the four subunits of AP-3 caused a pigmentation defect in Drosophila. Histological analyses revealed that the eye color defect in the AP-3 mutant flies was due to a severe reduction in the number of pigment granules in pigment cells.[5–8] This led us to speculate that some inherited pigmentation defects in mammals could be due to mutations in AP-3 subunits.

From the medical literature we learned that the most common inherited pigmentation defect in humans is caused by mutations in the gene encoding tyrosinase, a key enzyme in the biosynthesis of the mammalian pigment, melanin. However, we also found out that there are other inherited pigmentation disorders—all autosomal recessive—in which tyrosinase expression and activity are normal. One of these disorders, named Hermansky-Pudlak syndrome (HPS) after the two Czech internists who first described it in 1959, presents with reduced pigmentation of the skin and the eyes (FIG. 2).[9] The reduced pigmentation of the retina causes poor vision, to the extent that many of these patients are considered legally blind. As in the mutant flies, these pigmentation abnormalities are due to a severe depletion of pigment granules. In addition, these patients bruise easily and have prolonged bleeding due to the absence of platelet dense bodies. Over time, they develop fibrosis of the lungs and inflammatory colitis, probably due to accumulation of undegraded materials in lysosomes of reticuloendothelial cells. Some affected patients also exhibit immune system abnormalities such as neutropenia and loss of cytotoxic T lymphocyte (CTL)–mediated cytotoxicity. Most of these symptoms are consistent with defective biogenesis of a subset of LROs such as melanosomes, platelet dense bodies, cytotoxic granules and some types of lysosomes. Because of the phenotypic similarities to the Drosophila AP-3 mutants, we wondered whether HPS could be caused by defects in AP-3.

Fortunately for us, a group led by William Gahl was already studying a group of HPS patients at NICHD. We established a collaboration with this group to characterize the status of AP-3 in skin fibroblasts obtained from these patients and from normal individuals. Immunofluorescent staining of cells from normal individuals using antibodies to AP-3 subunits revealed the characteristic distribution of AP-3 to cytoplasmic puncta corresponding to endosomes (FIG. 3A). Most HPS patient cells exhibited a similar distribution and level of staining. Cells from two brothers affected with HPS, however, exhibited drastically reduced staining for AP-3 (FIG. 3A). Northern blot analyses showed normal levels of mRNAs encoding the four subunits of AP-3 in these two patients. However, immunoblot analyses revealed much lower levels of the four AP-3 subunits, particularly $\beta 3$ and $\mu 3$, in the brothers' cells as compared to cells from normal individuals (FIG. 3B). DNA sequencing revealed two mutations in the cDNA encoding the ubiquitous isoform of $\beta 3$ (i.e., $\beta 3A$).[10] Each mutation occurred on one chromosomal copy of the gene, meaning that the brothers were compound heterozygotes. The predicted mutant proteins had a single, non-conservative amino acid substitution (L^{580} to

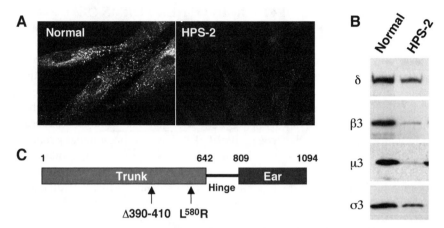

FIGURE 3. AP-3 defects in HPS-2. (**A**) Immunofluorescence microscopy of skin fibroblasts cultured from a normal individual and from a patient with HPS-2, stained for the β3A subunit of AP-3. (**B**) Immunoblot analysis of the same fibroblast cultures with antibodies to the four subunits of AP-3. (**C**) Schematic representation of the β3A subunit of AP-3 indicating two mutations found in patients with HPS-2. Amino acid numbers are indicated. Pictures in **A** and **B** are reprinted from ref. 10 with permission.

R) or a 21-amino acid internal deletion (Δ390–410) (FIG. 2C). These proteins were rapidly degraded by the proteasome, resulting in very low levels of β3A in the brothers' cells.[10]

Since AP-3 is capable of binding both tyrosine-based and dileucine-based sorting signals,[2] defects in AP-3 are likely to cause missorting proteins having either of those signals. Tyrosinase is a transmembrane protein that has a typical dileucine-based sorting signal within its cytosolic tail and this signal has been shown to bind to AP-3 *in vitro*.[11] Moreover, we have recently shown that this signal binds to a combination of the δ and σ3 subunits of AP-3.[3] Consistent with these interactions, tyrosinase is mislocalized in cells from the AP-3-deficient brothers.[12] It thus appears that the defective pigmentation observed in these patients is due to failure to sort tyrosinase to melanosomes. The cause for the abnormalities in platelet dense bodies and other LROs is currently unknown, although it is tempting to speculate that they could also result from impaired sorting of other transmembrane proteins having tyrosine-based or dileucine-based sorting signals. Indeed, fibroblasts from AP-3–deficient patients display increased trafficking of lysosomal membrane proteins such as Lamp-1, Lamp-2 and CD63 via the plasma membrane,[10] probably because of a partial block in their transport from early endosomes to late endosomes and lysosomes. The steady-state distribution of these lysosomal membrane proteins in the AP-3 deficient cells, however, is not visibly altered, meaning that the overall role of AP-3 in the sorting of these proteins is minor.

GENETIC DEFECTS IN OTHER FORMS OF
HERMANSKY-PUDLAK SYNDROME

Although highly informative of the molecular mechanisms of LRO biogenesis, mutations in β3A remain a rare cause for this disease. Moreover, mutations in the other three subunits of AP-3 have not been found in HPS patients. Instead, HPS has emerged as a genetically heterogeneous disorder in which mutations in at least seven distinct genetic loci give rise to the same disease in humans. The genetic heterogeneity of HPS has also been underscored by studies of mouse mutant strains having phenotypes resembling human HPS (FIG. 4A).[13] Mouse mutants with unusual coat colors have been collected throughout history, with documented examples in ancient China, 18th centu-

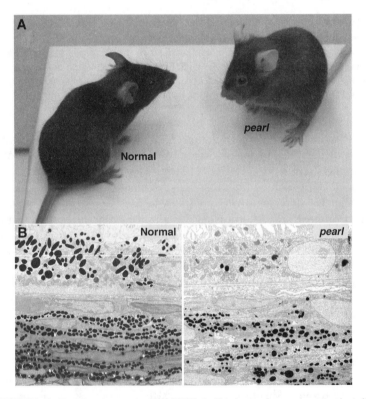

FIGURE 4. *Pearl*, a mouse model of HPS-2. (**A**) A *pearl* mouse next to its wild-type counterpart. Like HPS-2 patients, *pearl* mice have mutations in the gene encoding β3A. Picture courtesy of Richard Swank (Roswell Park Cancer Institute). (**B**) Ultrastructure of the retina from wild type (WT) and *pearl* mice. The electron micrographs show the retinal pigmented epithelium (*top layer*) and the choroid (*bottom layer*), both of which contain many melanosomes in normal mice. Notice the decreased number of melanosomes in the *pearl* mouse. Pictures are reprinted from ref. 17 with permission.

TABLE 2. Human and mouse HPS genes

Human	Mouse	Product
HPS1	Pale ear	BLOC-3 Subunit
HPS2	Pearl	AP-3 β3A Subunit
HPS3	Cocoa	BLOC-2 Subunit
HPS4	Light Ear	BLOC-3 Subunit
HPS5	Ruby eye-2	BLOC-2 Subunit
HPS6	Ruby eye	BLOC-2 Subunit
HPS7	Sandy	BLOC-1 Subunit
	Mocha	AP-3 δ Subunit
	Pallid	BLOC-1 Subunit
	Muted	BLOC-1 Subunit
	Cappuccino	BLOC-1 Subunit
	Reduced pigmentation	BLOC-1 Subunit
	Gunmetal	Rab geranylgeranyl transferase α subunit
	Buff	Vps33A
	Subtle gray	

ry Japan, and 19th century Europe. They gained in popularity in Victorian England with the foundation of "fancy mouse" clubs, and eventually captured the interest of geneticists in the early 20th century. Remarkably, many of these mouse mutants exhibit not only reduced pigmentation but also prolonged bleeding. As in HPS, these phenotypes arise from abnormalities in melanosomes (FIG. 4B) and platelet dense bodies, making these mice *bona fide* models for the human disease. To date, at least 15 such mouse strains have been described, each of which carries a mutation in a different gene. The seven human HPS genes and 15 mouse HPS genes have now been identified by the groups of Richard Spritz (University of Colorado), Richard Swank (Roswell Park Cancer Institute), Luanne Peters (Jackson Laboratory), Margit Burmeister (University of Michigan), William Gahl (NICHD), Stephen Kingsmore (University of Florida) and Esteban Dell'Angelica (UCLA), in most cases by positional cloning (TABLE 2).[13] HPS caused by mutations in β3A is now referred to as HPS type 2 (HPS-2) in humans and the *pearl* mutant in mouse.

Some of the mutated genes in mouse models of HPS encode proteins that are directly or indirectly involved in protein sorting or vesicular transport (TABLE 2). For example, the *mocha* gene encodes another subunit of AP-3, δ. The *buff* gene encodes Vps33A, a subunit of the Vps-C or HOPS complex involved in endosomal tethering/fusion events. Finally, the *gunmetal* gene encodes a Rab geranylgeranyl transferase α subunit (Rabggta) involved in isoprenylation of Rab GTP-binding proteins, which also mediate tethering/fusion and organelle translocation events.[13] All the other genes mutated in hu-

TABLE 3. Subunit composition of BLOCs

Complex	Subunits
BLOC-1	Pallidin, Muted, Cappuccino, Sandy/HPS7
	Reduced pigmentation, Snapin, BLOS1, BLOS2
BLOC-2	Ruby eye/HPS6, Ruby eye-2/HPS5, Cocoa/HPS3
BLOC-3	Pale ear/HPS1, Light ear/HPS4

man and mouse HPS encode products with no homology to any other proteins and no recognizable motifs. Recent biochemical analyses have shown that most of these proteins are subunits of at least three multi-protein complexes named BLOC (for Biogenesis of Lysosome-related Organelles Complex) (TABLE 3).[14] BLOC-1 comprises eight subunits, five of which are the products of HPS genes (pallidin, muted, cappuccino, sandy/HPS7 and reduced pigmentation), and three that have not yet been implicated in HPS (Snapin, BLOS1, and BLOS2). BLOC-2 comprises the products of the *ruby eye/ HPS6, ruby eye-2/HPS5* and *cocoa/HPS3* genes. Finally, BLOC-3 is composed of the *pale ear/HPS1* and *light ear/HPS4* gene products. It is still possible that some of these complexes could contain additional subunits. Like AP-3 mutants, humans and mice with mutations in the BLOC components exhibit reduced numbers of pigmented melanosomes and apparent absence of platelet dense bodies. Orthologs of some of the BLOC subunits also exist in Drosophila, and their mutation may likewise cause pigmentation defects. The mechanism of action of BLOC complexes, however, is likely to be different from that of AP-3, since BLOC mutants do not display increased trafficking of lysosomal membrane proteins via the plasma membrane.[15] The next challenge will be to determine the exact intracellular localization and function of these complexes. Possible functions include the tethering/fusion of transport carriers that deliver proteins to melanosomes or platelet dense bodies, and the dispersal of these organelles throughout the cytoplasm. Further studies of these proteins are likely to reveal details of a unique pathway for the biogenesis of LROs.

CONCLUDING REMARKS

In conclusion, the studies reviewed here have uncovered a molecular machinery involved in the biogenesis of LROs. This machinery is conserved from Drosophila to humans, and includes known effectors and regulators of protein trafficking (*i.e.*, AP-3, Vps33A and Rabggta), as well as novel proteins of unknown function (i.e., the BLOCs). The identification of this machinery has shed light into the pathogenesis of HPS and may yet yield clues to the pathogenesis of other human pigmentation disorders such as the

Chediak-Higashi syndrome. The elucidation of the functions of this machinery holds promise for better diagnosis of HPS and for therapeutic interventions that could alter the course of this disease. Finally, these studies illustrate the powerful synergy that results from the convergence of biochemical, cellular, genetic and clinical studies to study the causes of human disease.

ACKNOWLEDGMENTS

I thank all my co-workers and collaborators for their contributions to the research reviewed in this article. I also thank William Gahl and Richard Swank for pictures in FIGURE 2 and FIGURE 4, respectively. Finally, I am grateful to the Division of Intramural Research of NICHD for its generous support of this research. I apologize to those whose research I failed to cite because of space constraints.

REFERENCES

1. DELL'ANGELICA, E.C. *et al.* 2000. Lysosome-related organelles. FASEB J. **14:** 1265–1278.
2. BONIFACINO, J.S. & L.M. TRAUB. 2003. Signals for sorting of transmembrane proteins to endosomes and lysosomes. Annu. Rev. Biochem. **72:** 395–447.
3. JANVIER, K. *et al.* 2003. Recognition of dileucine-based sorting signals from HIV-1 Nef and LIMP-II by the AP-1 γ-σ1 and AP-3 δ-σ3 hemicomplexes. J. Cell Biol. **163:** 1281–1290.
4. ROBINSON, M.S. & J.S. BONIFACINO. 2001. Adaptor-related proteins. Curr. Opin. Cell Biol. **13:** 444–453.
5. OOI, C.E. *et al.* 1997. Altered expression of a novel adaptin leads to defective pigment granule biogenesis in the *Drosophila* eye color mutant *garnet.* EMBO J. **16:** 4508–4518.
6. MULLINS, C., L.M. HARTNELL & J.S. BONIFACINO. 2000. Distinct requirements for the AP-3 complex in pigment granule and synaptic vesicle biogenesis in *Drosophila melanogaster.* Mol. Gen. Genet. **263:** 1003–1014.
7. MULLINS, C. *et al.* 1999. Defective expression of the mu3 subunit of the AP-3 adaptor complex in the *Drosophila* pigmentation mutant carmine. Mol. Gen. Genet. **262:** 401–412.
8. SIMPSON, F. *et al.* 1997. Characterization of the adaptor-related protein complex, AP-3. J. Cell Biol. **137:** 835–845.
9. HUIZING, M., R.E. BOISSY & W.A. GAHL. 2002. Hermansky-Pudlak syndrome: vesicle formation from yeast to man. Pigment Cell Res. **15:** 405–419.
10. DELL'ANGELICA, E.C. *et al.* 1999. Altered trafficking of lysosomal membrane proteins in Hermansky-Pudlak syndrome due to mutations in the β3A subunit of the AP-3 adaptor complex. Mol. Cell. **3:** 11–21.

11. HÖNING, S., I.V. SANDOVAL & K. VON FIGURA. 1998. A di-leucine-based motif in the cytoplasmic tail of LIMP-II and tyrosinase mediates selective binding of AP-3. EMBO J. **17:** 1304–1314.
12. HUIZING, M. *et al.* 2001. AP-3 mediates tyrosinase but not TRP-1 trafficking in human melanocytes. Mol. Biol. Cell. **12:** 2075–2085.
13. LI, W. *et al.* 2004. Murine Hermansky-Pudlak syndrome genes: regulators of lysosome-related organelles. Bioessays **26:** 616–628.
14. DELL'ANGELICA, E.C. 2004. The building BLOC(k)s of lysosomes and related organelles. Curr. Opin. Cell Biol. **16:** 458–464.
15. DELL'ANGELICA, E.C. *et al.* 2000. Molecular characterization of the protein encoded by the Hermansky-Pudlak syndrome type 1 gene. J. Biol. Chem. **275:** 1300–1308.
16. SHOTELERSUK, V. *et al.* 2000. A new variant of Hermansky-Pudlak syndrome due to mutations in a gene responsible for vesicle formation. Am. J. Med. **108:** 423–427.
17. FENG, L. *et al.* 2002. The Hermansky-Pudlak syndrome 1 (HPS1) and HPS2 genes independently contribute to the production and function of platelet dense granules, melanosomes, and lysosomes. Blood **99:** 1651–1658.

Dynamics of Secretory Membrane Trafficking

JENNIFER LIPPINCOTT-SCHWARTZ, PHD

Section on Organelle Biology, Cell Biology and Metabolism Branch, NICHD, NIH, Bethesda, Maryland 20892, USA

ABSTRACT: The study of intracellular membrane trafficking and organelle dynamics has been revolutionized with the advent of GFP technology, which allows individual proteins to be tagged with GFP and monitored in living cells. Using GFP-based techniques such as selective photobleaching and time-lapse imaging of different GFP color variants, it is now possible to address a host of questions related to protein retention within the organelles, the origin and fate of transport intermediates, and the extent of trafficking through different transport pathways. This has provided unexpected new insights into the organization and function of secretory and endocytic pathways within cells.

KEYWORDS: GFP; Golgi apparatus; ER; secretory; membrane traffic; photobleaching

Within eukaryotic cells, the secretory pathway synthesizes, sorts and secretes a wide assortment of macromolecules that allow the cell to modify and respond to its surrounding environment. Protein and lipid molecules within this pathway are synthesized in the endoplasmic reticulum (ER) and transported to the Golgi apparatus for processing and maturation. The molecules are then sorted and packaged into post-Golgi carriers that move through the cytoplasm to fuse with the cell surface. The directional membrane flow through the secretory pathway (i.e., ER to Golgi to plasma membrane) is balanced by retrieval pathways that return specific types of proteins and lipids back to the Golgi or ER.

Only recently, through the advent of green fluorescent protein (GFP) technology, has it become possible to track and quantify the movement of pro-

Address for correspondence: Jennifer Lippincott-Schwartz, PhD, Section on Organelle Biology, Cell Biology & Metabolism Branch, Division of Intramural Research, NICHD, NIH, Building 18T, Room 101, 18 Library Drive, Bethesda, MD 20892-5430. Voice: 301-402-1010; fax: 301-402-0078.

jlippin@helix.nih.gov; <http://lippincottschwartzlab.nichd.nih.gov/>

Ann. N.Y. Acad. Sci. 1038: 115–124 (2004). © 2004 New York Academy of Sciences.
doi: 10.1196/annals.1315.019

teins within the secretory pathway in single cells. This has permitted unprecedented detailed measurements of the kinetic and morphological characteristics of secretory transport and organelle behavior. This, in turn, has provided the basis for addressing for the first time such key questions as: how are proteins retained in specific secretory compartments? what length of time does a typical cargo protein spend in a particular compartment? and, what are the origins, pathways and fates of secretory transport intermediates? In this chapter, I will discuss the GFP-based techniques and experiments that are helping to address these questions. The results from such experiments are providing new insights into how the secretory pathway is organized and functions, and how its molecular machinery functions on a system-wide basis within living cells.

GFP-BASED TECHNIQUES

Virtually any protein can be tagged with GFP—a compact, 23 kD protein containing an amino-acid triplet (Ser-Try-Gly) that rearranges into a fluorophore. The resulting chimeras are easily expressed within cells, are bright, and can be imaged repetitively without loss of fluorescence. The GFP tag also does not usually alter the parent protein's transport or function, so the chimeras can be used to track proteins through intracellular pathways. With high illumination levels, GFP chimeras can be photobleached—a process that causes a fluorophore's fluorescence to be permanently extinguished. This permits analysis of a chimera's diffusional mobility and transport itinerary under steady-state conditions—when the chimera's overall distribution may appear to be unchanging. Using sensitive light detection systems, it is also possible to quantify GFP fluorescence and thereby to correlate the signal from a chimera to the number of corresponding molecules. This can be used to determine how much of a particular protein resides within a given compartment and at what rate it moves out of the compartment. Finally, it is possible to label different proteins with different colored variants of GFP and to visualize them in the same cell. The ability to track, quantify and photobleach GFP-tagged proteins in this manner permit analysis of a host of central questions about secretory membrane function and trafficking.

PROTEIN RETENTION MECHANISMS

One question that GFP-based experiments are helping to clarify is how proteins are retained in a particular secretory compartment. Protein retention is vital for the proper functioning of the secretory pathway, as proteins responsible for the processing of secretory cargo and its packaging into transport intermediates need to be utilized repeatedly, and they function optimally only in specialized places in the secretory pathway. For example, chaperones involved in the folding and oligomerization of newly synthesized proteins (including BiP, calnexin, calreticulin and protein disulfide isomerase) reside exclusively in the ER, whereas enzymes that modify the sugar-side chains of glycoproteins localize primarily in the Golgi apparatus. How these proteins are retained in the ER or Golgi amidst the continuous forward flow of protein and lipid through the secretory pathway has been unclear. One possibility is that the proteins are physically retained within a compartment, for example, by binding to an immobilized scaffold. An alternative possibility is that retention is achieved by the failure of the protein to be sorted into export domains that bud off a compartment. In this case, the protein could diffuse and move freely within a compartment.

Using GFP-tagged organelle markers and the method known as fluorescence recovery after photobleaching (FRAP), it is now possible to distinguish between these possibilities (Lippincott-Schwartz et al., 2001). In this approach, the marker's fluorescence in a region of a compartment is irreversibly photobleached using a high-powered laser beam. Recovery of fluorescence into the photobleached region is then recorded at low laser power. If recovery is observed, it usually means that surrounding nonbleached fluorescence molecules have moved by diffusion into the bleached area replacing the bleached molecules. The speed that this occurs is dependent on the protein's diffusion constant, which varies based on the protein's size and the viscosity of the medium through which the protein is diffusing. In the event of no recovery, the fluorescent molecules are not moving. This indicates that the fluorescent proteins are immobilized in some fashion, since all proteins undergo diffusive, Brownian movement unless constrained in some fashion.

Using FRAP to measure the diffusional properties of GFP-tagged proteins residing in the ER or Golgi, it has been possible to determine whether these proteins are retained in these compartments by being physically immobilized or through their failure to be transported forward through the secretory pathway. Of the proteins examined so far, all seem to be retained by the latter mechanism since they exhibited rapid recovery in photobleaching experiments (FIG. 1). These proteins included ER chaperones and modifying enzymes, proteins misfolded in the ER and Golgi processing enzymes (Cole et al., 1996; Nehls et al., 2000; Snapp et al., 2003; Lippincott-Schwartz et al., 2000). The unhindered, free diffusion of ER and Golgi resident components revealed from FRAP experiments suggests that these proteins are retained in these compartments by lacking positive signals for being packaged into transport intermediates that move material forward through the secretory pathway. This property is likely to be important for allowing resident ER and Golgi components to rapidly and efficiently interact with and modify newly synthesized cargo molecules before the cargo proteins move further downstream through the secretory pathway.

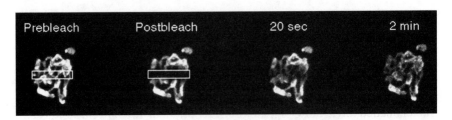

FIGURE 1. FRAP of Golgi apparatus in NRK cell expressing the Golgi enzyme marker, galactosyltransferase tagged with GFP. (Figure courtesy of K. Hirshberg.)

The ability to probe the diffusional characteristics of GFP-tagged proteins within secretory organelles using photobleaching techniques can also be used to study other secretory organelle functions, including interactions between protein complexes, and the membrane binding/dissociation rates of cytosolic protein complexes (Lippincott-Schwartz *et al.*, 2001). Results from studies using these approaches are providing exciting new perspectives into the mechanisms underlying protein folding and degradation processes in the ER (Marguet *et al.*, 1999; Nikonov *et al.*, 2002; Rotman-Pikienlny *et al.*, 2002), and the dynamics of COPII and COPI coat lattice assembly onto membranes (Stephens *et al.*, 2000; Ward *et al.*, 2001; Presley *et al.*, 2002), which regulate membrane budding and export out of the ER and Golgi, respectively.

FORMATION AND KINETICS OF MEMBRANE TRANSPORT INTERMEDIATES

A different area of the secretory pathway that GFP technology is providing important insights into is the characterization of transport carriers that mediate movement between secretory organelles. These carriers bud off from a donor compartment carrying selected cargo and lipid, translocate through the cytoplasm, and then dock and fuse with an acceptor compartment. While the machinery regulating carrier formation and targeting previously has been elegantly defined from genetic and biochemical approaches (Schekman & Orci, 1996), an understanding of the dynamics of these carriers—including where they originate, how long they persist, what path they follow, and what type and amount of cargo they carry—has only become attainable since the advent of GFP-based approaches.

By marking proteins so that they are visible to light, the GFP-based approaches allow cargo proteins to be tracked and quantified as they move through the secretory pathway in single living cells. An example of a cargo protein followed in this manner is the temperature-sensitive variant (ts045) of vesicular stomatitis virus G protein tagged with GFP (VSVG-GFP) (Presley *et al.*, 1997). VSVG-GFP reversibly misfolds and is retained in the ER at 40°C, but upon temperature shift to 32°C it correctly folds and is transported out of the ER into the secretory pathway. In cells expressing VSVG-GFP that were shifted from 40°C to 32°C, the chimera was found to rapidly concentrate (up to 8 fold) in small tubulovesicular domains of the ER (1–2 μm in diameter) called ER exit sites that were scattered all over the ER. Pre-Golgi structures containing VSVG-GFP then detached from the ER exit sites and moved into the Golgi region along microtubule tracks. The pre-Golgi structures then fused with the Golgi, delivering their contents enbloc (Presley *et al.*, 1997). After residing in the Golgi for 20–30 min on average, VSVG-GFP molecules then appeared in post-Golgi carriers. These carriers pulled off the Golgi as tubule elements depleted of Golgi enzymes (Hirschberg *et al.*, 1998; Toomre *et al.*, 1999; Polishchuk *et al.*, 2000). Upon detaching from the Golgi, they moved toward the cell periphery along microtubules at speeds of 2–3 μm/sec (FIG. 2). Enroute to the plasma membrane, the carriers exhibited dynamic shape changes, extending into long tubules or retracting into globule structures. The majority of the carriers did not interact with other membrane structures (i.e., endosomes) before fusing with the plasma membrane. At peak flux of VSVG-GFP out of the Golgi, individual post-Golgi carriers contained up to 10,000 VSVG-GFP molecules and occupied an area of 1.3 μm^2 (Hirschberg *et al.*, 1998)

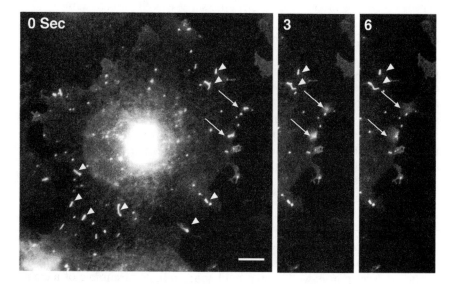

FIGURE 2. Post-Golgi trafficking of VSVG-GFP (adapted from Hirschberg *et al.*, 1998).

The conclusions derived from these observations were unexpected given earlier work examining fixed cells. For example, from the fixed cells it was assumed that ER-to-Golgi transport was not dependent on microtubules and that the pre-Golgi structures seen near ER exit sites represented a stable intermediate compartment between the ER and Golgi. By directly visualizing proteins moving between the ER and Golgi using GFP-tagged markers, however, it became clear that, in fact, microtubules have an important role in directing ER-derived carriers to juxtanuclear Golgi elements and that pre-Golgi structures represent transport vehicles for protein delivery to the Golgi.

From time-lapse experiments of cargo trafficking such as the above, it has also been possible to obtain detailed measurements of the kinetic characteristics of the secretory pathway (Hirschberg *et al.*, 1998). This has been accomplished by monitoring the amount GFP-tagged cargo in a compartment (based on its fluorescence intensity) as a bolus of the cargo passes through the secretory pathway. For VSVG-GFP, we found that the chimera moved between ER–Golgi and between Golgi–plasma membrane at a rate equal to a rate constant multiplied by the amount of VSVG-GFP in the donor compartment (Hirschberg *et al.*, 1998). For ER–Golgi transport, the mean rate constant for trafficking was 2.8% per min whereas for Golgi–plasma membrane transport it was 3% per min. Rate constants describe the fraction of material that moves by way of a process per unit time and represent the fundamental kinetic characteristic of the process. Therefore, the fact that export rate constants for VSVG-GFP out of the ER or Golgi remained constant irrespective of whether 4,000 VSVG-GFP molecules per sec were being exported (occurring soon after shift from 40°C to 32°C) or only 10 VSVG-GFP molecules per sec (occurring after 3 h of temperature shift) was significant. It meant that in our experiments VSVG-GFP did not pass any saturation bounds and that regulatory mechanism as a whole remained constant in the cell.

The finding that linear rate laws can accurately describe export of VSVG-GFP from the ER and Golgi also means that the rate-limiting steps for these export processes do not involve simple binary reactions between VSVG-GFP and some compartment constitutent (such as an ER or Golgi enzyme) because such reactions would be transiently altered by incoming/outgoing VSVG-associated membrane. Instead, it is likely that the rate-limiting steps for export involve phase-separation processes, such as lipid partitioning, which don't exhibit dilution effects (Hirschberg *et al.*, 1998).

RETRIEVAL PATHWAYS

A further topic that GFP-based approaches are helping to clarify is the extent of backward movement of proteins within the secretory pathway. Such retrograde transport is well known as playing an important role in retrieving ER proteins back to the ER whenever they "leak" into the secretory pathway.

Recent findings from GFP-based experiments has now revealed that retrograde pathways are being utilized to recycle Golgi enzymes back to the ER and to return certain types of plasma membrane proteins from the plasma membrane back to the Golgi. These constitutive recycling pathways are vital for the generation and maintenance of the Golgi apparatus.

Evidence that Golgi resident components are not stably retained in this organelle but are constitutively cycling between the ER and Golgi has come from photobleaching experiments using GFP-tagged Golgi enzymes (Cole et al., 1996; Zaal et al., 1999; Ward et al., 2001). In these experiments, the Golgi region of cells expressing a GFP-tagged Golgi protein was photobleached with high laser power under conditions in which new protein synthesis is inhibited. The Golgi region was then monitored at low laser power to determine whether nonbleached Golgi proteins in the ER or other sites could replenish the bleached Golgi pool. The same approach was then used to photobleach non-Golgi regions of the cell (including the ER) to determine whether nonbleached Golgi proteins would redistribute into the bleached non-Golgi areas. As nonbleached proteins were found to move to the areas occupied by bleached proteins in these experiments, the results supported the idea that Golgi proteins are continually cycling between Golgi and ER compartments.

The quantitative nature of the data obtained from these experiments has made it possible to estimate the rate constants for Golgi enzyme movement between Golgi and ER, and the residency time of Golgi enzymes in the Golgi (Zaal et al., 1999). This was accomplished by fitting the data to a simple two compartment model (including Golgi and ER) with one rate constant governing ER-to-Golgi and another governing Golgi-to-ER transport. From this kinetic model it was estimated that GalTase-GFP cycled between the Golgi and ER every 85 min, residing in the Golgi for ~58 min and in the ER for ~27 min. One prediction of such cycling is that conditions that block ER export should lead to Golgi proteins redistributing into the ER and Golgi integrity being lost. This has been observed when ER export is inhibited in cells over-expressing a Sar1p mutant that disrupts ER export (Ward et al., 2001; Miles et al., 2001). By revealing the magnitude of the Golgi to ER retrograde transport pathway in this quantitative fashion, GFP-based approaches have helped reveal the essential role of this pathway in the maintenance of Golgi structure.

Using similar selective photobleaching strategies with GFP chimeras, we have shown that glycosylphophatidylinositol (GPI)-linked proteins undergo constitutive cycling from the plasma membrane to the Golgi (Nichols et al., 2001). A characteristic feature of many GPI-linked proteins is their affinity for rafts—lipid domains enriched in cholesterol and glycosphingolipids—on the plasma membrane. The cycling of GPI-linked proteins was unexpected, since at steady-state these molecules appear to be stably residing in the Golgi and plasma membrane. However, by selectively photobleaching molecules in the Golgi and not the plasma membrane, we found that the two pools undergo dynamic and continuous exchange (FIG. 3). Through kinetic modeling ap-

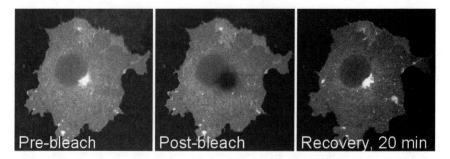

FIGURE 3. Cycling of GPI-GFP between plasma membrane and Golgi assessed by photobleaching (adapted from Nichols *et al.*, 2001).

proaches, we were able to determine how fast the proteins cycle between plasma membrane and Golgi and what conditions affect this cycling rate. As internalization of the proteins did not require the activity of clathrin-coated pits, the GPI-anchored proteins were following a nonclathrin pathway to the Golgi. Other molecules that associate with rafts (including Shiga and cholera toxin subunits) were also found to follow this pathway, so it appears to be a general route for returning raft-associated membrane components back to the Golgi.

In the Golgi, raft-domains are thought to play an important role in the lateral partitioning and sorting of cargo proteins into export competent domains of this organelle (Keller & Simons, 1997). The recycling of raft-associated proteins that we observed using GPI-linked GFP chimeras could play an important role in resupplying the Golgi with raft lipids. It might also function in the selective endocytosis of particular cell surface components during the generation of polarized cell surface domains. An additional potential role is in regulation of cell signaling events, since EGFR undergoes nonclathrin endocytosis in response to activating ligand (Yamazaki *et al.*, 2002). The existence of specific markers for this nonclathrin pathway that can be tracked using GFP will allow these and other issues related to the functional significance of the pathway to be addressed in future studies.

SUMMARY AND PERSPECTIVES

The ability to visualize, quantify and kinetically model protein trafficking in single cells using GFP technology provides a powerful approach for addressing a host of central questions about protein sorting and trafficking within the secretory pathway. As discussed above, these approaches already have provided important new insights into:

(1) protein targeting and retention within organelles,
(2) the processes by which transport intermediates form and move between compartments, and
(3) the extent and specificity of retrograde transport pathways.

Continued work using GFP chimeras for *in vivo* experimentation will require the further development of quantitative tools and methods for analyzing protein and organelle dynamics in living cells. This includes the continued exploration of new ways to analyze and quantify protein and organelle dynamics—such as with photoactivatable GFP variants (Patterson & Lippincott-Schwartz, 2002; Lippincott-Schwartz & Patterson, 2003) and with kinetic analysis tools of computational cell biology (Phair & Misteli, 2001). With these tools, it should be possible to generate sophisticated kinetic models for estimating rate constants for transport in and out of compartments, residency times in compartments and binding/dissociation rates. With this new information, a dynamic model for the secretory pathway that integrates protein localization, concentration, diffusion and interactions can be constructed and tested on a system-wide basis within living cells.

REFERENCES

COLE, N.B., C. SMITH, N. SCIAKY, *et al.* 1996. Diffusional mobility of Golgi proteins in membranes of living cells. Science **273:** 797–801.

HIRSCHBERG, K., C.M. MILLER, J.F. PRESLEY, *et al.* 1998. Kinetic and morphological analysis of secretory protein traffic in living cells. J. Cell Biol. **143:** 1485–1503.

KELLER, P. & K. SIMONS. 1997. Post-Golgi biosynthetic trafficking. J. Cell Sci. **110:** 3001–3009.

LIPPINCOTT-SCHWARTZ, J., T. ROBERTS & K. HIRSCHBERG. 2000. Secretory protein trafficking and organelle dynamics in living cells. Ann. Rev. Cell & Dev. Biol. **16:** 557–589.

LIPPINCOTT-SCHWARTZ, J., E. SNAPP & A. KENWORTHY. 2001. Studying protein dynamics in living cells. Nature Cell Biol. Rev. **2:** 444–456.

LIPPINCOTT-SCHWARTZ, J. & G. PATTERSON. 2003. Development and use of fluorescent protein markers in living cells. Science **300:** 87–91.

MARGUET, D., E.R. SPILIOTIS, T. PENTCHEVA, *et al.* 1999. Lateral diffusion of GFP-tagged H2Ld molecules and of GFP-TAP1 reports on the assembly and retention of these molecules in the endoplasmic reticulum. Immunity **11:** 231–240

NEHLS, S., E. SNAPP, N. COLE, *et al.* 2000. Dynamics and retention of misfolded proteins in native ER membrane. Nature Cell Biol. **2:** 288–295.

NICHOLS, B.J., A.K. KENWORTHY, T.H. ROBERTS, *et al.* 2001. Rapid cycling of lipid raft markers between the cell surface and Golgi complex. J. Cell Biol. **153:** 529–541.

NIKONOV, A.V., E. SNAPP, J. LIPPINCOTT-SCHWARTZ & G. KREIBICH. 2002. Active translocon complexes diffuse slowly in the membrane of the ER and behave as large polysome arrays. J. Cell Biol. **158:** 497–506.

PATTERSON, G. & J. LIPPINCOTT-SCHWARTZ. 2002. A photoactivatable GFP for selective photolabeling of proteins and cells. Science **297:** 1873–1877.

PHAIR, R.D. & T. MISTELI. 2001. Kinetic modeling approaches to in vivo imaging. Nat. Rev. Mol. Cell Biol. **2:** 898–907.

POLISHCHUK, R.S., E.V. POLISHCHUK, P. MARRA, *et al.* 2000. Correlative light-electron microscopy reveals the tubular-saccular ultrastructure of carriers operating between Golgi apparatus and plasma membrane. J. Cell Biol. **148:** 45–58.

PRESLEY, J.F., N.B. COLE, T.A. SCHROER, *et al.* 1997. ER to Golgi transport visualized in living cells. Nature **389:** 81–85.

PRESLEY, J.F., T.H. WARD, A.C. PFEIFER, *et al.* 2002. Dissection of COPI and Arf1 dynamics *in vivo* and role in Golgi membrane transport. Nature **417:** 187–193.

ROTMAN-PIKIENLNY, P., K. HIRSCHBERG, P. MARUVADA, *et al.* 2002. Retention of Pendrid in the endoplasmic reticulum is a major mechanism for Pendred Syndrome. Human Mol. Gen. **11:** 1–9.

SCHEKMAN R. & L. ORCI. 1996. Coat proteins and vesicle budding. Science **271:** 1526–1533.

SNAPP, E.L., R.S. HEGDE, M. FRANCOLINI, *et al.* 2003. Formation of stacked ER cisternae by low affinity protein interactions. J. Cell Biol. **163:** 257–269.

STEPHENS, D.J., N. LIN-MARQ, A. PAGANO, *et al.* 2000. COPI-coated ER-to-Golgi transport complexes segregate from COPII in close proximity to ER exit sites. J. Cell Sci. **113:** 2177–2185.

TOOMRE, D., P. KELLER, J. WHITE, *et al.* 1999. Dual-color visualization of trans Golgi network to plasma membrane traffic along microtubules in living cells. J. Cell Sci. **112:** 21–33.

WARD, T., R. POLISHCHUK, K. HIRSCHBERG, *et al.* 2001. Maintenance of Golgi structure and function depends on the integrity of ER export. J. Cell Biol. **155:** 557–570.

ZAAL, K., C.L. SMITH, R.S. POLISHCHUK, *et al.* 1999. Golgi membranes are absorbed into and re-emerge from the ER during mitosis. Cell **99:** 589–601.

Structure and Function of Glutamate Receptors

MARK MAYER, PHD

Head, Laboratory of Cellular and Molecular Neurophysiology, Division of Intramural Research, National Institute of Child Health and Human Development, National Institutes of Health, Bethesda, Maryland 20892, USA

ABSTRACT: Understanding how glutamate receptors, a group of molecules that mediate information between neurons in the brain, work at the molecular level has been the focus of my research. The key role of glutamate receptors is to mediate excitatory synaptic transmission throughout the brain and spinal cord. To understand the mechanisms by which this occurs requires a molecular understanding of the receptor proteins. Our experimental approach required breaking down the receptor into smaller assemblies that are easier to work with. We ended up, after a few years, with the first molecular model for how ion channel gating occurs.

KEYWORDS: glutamate receptors; neurons; synaptic plasticity; neurotransmitters

My scientific career has been devoted to understanding how glutamate receptors, a group of molecules that mediate information transfer between neurons in the brain, work at the molecular level. The first functional characterization of glutamate receptors was completed in 1955, the year I was born, and we are still engaged in this research today. The key role these molecules play is to mediate excitatory synaptic transmission throughout the brain and spinal cord (FIG.1).

Glutamate receptors are also involved in synaptic plasticity and have numerous roles in development. Like many molecules, they were first cloned in the late 1980s. They fall into seven gene families and are all membrane proteins; but because they are membrane proteins, there has been very little progress in understanding their structure or their molecular mechanisms of action.

Address for correspondence: Mark Mayer, PhD, Head, Laboratory of Cellular and Molecular Neurophysiology, Division of Intramural Research, NICHD, NIH, Building 36, Room 2D02 MSC 4066, 36 Convent Drive, Bethesda, MD 20892. Voice: 301-496-9346; fax: 301-496-2396. mm18a@nih.gov

Ann. N.Y. Acad. Sci. 1038: 125–130 (2004). © 2004 New York Academy of Sciences. doi: 10.1196/annals.1315.020

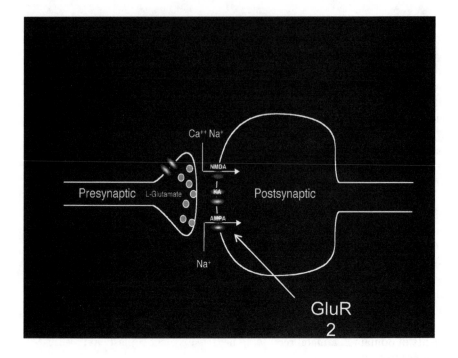

FIGURE 1. A family of glutamate receptor ion channel genes is expressed at excitatory synapses in the brain.

These proteins are present mostly in the postsynaptic membranes; there are 18 known glutamate receptor genes in the human genome and also in those of mice and rats. With the exception of two genes of unknown function they all encode proteins that mediate neural transmission. To measure the kinetics of their response to the neurotransmitter glutamate, we use a membrane patch and a fast perfusion system. When one applies the neurotransmitter glutamate to the receptor for a period of one millisecond, the receptor rapidly activates, and when one removes the neurotransmitter, the channels switch off again. At synapses the activation and deactivation can occur at rates of close to 1000 times per second, which is what allows us to process information quickly in the brain.

To understand the mechanisms by which this occurs requires a molecular understanding of the receptor proteins. We now know that they have four domains, including two extracellular domains that have amino acid sequence homology to bacterial periplasmic proteins and both of which bind a small ligand, such as glutamate or an allosteric modulator; a membrane-spanning portion, which makes up the pore itself; and a cytoplasmic tail that can be up to 500 amino acids in length.

Our experimental approach required breaking down the receptor into smaller assemblies that are easier to work with. For example, we made deletion mutants to remove 400 acids encoding the first extracellular domain from the glutamate binding site and membrane-spanning domain, expressed the mutant protein, and looked at its physiology. The activation and desensitization in this case look almost identical to wild type. By applying this technique further, we trimmed out the parts of the proteins that were difficult to work with in biochemical experiments and were able to engineer a soluble protein, which we could express at the multi-milligram quantities suitable for structural studies. The soluble protein contains the binding site for glutamate and variety of agonists, antagonists, and allosteric modulators.

Our results suggest that conformational changes observed on the binding of glutamate to the portion of the molecule isolated as a soluble protein activates ion channel gating in the intact receptor. The isolated protein has two-domains and the binding of the ligand stabilizes a conformation like a closed Venus clamshell. The proteins also assemble as dimers and the dimer formation occurs exclusively through domain 1. From these observations we were able to propose a model for gating, a simple mechanical model in which the domain closure associated with the binding of agonist, which stabilizes this conformation, causes mechanical work on the ion channel portion by movements of domain 2, and, either by a twisting or pulling motion, causes the ion channel to open. Some of the experimental evidence of this came from studies of molecules that have been complexed with ligands with different efficacies for activating ion channel gating.

These experiments relied upon 5-substituted willardiines, a series of compounds on which I first worked seven or eight years ago. We now have crystal structures for complexes of several of these compounds with glutamate receptors, which have revealed that their mode of binding is similar to glutamate. Specifically, the placement of these compounds, including key water molecules, in the pocket of the ion channel is nearly identical to that for glutamate. What does change, however, is the response of the receptor as the size of the ligand increases, which has two consequences. First, selected amino acid side chains in the binding pocket undergo a conformational change to relieve collision with the ligand 5-positions atoms. But for the largest ligands that is not sufficient to fully relieve bad contacts, so that the global conformation of the receptor also has to adapt. Thus each willardiine bound structure has a slightly different, unique conformation. Glutamate produces the most closed conformation, and as we gradually increase the size of the willardiine agonists, the whole of domain 2 is pushed out of the way by rigid body movements so that the cleft becomes progressively more and more open as larger ligands are bound to the receptor.

We were able to alter the efficacy of activation experimentally by slight changes in the size of amino acid side chains in the ligand binding pocket. The design of these experiments was based upon structural information that

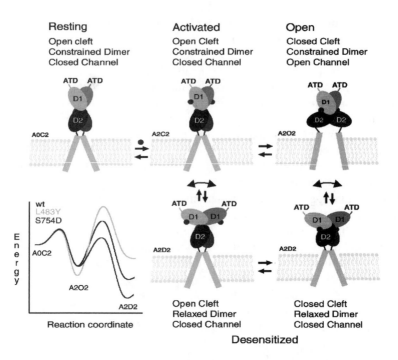

FIGURE 2. Structural model for GluR desensitization.

we already had. When we plotted the separation in the protein crystal dimer as a function of occupation with different ligands a number of quite remarkable things happened. The first is that the initial response required to activate ion channel gating is quite large, suggesting that the coupling mechanism has a threshold, but then activation progressively increases with domain closure. The second thing we got out of our experiments, which was unexpected and quite remarkable, was an explanation for the process of desensitization for the AMPA family of ion channel genes.

FIGURE 2 illustrates that activation is the result of agonist triggered domain closure of the binding core. We have experimental evidence that desensitization occurs by relaxation of the ligand-binding core dimer. Some of the experimental evidence came from the study of mutants that altered the process. One of the most interesting was the L483Y mutation, which changes the response to glutamate—normally very strongly desensitizing—to one that is barely desensitizing at all (FIG. 3).

When we compare the crystal structures of the wild-type protein with that of the L483Y mutant, we saw that the in the wild-type protein the leucine side chain is trying to fit into the a pocket between another leucine and a lysine in

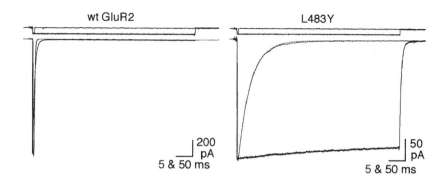

FIGURE 3. Point mutations in the dimer interface block desensitization.

the adjacent subunit but is not very well accommodated by this pocket. When this amino acid is replaced by tyrosine, it interacts very nicely with this pocket. It makes a very nice series of bonds here including cation pi interactions with the lysine side-chain ammonium group. Biochemical studies revealed that there is a much stronger interaction in the dimer for this mutant protein than for the wild type. We also identified mutants that can do the opposite. When tested in functional experiments we found a striking correlation between the extent of desensitization in intact receptors and the strength of dimer formation for the isolated ligand-binding cores, the crystal structures of several of which have been solved.

We ended up after a few years with the first molecular model for how ion channel gating occurs. I feel lucky to have played a role in this unprecedented advance through experiments done in collaboration with Eric Gouaux at Columbia University, where I was fortunate to be able to spend a year on sabbatical leave. It was there that I made a mid-career transition after being a physiologist to doing crystallography, which is now being done in my own lab here at the institute where we have solved structures of the ligand-binding cores for kainate receptors, which have their own unique structural and functional properties that we are now beginning to explore in depth.

SELECTED RECENT PUBLICATIONS

MAYER, M.L. Crystal structures of the GluR5 and GluR6 ligand binding cores: molecular mechanisms underlying kainate receptor selectivity. Neuron. In press.

HORNING, M.S. & M.L. MAYER. 2004. Regulation of AMPA receptor gating by ligand binding core dimers. Neuron **41:** 379–388.

MAYER, M.L. & N.A. ARMSTRONG. 2004. Structure and function of glutamate receptor ion channels. Annu. Rev. Physiol. **66:** 161–181.

ARMSTRONG, N.A., M.L. MAYER & E. GOUAUX. 2003. Tuning activation of the AMPA-sensitive GluR2 ion channel by genetic adjustment of agonist-induced conformational changes, PNAS **100:** 5736–5741.

SUN,Y., R. OLSON, M. HORNING, *et al.* 2002. Mechanism of glutamate receptor desensitization, Nature **417:** 245–253.

Neuroendocrine Basis of Human Disease

ROGER GUILLEMIN, MD, PHD

The Salk Institute for Biological Studies, La Jolla, California 92037, USA

ABSTRACT: This paper is a short review of the traditionally obvious diseases of neuroendocrine origin (diabetes insipidus, Kallman syndrome, etc.), but also of the newly recognized participation of several peptides originally characterized in the hypothalamus and of their receptors, in a series of diseases, both in internal medicine and in psychiatry (rheumatoid arthritis, inflammation, carcinoids, anxiety, depression, etc.). The concept of neuropeptides is now vastly expanded, as these molecules and their several receptors are now known to be widely distributed throughout the brain and the periphery with increasing evidence of paracrine and autocrine modes of action.

KEYWORDS: neuropeptides; receptors; hypothalamus; paracrine secretions

I am delighted to participate in this symposium, which, just by the titles of its many presentations, shows the extraordinary contribution of the National Institute for Child Health and Human Development to the progress of medicine over the last 40 years. I have an immense debt of gratitude to the successive leaders of NICHD, which for 30 years supported the research of our Laboratories for Neuroendocrinology at the Salk Institute.

Let me say also that I have never agonized in preparing a 15 minute talk as I did for this one when I saw the proposed title for this exercise of mine—the "neuroendocrine basis of human disease." I felt totally overwhelmed by the scope of the assignment. But while I may have attracted that load upon myself (FIG. 1), reflections for this short talk also led to a great deal of satisfaction and intellectual humility.

The Web site of the National Library of Medicine lists more than 100,000 papers dealing one way or another with the peptides originally recognized in the hypothalamus. The original hypophysiotropic hypothalamic peptides with which we were dealing are now seen to be ultimately involved in many

Nobel Prize in Physiology or Medicine, 1977; Lasker Award, Basic Medical Research, 1975.
Address for correspondence: Roger Guillemin, MD, PhD, The Salk Institute for Biological Studies, 10010 North Torrey Pines Road, La Jolla, CA 92037. Voice: 858-455-9322; fax: 858-625-0688.
Guillemin@salk.edu

Ann. N.Y. Acad. Sci. 1038: 131–137 (2004). © 2004 New York Academy of Sciences.
doi: 10.1196/annals.1315.021

Reprint Series
27 October 1978, Volume 202, pp.390-402

SCIENCE

528

Peptides in the Brain: The New Endocrinology of the Neuron

Roger Guillemin

Copyright © The Nobel Foundation 1978

FIGURE 1. Cover page of reprint from *Science* magazine.

aspects of many human diseases, some expected, some unexpected. The endocrinology of the neuron I mentioned above is no longer exclusively of hypothalamic neurons but is of widely and not randomly distributed neurons throughout the central and peripheral nervous system. Moreover, what we originally recognized as neuropeptides are now known to be expressed and functional in tissues of the gastrointestinal tract, the lungs, the hematopoietic system, and the immune system. The same is true regarding the recently acquired knowledge of the multiple receptors for these same peptides. The neuroendocrine basis of human disease, to come back to my assigned title, is now a proposition with ubiquitous answers.

Thus, what I will be giving here is pretty much a listing, a recital, rather than details of any mechanism of action.

Probably the first disease of neuroendocrine origin so recognized was diabetes insipidus, recognized when vasopressin was characterized by du-Vigneaud in 1952 and its true biosynthetic origin in the supraoptic nucleus of the hypothalamus definitely confirmed.[1,2]

Isolated pituitary deficiencies for TSH, growth hormone or gonadotropins are usually of hypothalamic origin. They respond well to administration of the corresponding hypothalamic-releasing factors, actually, to any one of the analogues now available from the pharmaceutical industry.[3]

True, uncomplicated precocious puberty due to early activation of the hypothalamo-pituitary GnRH-gonadotropins axis is very responsive to administration of any of the GnRH-superagonists now available, through well understood mechanisms of downregulation.[4]

Similarly, pituitary hyperfunction such as in acromegaly due to ectopic secretion of the corresponding releasing factor, in this case GRH, is of neuroendocrine origin and responds usually dramatically to the surgical removal of the secreting ectopic source.[5] I will say more later about the carcinoids usually involved.

Many, possibly all, prolactin-secreting microadenomas of the pituitary have a neuroendocrine basis as they usually respond not only to dopamine agonists, but also to somatostatin in one of its long-acting forms (Octreotide, Somatulin, Lanreotide).[6] This is probably also the case for the rare thyrotropin-secreting pituitary adenomas.

The complex clinical picture of hypogonadotropic hypogonadism or Kallmann syndrome is due to failure of migration of the GnRH-secreting neurons from the nasal placode to the hypothalamus during fetal development.[4] Some of these patients do respond well to pulsatile administration of GnRH. Similarly, hypothalamic amenorrhea due to inhibition of GnRH biosynthesis also responds to pulsatile administration of GnRH.[4,7]

Neoplasms of tissues embryologically derived from the neural crest, or more precisely what is now referred to as the neuroendocrine-programmed epiblast, the so called cristopathies or neurocristopathies[8] are obviously of neuroendocrine origin. These include the carcinoids,[9] which can be located throughout the body leading to a multiplicity of clinical syndromes, including those due to pheochromocytomas. Insulinomas, glucagonomas, gastrinomas belong to this group. When surgery is difficult or impossible, a long-acting somatostatin usually inhibits the abnormal secretion of the corresponding peptide. Some neurofibromatoses are now considered by some to be neurocristopathies,[10] though it appears difficult to separate the original neurofibrosis lesion(s) from the often contemporary neuroblastic tumors.

With the recent and explosive knowledge on leptin and its mechanism of action at the hypothalamic level, its complex interactions with α-MSH and ghrelin as well as with the recently reported oleyl-ethanolamide or OEA, we may well say also that there is a neuroendocrine basis for the human disease known as obesity.[11] Anorexia nervosa is a compendium of complex neuroendocrine involvement. Pseudocyesis, rare but real, is probably the ultimate psychoneuroendocrine disease. Spectacular when dealing with a Queen of England—the well-known case of Mary Tudor, pseudocyesis is still occasionally reported in the literature.

The recently reported dramatic results on the use of RU-486 the progesterone-glucocorticoids receptor-antagonist in acute psychotic depression[13] is best explained by its action at the level of the brain receptors for glucocorticoids. And there is increasing evidence that CRF (corticotropin releasing factor) and its several variants along with their recognized multiple receptors, are involved in the pathophysiology of affective disorders. Recent studies with CRF-receptors antagonists appear to confirm this dramatic proposal. Indeed, hyperactivity of the hypothalamo-pituitary-adrenal (HPA) axis in a large number of patients with major depression is one of the most consistent observation in functional psychiatry.[14,15] The very recent description of type 1 and 2 receptors for CRF on fetal Purkinje cells may open new vistas on the pathogenesis of well-recognized cerebellar ataxias for which we have no explanation so far.[27]

Let me say here that it is with great personal pleasure that I wish to give unique credit to Wylie Vale and his group for opening this new chapter of neuroendocrinology following their isolation and characterization of CRF.

But I would like now to take a somewhat different tack and discuss with you the extraordinary development of the significance of somatostatin and its multiple receptors in a series of unexpected diseases for which we can now propose a neuroendocrine basis.

When we first isolated from hypothalamic tissues, sequenced, and synthesized somatostatin in 1972,[16] it was a physiologically unexpected inhibitor of the pituitary secretion of growth hormone. Rapidly it was shown by Charlie Gale in Seattle to produce hypoglycemia in baboons, related to inhibition of the secretion of glucagon and insulin, a fact confirmed by Sam Yen in acromegalic patients, and Dubois in France and Rolf Luft and Høkfelt in Stockholm showed that somatostatin was indeed synthesized in the delta cells of the endocrine pancreas.

That was truly a remarkable and unexpected series of observations.

Rapidly again, the group around Michael Besser in London was to show effects of somatostatin on the secretion of gastrointestinal peptides as well as immunolocalization of somatostatin in the pertinent secretory elements.

That was followed by the synthesis both in academia and the pharmaceutical industry of a very large number of analogues of the native structure of somatostatin with the aim of dissociating the multiple activities of the native peptide. Availability of these analogues led to the characterization of somatostatin receptors in multiple tissues. We know now that there exist five different receptors, with isoforms, and their tissues distribution is now well known.[17] They have been cloned, expressed and knock-out animals have been prepared. And the results are remarkable and I will say somewhat unexpected.

Thus, there is now extensive evidence that somatostatin also originates from the immune system and has significant immunomodulatory activity. The thymic epithelial and dendritic cells synthesize somatostatin and express type 2 somatostatin receptors. The thymus seems to have a complete somatostatin regulatory compartment. George Chrousos was one of the first to propose that somatostatin is part of an immunoregulatory circuit that inhibits production of interferon-γ at sites of chronic inflammation.[18,19] A recently discovered variant of somatostatin, named cortistatin because of its prevalence in the brain cortex, has also been shown to be expressed in human monocytes, monocyte-derived macrophages, and dendritic cells both in the normal state and when activated by various lipopolysaccharides. Both cortistatin and somatostatin bind to type 2 somatostatin receptors,[19,20] more specifically the isoform 2A. T cells and B cells, like macrophages, express mRNA for the receptor type 2. Thus, somatostatin can be considered as an immunoregulatory cytokine that regulates inflammation. Indeed, intraarticular injection of somatostatin or one of the analogues, has been reported to reduce synovitis and inflammation in patients with rheumatoid arthritis.[21] It also reduces the concomitant pain possibly because, in a recently demonstrated new twist, somatostatin also binds to the μ-opioid receptor. μ-Opioid receptors in the skin, particularly in the keratinocytes are involved in the perception of peripheral pain. Analogues of somatostatin such as Octreotide and Lanreotide have much greater affinity to the μ-opioid receptor than the native peptide. Several years ago, George Chrousos (again) and his group here at NICHD showed that locally released somatostatin was involved in the classic antiinflammatory action attributed to glucocorticoids.[22]

Thus we can now add chronic inflammatory states from rheumatoid arthritis to the granulomas due to parasites like shistosomiasis to the list of human diseases with a major neuroendocrine basis.

Scintigraphy with labeled analogues of somatostatin has shown the presence of several types of receptors in pathological peripheral tissues, including the retroorbital tissue in Graves disease. Accumulation of the radionuclide is correlated with presence in the orbital tissue of activated lymphocytes and treatment with octreotide has been reported to improve the ophthalmopathy.[23]

The same technique of scintigraphy with a labeled analogue such as octreoscan has led to the recognition that many cancers do express specific somatostatin receptors. Somatostatin receptor scintigraphy in primary breast cancer has been reported to correlate with expression of the subtype 2A and type 5 receptors, including in metastases.[24]

But the largest number of reports deals with adenocarcinoma of the prostate. It has been known for many years that all prostatic tumors contain cellular elements known as neuroendocrine cells as they are positive in immunocytochemistry for a variety of peptides such as bombesin, somatostatin and also serotonin.[25] The degree of differentiation and proliferation of these cells appear to correlate inversely with tumor progression and the appearance of the androgen-independent state.

It has been proposed[26] that cancerous epithelial cells become responsive to paracrine and autocrine factors from the neuroendocrine cells by upregulation of receptors for these neuropeptides. In cell lines like PC3, analogues of somatostatin binding to type 2 and 5 inhibit proliferation.

Thus, choosing the correct analogue of somatostatin in relation to the particular receptor expressed may become part of the therapy of some of these tumors.

Jonas Salk used to say "We must be good ancestors...." Looking back over these 40 years, I think that it is what we have been, thanks to the support of NICHD.

REFERENCES

1. DU VIGNEAUD, V. 1955. A trail of sulfa research: from insulin to oxytocin. Nobel lecture. *In* Nobel Lectures, Chemistry 1942–1962, Elsevier Publishing Co. Amsterdam, the Netherlands.
2. SOKOL, H.W. & H. VALTIN. 1965. Morphology of the neurosecretory system in rats homozygous and heterozygous for hypothalamic diabetes insipidus (Brattleboro strain). Endocrinology **77:** 692–700.
3. YEN, S.S.C., R.B. JAFFEE, R.L. BARBIERI, EDS. 1999. Reproductive Endocrinology: Physiology, Pathophysiology, and Clinical Management, 4th edit. W.B. Saunders Company, Philadelphia, PA.
4. YEN, S.S.C. 1999. *In* Reproductive Endocrinology: Physiology, Pathophysiology, and Clinical Management, 4th edit. S.S.C. Yen, R.B. Jaffee, R.L. Barbieri, Eds.: 30–80. W.B. Saunders Company, Philadelphia, PA.
5. GUILLEMIN, R., P. BRAZEAU, P. BOHLEN, *et al.* 1982. Growth-hormone releasing factor from a human pancreatic tumor that caused acromegaly. Science **218:** 585–587.
6. SHIMON, I., X. YAN, G.E. TAYLOR, *et al.* 1997. Somatostatin receptor (SSTR) subtype-selective analogues differentially suppress in vitro growth hormone and prolactin in human pituitary adenomas. Novel Potential therapy for functional pituitary tumors. J. Clin. Invest. **100:** 2386–2392.
7. OLIVEIRA, L.M., S.B. SEMINARA, M. BERANOVA, *et al.* 2001. The importance of autosomal genes in Kallmann syndrome: genotype-phenotype correlations and neuroendocrine characteristics. J. Clin. Endocrinol. Metab. **86:** 1532–1538.
8. JONES, M.C. 1990. The neurocristopathies: reinterpretation based upon the mechanism of abnormal morphogenesis. Cleft Palate J. **27:** 126–140.
9. CHEJFEC, G., S. FALKMER, U. ASKENSTEN, *et al.* 1988. Neuroendocrine tumors of the gastrointestinal tract. Hol. Res. Pract. **183:** 143–154.
10. QUALMAN, S.J., W.R. GREEN, C. BROVALL & B.G. LEVENTHAL. 1986. Neurofibromatosis and associated neuroectodermal tumors: a congenital neurocristopathy. Pediatr. Pathol. **5:** 65–78.
11. ALTMAN, J. 2002. Weight in the balance. Neuroendocrinology **76:** 131–136.
12. DEWHURST, J. 1980. Royal pseudocyesis. Hist. Med. **8:** 12–17.
13. BELANOFF, J. K., B.H. FLORES, M. KALEZHAN, *et al.* . 2001. Rapid reversal of psychotic depression using mifepristone. J. Clin. Psychopharmacol. **21:** 516–521.

14. BALE, T.L. & W.W. VALE. 2004. CRF and CRF receptors. Role in stress responsivity and other behaviors. Annu. Rev. Pharmacol. Toxicol. **44:** 525–557.
15. OWENS, M.J. & C.B. NEMEROFF. 1999. Corticotropin releasing factor antagonists in affective disorders. Expert Opin. Investig. Drugs. **8:** 1849–1858.
16. BRAZEAU, P., W. VALE, R. BURGUS, *et al.* 1973. Hypothalamic polypeptide that inhibits the secretion of immunoreactive pituitary growth hormone. Science. **179:** 77.
17. RAULF, P.J., D. HOYER & C. BRUNS. 1994. Differential expression of five somatostatin receptor subtypes, SSTR 1-5, in the CNS and peripheral tissue. Digestion **55:** 46–53.
18. KARALIS, K., G. MASTORAKOS, H. SANO, *et al.* 1994. Somatostatin analogues suppress the inflammatory reaction in vivo. J. Clin. Invest. **93:** 2000–2006.
19. WEINSTOCK, J.V. & D. ELLIOTT. 2000. The somatostatin immunoregulatory circuit present at sites of chronic inflammation. Eur. J. Endocrinol. **143:** S15–19.
20. ELLIOT, D.E., J. LI, A.M. BLUM, *et al.* 1999. SSTR2A is the dominant somatostatin receptor subtype expressed by inflammatory cells, is widely expressed and directly regulates T cell IFN-γ release. Eur. J. Immunol. **29:** 2454–2463.
21. COARI, G., M. DI FRANCO, A. IAGNOCOCCO, *et al.* 1995. Intra-articular somatostatin 14 reduces synovial thickness in rheumatoid arthritis: an ultrasonographic study. Int. J. Clin. Pharmacol. Res. **15:** 27–32.
22. KARALIS, K., G. MASTORAKOS, H. SANO, *et al.* 1995. Somatostatin may participate in the anti-inflammatory actions of glucocorticoids. Endocrinology **136:** 4133–4138.
23. KRASSAS, G.E. & G.J. KAHALY. 1999. The role of octreoscan in thyroid eye disease. Eur. J. Endocrinol. **140:** 373–375.
24. SCHULZ, S., T. HELMHOLZ, J. SCHMITT, *et al.* 2002. True positive somatostatin receptor scintigraphy in primary breast cancer correlates with expression of sst2A and ss5. Breast Cancer Res. Treat. **72:** 221–226.
25. HANSSON, J. & P.A. ABRAHAMSSON. 2001. Neuroendocrine pathogenesis in adenocarcinoma of the prostate. Ann. Oncol. **12:** S145–152.
26. ZAPATA, P.D., R.M. ROPERO, A.M. VALENCIA, *et al.* 2002. Autocrine regulation of human prostate carcinoma cell proliferation by somatostatin through the modulation of the SH2 domain containing protein tyrosine phosphatase (SHP)-1. J. Clin. Endocrinol. Metab. **87:** 915–926.
27. SWINNY, J.D., D. KALICHARAN, E.H. BLAAUW, *et al.* 2003. Corticotropin-releasing factor receptor types 1 and 2 are differentially expressed in pre- and post-synaptic elements in the post-natal developing rat cerebellum. Eur. J. Neurosci. **18:** 349–362.

Role of Growth Factors in the Nervous System

IRA B. BLACK, MD

Professor and Chairman, Department of Neuroscience and Cell Biology, UMDNJ-Robert Wood Johnson Medical School, Director of the Joint Graduate Program in Physiology and Neurobiology, Robert Wood Johnson Medical School and Rutgers University, Piscataway, New Jersey 08854, USA

ABSTRACT: We are studying brain and stem cell plasticity. How do brain, mind, and cell change with environmental alteration? Combining molecular biology, cell culture, single cell electrophysiology, synaptic physiology, and whole animal experimentation, we have found that experience alters function.

KEYWORDS: brain-derived neurotrophic factor; synaptic plasticity; bone marrow stromal stem cells

Approximately fifteen years ago, we and others discovered that the brain contains multiple growth factors that regulate long-term development and survival of brain neurons over days to weeks. We found that one of the factors, BDNF (brain-derived neurotrophic factor), also acutely increases neuronal synaptic communication within minutes. This increased neural transmission occurs in hippocampal neurons that subserve memory. Detailed analysis in a number of laboratories indicated that BDNF enhanced transmission through actions both on the signal sending and signal receiving neurons. Focusing initially on the receiving neurons in cell culture, we found that BDNF increased the activity of the receptor lock for the neurotransmitter signal key that transmits nerve impulses. In sum, BDNF increases responsiveness of the receiving memory neuron to neurotransmitter signals. We were able to identify the biochemical changes that increased re-

Address for correspondence: Ira B. Black, MD, Professor and Chairman, Department of Neuroscience and Cell Biology, UMDNJ-Robert Wood Johnson Medical School, CABM, Room 342, 675 Hoes Lane, Piscataway, NJ 08854. Voice: 732-235-5388; fax: 732-235-4990.
black@mbcl.rutgers.edu
The material presented here is available in almost identical form on the author's website <http://www2.umdnj.edu/blackweb/index.htm>.

Ann. N.Y. Acad. Sci. 1038: 138–141 (2004). © 2004 New York Academy of Sciences.
doi: 10.1196/annals.1315.022

ceptor activity: Specific subunits of the receptor were phosphorylated indirectly by BDNF, increasing responsiveness. In parallel studies, BDNF also increased the release of transmitter signal by the transmitting neuron. In summary, the growth factor potentially increases memory function by acting both on the sending and receiving neurons.

To define the genomic basis of the growth factor action, we combined electrophysiological and molecular biological investigation at the *single neuron* level. Exposure to BDNF markedly increased synaptic transmission, as expected, and transcriptional analysis identified increases in 11 genes. We examined one gene, Rab3A, in detail as a prototype. The Rab3A gene product is a small GTP-binding protein that plays a critical role in transmitter release. To analyze function, we examined hippocampal neurons from mutant mice lacking Rab3A. Although basal synaptic transmission was normal, the neurons failed to respond to the growth factor with enhanced transmission, indicating that Rab3A is required for BDNF-induced synaptic plasticity associated with learning and memory. More generally, our studies suggest that gene expression governing mental function can be approached at the single cell level. Since BDNF is regulated by a variety of environmental stimuli from stress to seizures, our findings integrate experience, gene expression and brain function.

The striking synaptic plasticity uncovered by BDNF raised a host of general questions concerning cellular plasticity and cellular identity. What are the limits of plasticity? We approached this question by studying stem cells, the paradigm of plasticity. These undifferentiated elements can differentiate into a variety of specialized cell types and also retain the ability to self-renew.

We recently differentiated adult human and rat bone marrow stromal stem cells (BMSCs) into neurons. Our ultimate goal is to use these cells in Alzheimer's and Parkinson's diseases and in spinal cord injury. BMSCs normally differentiate only into mesenchymal cells, including bone, cartilage, muscle, tendon and fat. Differentiation into non-mesenchymal fates had not been demonstrated. A relatively simple treatment protocol induced the stromal cells to differentiate into neurons, exhibiting neuronal morphological traits, and expressing a variety of neuron-specific genes. Clonal cell lines, established from single cells, proliferated, yielding both undifferentiated and neuronal cells. Our observations suggest that intrinsic genomic mechanisms of commitment, lineage restriction and cell fate are mutable. Environmental signals apparently can elicit the expression of pluripotentiality that extends well beyond the accepted fate restrictions of cells originating in classical embryonic germ layers.

We have transplanted these neurons into various regions of the rat brain and spinal cord. The neurons survive and the rats exhibit no untoward effects. We are now transplanting the cells into rats with experimental diseases. Our approach, using adult stem cell-derived neurons, confers several potential future advantages:

(1) Use of the patient's own cells for autologous transplantation eliminates the danger of immunorejection and the need for toxic immunosuppressive agents;
(2) The self-renewing BMSCs and the neurons grow vigorously in culture providing a vast reservoir of source material;
(3) Neuronal differentiation is achieved by environmental manipulation only, without altering the genome, eliminating the need for immortalization and minimizing the probability of neoplastic transformation;
(4) The use of adult cells circumvents the ethical concerns associated with the use of embryos.

KEY REFERENCES

LEVINE, E., C.F. DREYFUS, I.B. BLACK & M. PLUMMER. 1995. Brain derived neurotrophic factor rapidly enhances synaptic transmission in hippocampal neurons via postsynaptic tyrosine kinase receptors. Proc. Natl. Acad. Sci. USA **92**(17): 8074–8077.

BLACK, I.B. 1995. Trophic interactions and brain plasticity. *In* The Cognitive Neurosciences. M.S. Gazzaniga, Ed. MIT Press. Cambridge, MA.

SUEN, P-C., K. WU, E.S. LEVINE, H.T.J. MOUNT, J-L. XU, S-Y. LIN & I.B. BLACK. 1997. Brain-derived neurotrophic factor rapidly enhances phosphorylation of the postsynaptic N-methyl-D-aspartate receptor subunit 1. Proc. Natl. Acad. Sci. USA **94**: 8191–8195.

LEVINE, E.S. & I.B. BLACK. 1997. Trophic factors, synaptic plasticity, and memory. Ann. N.Y. Acad. Sci. **835**: 12–18.

LIN, S-Y., K. WU, E.S. LEVINE, H.T.J. MOUNT, P-C. SUEN, I.B. BLACK. 1998. BDNF acutely increases tyrosine phosphorylation of the NMDA receptor subunit 2B in cortical and hippocampal postsynaptic densities. Mol. Br. Res. **55**: 20–27.

LEVINE, E.S., R.A. CROZIER, I.B. BLACK & M.R. PLUMMER. 1998. Brain-derived neurotrophic factor modulates hippocampal synaptic transmission by increasing NMDA receptor activity. Proc. Natl. Acad. Sci., USA, **95**: 10235–10239.

WOODBURY, D., E.J. SCHWARZ, D.J. PROCKOP & I.B. BLACK. 2000. Adult rat and human bone marrow stromal cells differentiate into neurons. J. Neurosci. Res. **61**: 364–370.

BLACK, I.B. 2001. The Dying of Enoch Wallace: Life, Death, and the Changing Brain. McGraw-Hill.

ALDER, J., S. THAKKER-VARIA & I.B. BLACK. 2002. Transcriptional analysis in the brain: trophin-induced hippocampal synaptic plasticity. Neurochem. Res. **27**: 1079–1092.

MUNOZ-ELIAS, G., D. WOODBURY & I.B. BLACK. 2003. Marrow stromal cells, mitosis, and neuronal differentiation: stem cell and precursor functions. Stem Cells **21**: 437–448.

ALDER, J., S. THAKKER-VARIA, D.A. BANGASSER, M. KUROIWA, M.R. PLUMMER, T.J. SHORS & I.B. BLACK. 2003. Brain-derived neurotrophic factor-induced gene expression reveals novel actions of VGF in hippocampal synaptic plasticity. J. Neurosci. **23**: 10800-10808.

WU, K., G.W. LEN, G. MCAULIFFE, C. MA, J.P. TAI, F. XU & I.B. BLACK. 2004. Brain-derived neurotrophic factor acutely enhances tyrosine phosphorylation of the AMPA receptor subunit GluR1 via NMDA receptor-dependent mechanisms. Brain Res. Mol. Brain Res. **130:** 178–186.

MUNOZ-ELIAS, G., A.J. MARCUS, T.M. COYNE, D. WOODBURY & I.B. BLACK. 2004. Adult bone marrow stromal cells in the embryonic brain: engraftment, migration, differentiation, and long-term survival. J. Neurosci. **24:** 4585–4595.

Activins and Inhibins and Their Signaling

WYLIE VALE, PHD, EZRA WIATER, PHD, PETER GRAY, PHD, CRAIG
HARRISON, PHD, LOUISE BILEZIKJIAN, PHD AND SENYON CHOE, PHD

*Clayton Foundation Laboratories for Peptide Biology and Structural Biology
Laboratory, Salk Institute for Biological Studies,
San Diego, California 92037, USA*

ABSTRACT: Activins and inhibins, which were discovered by virtue of their
abilities to stimulate or inhibit, respectively, the secretion of FSH, are
members of the transforming growth factor-β (TGFβ) superfamily and exert a broad range of effects on the diffentiation, proliferation and functions
of numerous cell types. Activins interact with two structurally related
classes of serine/threonine kinase receptors (type I and type II). Inhibin antagonizes activin by binding to the proteoglycan, betaglycan, and forming
a stable complex with and, thereby, sequestering type II activin receptors
while excluding type I receptors. If betaglycan is present, inhibin can also
antagonize those bone morphogenic proteins (BMPs) whose signaling is
dependent upon access to type II activin receptors. Recent insights regarding the structures of ligands, receptors and their signaling complexes are
providing the basis for the development of therapeutics capable of modulating fertility and numerous pathophysiologic processes.

KEYWORDS: activin; inhibin; betaglycan; FSH; receptor; co-receptor

The inhibin hypothesis was born more than 70 years ago with observations
of the effects of a water-soluble testicular extract on the appearance of post-
castration pituitary cells in rats. Over ensuing years, the concept was refined
to suggest that gonadal inhibin would selectively reduce secretion of one gonadotropin, FSH, and not the other, LH, by the pituitary gland. The existence
of inhibin remained controversial until the isolation from gonadal fluids,
characterization and cloning of inhibins in 1985.[1-4] Inhibins are het-
erodimers with common alpha (α) and distinct but related beta (β) subunits,
βA and βB comprising inhibin-A or inhibin-B. Additional related β-subunits
have been identified, but their biological roles remain less clear. Experiments measuring or immunoneutralizing inhibin-A or inhibin-B or deleting
the common α-subunit gene supported the important roles played by gonad-

Address for correspondence: Wylie Vale, PhD, Helen McLoraine Professor and Head, Clayton
Foundation Laboratories for Peptide Biology, Salk Institute for Biological Studies, 10010 N.
Torrey Pines Road, La Jolla, California 92037. Voice: 858-453-4100 X1307.
vale@salk.edu

Ann. N.Y. Acad. Sci. 1038: 142–147 (2004). © 2004 New York Academy of Sciences.
doi: 10.1196/annals.1315.023

al inhibins in the feedback regulation of FSH secretion and gametogenesis. Broader roles for inhibins were proposed based on the broad distribution of subunit proteins and mRNAs as well as the phenotype of mice null for the inhibin alpha gene, namely the appearance of gonadal and adrenal tumors and liver dysplasia.[5]

The purification of FSH releasing fractions led to the discovery of activins. Composed of two inhibin β-subunits, activins could stimulate FSH secretion and overcome the inhibitory effects of inhibins.[6,7] The localization of activin-B to gonadotropes and the consequences of immunoneutralizing activin-B revealed an autocrine loop whereby activin produced by gonadotropes acts to drive FSH, but not LH production.[8] Blood-borne inhibin from mainly gonadal sources acts at the pituitary level to antagonize the effects of local activins. Superimposed upon these slow-acting proteins and sex steroids (not discussed here) is rapidly acting GnRH, episodically secreted by the hypothalamus. In addition to pituitary effects, locally produced activins and inhibins can modify hormone production in the gonads and placenta, and regulate ovarian and testicular gametogenesis.[9] Activins and inhibins have been implicated in the progression of cancers and proliferative disorders of gonads and endometrium.[10]

Activins and inhibins are members of the TGFβ superfamily of pleiotropic hormones/growth factors and have powerful actions on erythropoiesis, liver proliferation, immune function, bone formation, skin morphogenesis and cutaneous wound repair, and angiogenesis. In the central nervous system, activins stimulate oxytocin and GnRH production. Activins behave as neuronal survival factors under some, but not all, circumstances and can induce terminal differentiation of some neurons. Activin has profound effects on early mesoderm development, axis formation, and cell fate determination. Activin receptors and endogenous activin-related ligands may be important determinants of vertebrate developmental steps including left-right asymmetry.[10]

Activins and other members of the TGFβ superfamily exert their biological effects by interacting with two types of transmembrane receptors (type I and type II) with intrinsic serine/threonine kinase activities, now called receptor serine kinases (RSKs). The first vertebrate RSK to be characterized was the type II activin receptor, ActRII;[11] subsequently, a dozen RSKs have been identified in mammals.[12,13] The initial step in activin signaling involves the binding of activin to a type II receptor, ActRII or ActRIIB and subsequent association with type I receptors. Type I RSKs are referred to as ALKs (ALK 1–7), for Activin receptor-Like Kinases. Functional studies have indicated that ALK4 is the type I receptor for activin.

The type II receptors exist as dimeric membrane molecules, each with a extracellular ligand binding domain, a single transmembrane domain, and a large cytoplasmic region, which includes a kinase domain activated as a result of phosphorylation in the juxtamembrane region by the type II receptor. The crystal structure of the extracellular domain of ActRII was solved and subsequently, the structure of ActRII bound to BMP7 and ActRIIB bound to activin A were determined.[14–16] In the complex, interactions occur between a convex surface on the receptor and an extended loop of the ligands. In binding, the receptor undergoes minimal structural rearrangement, but the ligand exhibits complex conformational changes that appear to differ amongst different ligand family members. In the case of activin, the bound dimer may be extended and rotated extending a previously inaccessible type I binding site thereby allowing the recruitment of ALK4 into the complex.

RSK signals are transduced through cytoplasmic proteins called pathway specific Smads (Smad1, 2, 3, 5 and 8), which, following phosphorylation by a type I kinase, associate with the common Smad (Smad4) and migrate to the nucleus where they modulate transcription of numerous genes. In addition, there are two inhibitory Smads (Smad6 and Smad7) that block phosphorylation of pathway specific Smads. The ActRII/activin/ALK complex signals through Smad2 or Smad3 and can be inhibited by Smad7.[13,17]

Activin signaling uses ActRII or ActRIIB as type II receptors, ALK4 as the type I receptor and Smad2 or Smad3. It is interesting that TGFβs have their own type II and type I (ALK5) receptors, yet share Smad2 and Smad3 with the activins. Activins share the type II receptors with many BMPs. Almost all BMPs bind ActRIIs with high affinity, but they signal through BMP specific type I receptors and Smads. Thus, although there is promiscuity at each level, overall there is a unique pathway for activins, TGFβs and BMPs. Specificity is achieved by the involvement of numerous membrane and cytoplasmic proteins as well as other soluble extracellular binding proteins, such as follistatin, which sequesters activins and some BMPs.

In considering the mechanism by which inhibin antagonizes activin, several observations are relevant. Inhibin fails to block signaling induced by constitutively active mutant type I receptors, in keeping with the site of action of inhibin occurring upstream of ALK4 activation. Inhibin can bind to ActRII and block activin binding, but with only low affinity, yet in some cellular systems, inhibin is a very potent inhibitor of activin. Thus, simple competition between the two proteins for access to ActRII would appear to be an unlikely explanation. Over-expression of ActRII abrogates the ability of inhibin to block activin, suggesting that sequestering activin type II receptors would be a plausible mechanism. However, some cell systems respond to activin but not to inhibin, so it seemed likely that some cell-specific component is required for inhibin action that would form a stable complex with inhibin and ActRII/IIB.

While screening for inhibin-binding proteins we found that the proteoglycan, betaglycan, bound inhibin, and formed a very stable complex with inhibin and ActRII. Furthermore, betaglycan could increase the functionality of inhibin and could confer sensitivity even on cells that were previously non-responsive to inhibin.[18] The most accepted current hypothesis is that betaglycan is an inhibin co-receptor (there may be others), which by associating strongly with the α-subunit, forms a very stable complex and reduces the concentration of type II receptors available to transduce activin signals. Betaglycan was initially characterized as a type III TGFβ receptor, which was not a signaling receptor, but facilitated the binding and biological response of cells to TGFβ-2. Mutagenesis studies have shown partial but not complete overlap between the TGFβ and inhibin binding sites on betaglycan[19] and it is interesting to consider the integrative roles of betaglycan, which could enhance TGFβ while suppressing activin signaling.

In keeping with the proposed mechanism of action of inhibin to sequester type II activin receptors, we hypothesized that inhibin could antagonize ligands of the BMP family, including myostatin, that utilize ActRII and ActRIIB. We have found that inhibin can indeed block BMP responses in several cell types including TM4 Sertoli cells.[20] These observations raise the possibility that inhibin, of either local or blood-borne origin, might under some circumstances interfere with BMP as well as activin signaling, and hence play a much broader role than previously appreciated.

Given the diverse actions and roles of members in this family, it is important to have tools with which to study them and ultimately to develop drugs for therapeutically modulating their actions. Advancements in unraveling the structures of ligand/receptor complexes will hopefully provide important clues for the development of such modalities. Recently, using the structure of BMP2 bound to its type I receptor ALK3[21] as a guide, we have developed a mutant activin (M108A) with modifications to the putative type I binding site, but which retained an intact type II, binding site. This mutant psuedoligand, indeed binds ActRII, but the complex fails to attract ALK4 and does not initiate a signaling cascade.[22] Like the heterodimeric inhibin, this homo-dimeric activin mutant antagonizes responses to activin and BMPs including myostatin. This is a prototype of what will be many modulators of TGFβ family signaling, which we anticipate will be developed with improved potency and selectivity as we better understand the subtle differences in the binding surfaces of various ligand/receptor interactions. Other approaches for developing drugs and biologics of improved specificity will target key binding proteins and co-receptors for each network. It is hoped that such agents will be important tools for studying and therapeutically managing physiologic and pathophysiologic processes dependent upon signaling by RSK's and their ligands.

REFERENCES

1. MASON, A.J., J.S. HAYFLICK, N. LING, *et al.* 1985 Complementary DNA sequences of ovarian follicular fluid inhibin show precursor structure and homology with transforming growth factor-beta. Nature **318:** 659–663.
2. DE KRETSER, D.M., D.M. ROBERTSON, G.P. RISBRIDGER, *et al.* 1988. Inhibin and related peptides. Progress in Endocrinology, pp. 13–23

3. DeJong, F.H. 1988. Inhibin. Physiol. Rev. **68:** 555–607.
4. Vale, W, C. Rivier, A. Hsueh, *et al.* 1988. Chemical and biological characterization of the inhibin family of protein hormones. Laurentian Hormone Conference, 1988, pp. 1–34.
5. Matzuk, M.M., T.R. Kumar, W. Shou, *et al.* 1996 Transgenic models to study the roles of inhibins and activins in reproduction, oncogenesis, and development. Recent Prog. Horm. Res. **51:** 123–154; discussion 155–157.
6. Vale, W., J. Rivier, J. Vaughan, *et al.* 1986 Purification and characterization of an FSH releasing protein from porcine ovarian follicular fluid. Nature **321:** 776–779.
7. Ling, N., S.A. Ying, N. Ueno, *et al.* 1986 Pituitary FSH is released by a heterodimer of the β-subunits from the two forms of inhibin. Nature **321:** 779–782.
8. Corrigan, A.Z., L.M. Bilezikjian, R.S. Carroll, *et al.* 1991 Evidence for an autocrine role of activin B within rat anterior pituitary cultures. Endocrinology **128:** 1682–1684.
9. Mather, J.P., K.M. Attie, T.K. Woodruff, *et al.* 1990 Activin stimulates spermatogonial proliferation in germ-sertoli cell cocultures from immature rat testis. Endocrinology **127:** 3206–3214.
10. Petraglia, F., D. D'Antona, P. Florio & S. Luisi, Eds. 2004. Serono Foundation for the Advancement of Medical Science, Special Issue, Proceedings of the International Workshop on Inhibins, Activins and Follistatins, Sinea, Italy, July 3–4, 2003. Mol. Cell. Endocrinol. **225:** 1–132.
11. Mathews, L.S. & W.W. Vale. 1991. Expression cloning of an activin receptor, a predicted transmembrane serine kinase. Cell **65:** 973–982.
12. ten Dijke, P., H. Yamashita, H. Ichijo, *et al.* 1994. Characterization of type I receptors for transforming growth factor-beta and activin. Science **264:** 101–104.
13. Massague, J. & Y-C. Chen. 2000. Controlling TGF-β signaling. Genes & Dev. **14:** 627–644.
14. Greenwald, J., W.H. Fischer, W.W. Vale & S. Choe. 1999 Three-finger toxin fold for the extracellular ligand-binding domain of the type II activin receptor serine kinase. Nature Struc. Biol. **6:** 18–22.
15. Greenwald, J., J. Groppe, P. Gray, *et al.* 2003 The BMP7/ActRII extracellular domain complex provides new insights into the cooperative nature of receptor assembly. Mol. Cell **11:** 605–617.
16. Thompson, T.B., T.K. Woodruff & T.S. Jardetzky. 2003 Structures of an ActRIIB:activin A complex reveal a novel binding mode for TGF-beta ligand:receptor interactions. EMBO J. **22:** 1555–1566.
17. Heldin, C.H., K. Miyazono & P. ten Dijke. 1997 TGF-beta signalling from cell membrane to nucleus through SMAD proteins. Nature **390:** 465–471.
18. Lewis, K.A., P.C. Gray, A.L. Blount, *et al.* 2000. Betaglycan binds inhibin and can mediate functional antagonism of activin signaling. Nature **404:** 411–414.
19. Esparza-Lopez, J., J.L. Montiel, M. Vilchis-Landeros, *et al.* 2001 Ligand binding and functional properties of betaglycan, a co-receptor of the transforming growth factor-{beta} superfamily. Specialized binding sites for transforming growth factor-beta and inhibin A. J. Biol. Chem. **5:** 5.
20. Wiater, E. & W. Vale. 2003. Inhibin is an antagonist of bone morphogenetic protein signaling. J. Biol. Chem. **278:** 7934–7941.

21. KIRSCH, T., W. SEBALD, M.K. DREYER. 2000. Crystal structure of the BMP-2-BRIA ectodomain complex. Nat. Struct. Biol. **7:** 492–496.
22. HARRISON, C., P. GRAY, W. FISCHER, *et al.* 2004 An activin mutant with disrupted ALK4 binding blocks signaling via type II receptors. J. Biol. Chem. **279:** 28036–28044.

Neurobiology of Rehabilitation

BRUCE H. DOBKIN, MD

Department of Neurology, Director, Neurologic Rehabilitation and Research Program, Geffen School of Medicine, University of California Los Angeles, Reed Neurologic Research Center, Los Angeles, California 90095-1769, USA

ABSTRACT: Rehabilitation aims to lessen the physical and cognitive impairments and disabilities of patients with stroke, multiple sclerosis, spinal cord or brain injury, and other neurologic diseases. Conventional approaches beyond compensatory adjustments to disability may be augmented by applying some of the myriad experimental results about mechanisms of intrinsic biological changes after injury and the effects of extrinsic manipulations on spared neuronal assemblies. The organization and inherent adaptability of the anatomical nodes within distributed pathways of the central nervous system offer a flexible substrate for treatment strategies that drive activity-dependent plasticity. Opportunities for a new generation of approaches are manifested by rodent and non-human primate studies that reveal morphologic and physiologic adaptations induced by injury, by learning-associated practice, by the effects of pharmacologic neuromodulators, by the behavioral and molecular bases for enhancing activity-dependent synaptic plasticity, and by cell replacement, gene therapy, and regenerative biologic strategies. Techniques such as functional magnetic resonance imaging and transcranial magnetic stimulation will help determine the most optimal physiologic effects of interventions in patients as the cortical representations for skilled movements and cognitive processes are modified by the combination of conventional and biologic therapies. As clinicians digest the finer details of the neurobiology of rehabilitation, they will translate laboratory data into controlled clinical trials. By determining how much they can influence neural reorganization, clinicians will extend the opportunities for neurorestoration.

KEYWORDS: neurologic rehabilitation; neuroimaging; plasticity; neural regeneration

Address for correspondence: Bruce H. Dobkin, MD, Department of Neurology, Director, Neurologic Rehabilitation and Research Program, Geffen School of Medicine, University of California Los Angeles, Reed Neurologic Research Center, 710 Westwood Plaza Los Angeles, California 90095-1769, USA. Voice: 310-206-6500; fax: 310-794-9486.
  bdobkin@mednet.ucla.edu

Ann. N.Y. Acad. Sci. 1038: 148–170 (2004). © 2004 New York Academy of Sciences.
doi: 10.1196/annals.1315.024

Neurologic rehabilitation has been a peculiar undertaking for modern medicine. More a clinical art than science since formal programs started about 60 years ago, diagnostic and treatment options have lagged behind other medical specialties. Care for the victims of war and of polio in the 1950s was organized around lengthy hospitalizations, because the burden of care was too great for families. The theories of educators, psychologists, and social scientists, along with highly selected data drawn from physiologists such as Sherrington, served as an untested conceptual basis for rehabilitation services.[1] In the past 15 years, an infusion of studies from neuroscience on mechanisms of cell and neural network injury, development, activity-dependent synaptic plasticity, and motor control offer interesting hypotheses to be tested.[1] When added to new information about the induction of neurogenesis and axonal regeneration, a neurobiology for rehabilitation practices comes into focus.[2] The resources for neurorestoration include both intrinsic and extrinsic signals (TABLE 1). Success in applying these new approaches and demonstrating robust enough improvements in outcomes to warrant their potential risks will take thoughtful planning and execution of clinical trials. This review emphasizes the bases for enhancing motor skills.

ANATOMICAL REORGANIZATION

Cerebral Sensorimotor System

The cortex in humans contributes to reaching, grasping, individuated finger movements, and walking-related motor control. At least six motor projections, in addition to the dominant ones from the primary motor cortex (M1), excite the motor pools. Descending fibers from the primary sensory cortex (S1) also project within the corticospinal tract to the dorsal horns.[3] Axons from M1 pass through the posterior limb of the internal capsule, dorsal and ventral premotor neurons project through the knee, and the supplementary motor area (SMA) fibers pass through the anterior limb of the internal capsule. Dorsal and ventral cingulate fibers are distributed among the latter regions. For example, the macaque's L-6–S-1 neurons, which contribute to hindlimb stepping, receive descending corticospinal tract projections from about 24,000 neurons in M1, 6000 from SMA, 6200 from dorsal and ventral cingulate, 5000 from dorsal premotor, and 10 from ventral premotor cortices.[4] Each of these cortical regions interacts with visual, vestibular, aural, proprioceptive, cutaneous and other inputs to help plan, select, initiate, and maintain unilateral and bilateral skilled movements. Thus, the corticospinal tract, which includes some uncrossed fibers within the lateral and ventral funiculi, draws from neurons that are distributed and separated by somewhat different vascular territories. One assembly of neurons may partially com-

TABLE 1. Potential biological mechanisms for neurorestoration

Intrinsic

Restore excitation, inhibition, and modulation by neurotransmitter projections to reverse diaschisis

Alter ion channel changes to reverse conduction block

Activate neuronal intracellular signaling for trophic functions

Increase synaptic efficacy

    Denervation hypersensitivity of postsynaptic receptors

    Activity-dependent unmasking of synapses

    Hebbian experience–dependent long-term potentiation

    Modulate basal synaptic transmission by changes in membrane- or neurotransmitter-mediated excitability

    Upregulate number or type of receptors, e.g., AMPA receptors

Axonal and dendritic collateral sprouting

Axonal regeneration

Remyelination

Neurogenesis

Extrinsic

Rehabilitation training-induced plasticity

Preserve neurons and axons by acute neuroprotection: block glutamate and free radical toxicity

Prevent apoptosis and transsynaptic degeneration: neurotrophins, caspase inhibitors

Prevent glial scar: modulate immune response and extracellular matrix molecules

Replace neurotransmitters or activate second messenger cascades: norepinephrine, dopamine, serotonin, acetylcholine, cAMP

Improve axon conduction: 4-aminopyridine potassium channel blockade

Sprout uninjured axons and dendrites: neurotrophins

Regenerate axons: increase intracellular signaling for actin and cytoskeletal proteins: neurotrophins BDNF, NT-3, GDNF; NCAMs; inhibit Rho or block Nogo receptor; chondroitinase to inhibit proteoglycans

Guide axons to targets: gradient of neurotrophins and laminin; modulate chemoattractants and repellants (netrins, semaphorins)

Remyelinate axons: implant olfactory ensheathing cells, oligodendrocyte precursors

Replace neurons and glia: implant stem cells, neural precursors

Reimplant ventral roots to key muscles or bladder

Prevent muscle atrophy; resistance exercise; drugs that alter myosin proteins

Replace a neural network: silicon biochips, microstimulators, neuroprosthetic brain-to-muscle bypass

ABBREVIATIONS: AMPA, alpha-amino-3-hydroxy-5-methyl-4-isoxazoleproprionic; cAMP, cyclic adenosine monophosphate; BNDF, brain-derived neurotrophic factor; NT-3, neurotrophin-3; GDNF, glial-derived neurotrophic factor; NCAM, neural cell adhesion molecule.
Adapted from Dobkin.[1]

pensate for loss of another when subjects find a strategy to activate spared neurons.

The neurons within M1 and other somatotopically organized sensorimotor regions are also mutable controllers of muscles and movements. Clusters of neurons connected by horizontal fibers alter their relative ability to represent a shoulder, wrist and finger movement depending on how much the practice of a skilled movement fires these neurons together.[5] Electrical stimulation of clusters of neurons in M1 in trains lasting 500 ms reveals cells within adjacent sites that conduct rather stereotyped, but commonly employed movements, such as elbow flexion or extension that depends on the initial position of the arm, a hand-to-mouth pattern for feeding, and defensive postures.[6] These homuncular organizations increase the flexibility of M1 in guiding complex actions. In addition, an injury that disrupts one assembly of neurons that participate in a movement may have nearby neurons come to represent aspects of that movement with motor skills retraining,[7] although some of the improvement in behavior may arise from other portions of the cortical, subcortical, or spinal motor network.[8]

Rapid representational plasticity has been demonstrated using transcranial magnetic stimulation (TMS) of motor cortex by the practice of simple directional finger movements, which can be augmented by neuromodulators such as amphetamine.[9,10] One correlate of learning-induced plasticity is the synaptic expression of long-term potentiation (LTP) and long-term depression (LTD) in neocortex[11] as well as in the hippocampus. LTP is associated with the proliferation of dendritic spines.[12] This morphologic change has been found in homologous cortex opposite from the site of an experimental sensorimotor cortical lesion when the unaffected limb works to compensate for the paretic one.[13]

Corticostriatal neurons from primary and secondary motor areas are distinct from those within the corticospinal tract and respond especially to sensory inputs associated with the direction and force of movements. Uninjured cortical descending tracts from crossed and uncrossed projections may play a greater role during rehabilitation based on their inherent connectivity, perhaps especially if sensory feedback to the sensorimotor cortices is as typical of the desired movement as feasible. Cues from therapists to evoke cognitive strategies that bring these regions into greater play during training may increase the level of descending drive on motoneurons of the spinal cord. For example, ventral premotor neurons are most active during shaping and grasping the hand to hold an object. A visual cue, such as an object, may engage these neurons to enable a subject with a hemiparetic hand to reach and grasp, a movement that cannot otherwise be initiated when no object is present. Imagining a movement and watching a movement will activate many of the nodes in the sensorimotor network that are also active when a person carries out the actual movement.[14,15] Thus, visual practice could produce the cerebral reiterations that increase synaptic efficacy for learning a skill.

Brain Stem Nodes

The brain stem contains centers that contribute to the initiation of rhythmic flexion and extension for walking. The basal ganglia and cerebellum project to these locomotor regions. The dorsal mesencephalic locomotor center and the mesopontine locomotor center with its cholinergic and glutaminergic cells activate the lumbar spinal central pattern generators (CPGs) when stimulated electrically or with certain drugs. These brain stem regions project to reticulospinal nuclei that pass bilaterally into the ventral funciuli, providing another route for spared cortical and brain stem drives to activate motoneurons for movements. This pathway provides a slower and less precise control for flexor movements than the direct descending corticospinal tract. Several brain stem pathways have been shown in animal models to generate new dendrites after being damaged. For example, the corticorubrospinal fibers, which participate in distal more than proximal upper extremity movements for grasping, show spontaneous collateral sprouting[16] from the intact hemisphere and functional reorganization[17] that includes the corticospinal tract. Of interest, atrophic rubrospinal neurons can be coaxed with neurotrophins to regenerate axons after a chronic SCI.[18] This pathway, with its connections to the cerebellum, can potentially substitute for corticospinal fibers for making fine hand movements.

The cerebellum monitors the outcome of every movement using proprioceptive inputs from the dorsal and ventral spinocerebellar tract. These inputs are also copied to the thalamus and motor cortex, as well as the brain stem locomotor centers. The timing of coordinated movement sequences, as well as computations on the position, velocity, acceleration, and inherent viscous forces of the moving limbs, is partly orchestrated by the cerebellar nuclei and Purkinje cells. The great interest in these afferent signals within cortical regions for motor control suggests that motor skills training during rehabilitation should aim to optimize kinematic and kinetic inputs that are associated with normal walking, reaching, grasping, and pinching.

Spinal Cord Systems

The spinal cord of humans probably includes CPGs for locomotor movements. These neural circuits produce oscillating patterns of flexion and extension, independent of sensory input or supraspinal commands. Elemental CPGs may control different muscles around each joint. These oscillators are interlocked by intrinsic connections and by their responses to segmental afferents and descending command centers.

Evidence for pattern generation comes from experiments in vertebrates, including non-human primates, in which the spinal cord is transected in the low thoracic region and deafferented from all dorsal root inputs below that level. Electrical stimulation and monamines placed on the isolated lumbar cord produce alternating electrical activity in the ventral roots of limb flexors and extensors.[19] When cats and rats undergo spinal transection, their paraplegic hindlimbs lose the ability to step on a treadmill. With practice that emphasizes hindlimb loading and treadmill-induced hip extension, they regain alternating stepping movements, though the paws do not readily clear the surface. Noradrenergic agents may help initiate stepping and the training has lasting effects.[20,21] The cats and rats generally cannot step very well over ground with their hindlimbs, however. Animals trained to stand, rather than to step, walk poorly on the treadmill, pointing to the specificity of the type of practice on spinal cord learning.[22] These findings suggest that a CPG is at work. Evidence for a CPG in humans has been found in both the spontaneous rhythmic movements made by some patients after SCI[23,24] and from the evolution of EMG activity in the legs of patients with paraplegia who are manually stepped on a treadmill[25] or undergo electrical stimulation of the dorsal horns at L-2.[26]

Modulation of the CPG involves the organization of several neurotransmitters that seem to be conserved from lampreys to mammals[27-29] For example, glutaminergic reticulospinal neurons excite ipsilateral spinal motoneurons and interneurons and contralateral glycinergic inhibitory neurons. Glycinergic neurons also have axons that cross to the opposite half of the spinal cord CPG. Other amines and peptides modulate the initiation, maintenance, and termination of cell bursts. Metabotropic receptors for serotonin (5-HT), gamma-aminobutyric acid (GABA), and glutamate are also activated within the CPG network during locomotion. These neurotransmitters could be restored to the lumbar cord after a brain or SCI by systemic or intrathecal drugs, by implanted cells that release a neurotransmitter, or by regeneration of specific axons.

Other intrinsic systems may contribute to the flexibility of spinal control for reaching and for walking. A small set of modules appear to store components of flexor and extensor synergistic movements within the typical workspace of the extremities.[30] The modules may be activated in chains to achieve functional movements. This synaptic organization probably shares connections with the CPG and responds to segmental sensory inputs and descending controllers of the kinematics for reaching into space and walking.[31] In addition, interconnections among columns of motor pools via propriospinal pathways aid postural adjustments and movement during reaching and ambulation, as do spinal reflex pathways and vestibulospinal inputs.

Sensory inputs provide a powerful source for functional modulation of the CPG, as well as for positive and negative force feedback during walking.[32] In studies of higher vertebrates and human subjects, cutaneous inputs from the sole and Ia and Ib inputs to the hips and ankles are especially important drives for walking.[32,33] For example, the spinal cord responds to varying levels of weight bearing on the legs in patients with clinically complete SCI, reflected in changes in the amplitude and timing of electromyographic bursts from lower extremity muscles.[34] Studies of cats and humans reveal the impact of the timing of hip extension at the end of stance of one leg and simultaneous loading of the opposite leg for successful initiation of the swing phase.[35,36] These sensory inputs presumably contribute to the internal models the brain possesses about the properties of limbs and limb mechanics.[37]

NEUROBIOLOGICALLY BASED INTERVENTIONS FOR PATIENTS

Exercise and practice are the *sine qua non* in rehabilitation for regaining the ability to walk, reach, grasp, and carry out self-care and community activities. Greater intensity of task-specific practice tends to improve motor[38–44] and cognitive[45,46] outcomes for what patients practice. The optimal style, intensity, duration, and feedback needed to relearn most skills have not yet been established. Practice does induce activity-dependent adaptations within the distributed neural networks needed for skilled movement and produces cortical representational plasticity.[47,48]

Motor Control

Theories about motor control and the acquisition and recall of motor skills are beginning to play an important role in the development of more sophisticated rehabilitation strategies. M1 is involved in the initial phase of learning a motor skill, as well as in early consolidation from an unstable to a stable state.[49] Lasting learning of a simple, but novel motor skill in non-human primate studies requires a considerable number of practice repetitions, from 300–1500, to reveal behavioral and neuronal reorganization changes.[50,51] After a brain or spinal cord lesion, the nervous system has less information about how to select, initiate, and correct movements, and even the mechanical properties of the joints and muscles may change, so both attempted actions and the process for relearning functional movements may suffer. Even greater intensity and duration of practice become necessary.

Many parameters for an internal model of interactions with the environment have been investigated. At the neuronal level, for example, firing rates during learning to reach to a target at a specific angle within the body's workspace increase within the subpopulation of cells that are preferentially tuned to the direction of the target. This activity seems most related to a modification in the internal model of movement kinematics for computation of a visuomotor transformation, rather than to movement dynamics.[52] One especially relevant theory of motor control suggests that enough feedback control for movement can be obtained from optimal estimates of the state of a limb, using parameters such as joint angles or muscle lengths.[37,53,54] The system controls the global goal of a task from low-level signals, each concerned with a portion of the system. Errors that influence motor performance are corrected and signals that are not relevant are ignored. This theory suggests that spared neural nodes may be able to act as controllers by optimally selecting afferent feedback.

Another theory suggests that neural signals may explicitly encode the end-point of the limb, such as the cat's paw during walking, and that the dorsal spinocerebellar tract provides this kinematic information.[31] Translating models built upon studies in cats with their bi-articular hindlimb muscles into humans may be misleading, however, since these muscles may naturally reflect end-points more than joint angles. Another point of view is that the brain may issue motor commands based on a prediction of the forces for an upcoming movement. An internal model of experienced forces also generalizes to upper extremity parameters such as velocity and position in space.[55,56] Activation of the N-methyl-D-aspartate (NMDA) receptor and inhibition by GABA were shown to be involved in the acquisition, but not the recall of a new internal model of the dynamics for reaching.[57] These theories are important to the neurobiology of rehabilitation, because they help set the tone for styles of practice, the sensorimotor parameters to be monitored to optimize training, the neural pathways that need to be engaged for skills learning, and the potential for pharmacologic interventions to augment motor learning.

Massed Practice of Task-Oriented Motor Skills

The essence of therapy for any disability is *practice*. A practice session can have a powerful, but only temporary effect. A positive effect on performance during a training session by repeatedly practicing the same movement may not lead to long-term learning. Studies of interventions should include a dose-response curve to establish how much practice is needed to achieve a retraining goal. During practice, contextual interference from intermixing other related tasks may enhance learning, unless cognitive impairment impedes attention or procedural learning.

Treadmill Training

Body weight-supported treadmill training (BWSTT) was derived from the treadmill training approach for cats after complete spinal cord transection in studies of CPG activity. BWSTT, in theory, allows the spinal cord and supraspinal locomotor regions to experience sensory inputs that are more like ordinary stepping compared to the atypical locomotor inputs created by compensatory gait deviations and difficulty loading a paretic limb.[58,59] More typical proprioceptive and cutaneous input, as noted earlier, may improve the timing and increase the activation of residual descending locomotor outputs on the motor pools. Most important, BWSTT allows massed practice at different walking speeds and levels of limb loading with repetitions guided by the cues of the therapist. Randomized clinical trials for patients with hemiparetic stroke have produced mixed results,[60,61] but treadmill speeds have not been optimized.[44] A multi-center trial of patients with acute incomplete SCI tried to optimize training at high treadmill and overground walking speeds for 12 weeks with best-of-possible kinematics and kinetics, but demonstrated no significant differences from the conventionally trained subjects.[62] The trial established a reproducible retraining approach that can serve as an experimental control for the style and intensity of locomotor rehabilitation in future clinical trials of pharmacologic and biologic interventions.

Constraint-Induced Movement Therapy (CIMT)

Rehabilitation practice-induced neuroplasticity and behavioral gains have been repeatedly demonstrated for the upper extremity in patients who retain at least modest motor control.[63] In the most common paradigm, subjects practice with a therapist for at least six hours a day for two weeks on a variety of tasks with the affected arm plus restraint of the normal hand for most of the day. These patients can, at onset, dorsiflex the wrist at least 10 degrees and partially extend the fingers of the paretic hand.[64,65] Less intensity may work as well.[66] The most important aspect of this approach is massed practice and feedback about movement skills that are important to the subject, rather than the type of restraint. Animal models of forced use early after an ablative or traumatic focal cortical injury suggest an increase in the volume of the lesion and behavioral deficits, probably on the basis of glutaminergic toxicity.[67] The intensity of use of the limb, however, was far greater than any clinical situation could allow. Forced nonuse of the limb affected by experimental damage restricted to the striatonigral dopamine projections, in contrast, augmented dopamine loss and Parkinsonian symptoms.[68] One acute clinical trial of the approach showed positive results[64] and data from a multicenter trial for hemiparetic patients who are 3–9 months post-stroke are pending.[69]

Biofeedback and Automated Robot-Assisted Devices

Biofeedback (BFB) includes a variety of instrumented techniques that try to make the treated subject aware of physiologic information that can be used to better train an activity. Electromyographic BFB to increase the amplitude of muscle contractile bursts, decrease co-contraction of muscles, improve the timing of a contraction, can enhance skilled movements.[70] Robotic devices

aim to maximize practice with only intermittent therapist oversight.[1] One robotic exoskeleton manipulates a patient's paretic elbow and shoulder by a
two-degrees-of-freedom impedance controller system, much as a therapist
might provide hand-over-hand therapy for reaching in a plane across a table.
Motor power and control improved at the shoulder and elbow with this form
of robotic training, consistent with the greater intensity of practice with those
muscle groups.[71] Active participation improves function more than passive
movement, as might be expected during motor learning.[72] By providing data
on the intensity, duration, and accuracy of practice, these devices allow future
studies of parallels between therapy-induced behavioral gains and activity-
dependent reorganization, perhaps monitored by functional neuroimaging
techniques.

Pharmacologic Augmentation

Any neurobiology of rehabilitation must consider the potential to augment
training strategies with medications that act on neurotransmitters, neuromodulators, and intracellular second messengers. The goals include strengthening
synaptic efficacy within perilesional neurons and other nodes of the motor
network during task learning, replenishing neurotransmitter projections that
have been disconnected to reverse diaschisis, and preventing transsynaptic
degeneration of neurons.

Among these drugs, dextroamphetamine increases the cortical signal-to-
noise ratio.[73] Cholinergic projections serve as a gate for behaviorally relevant
sensory information.[74] Human and animal studies have provided preliminary
evidence that a variety of medications, such as dopaminergic and noradrenergic,[75–78] cholinergic,[79] and serotonergic[80] agents, may facilitate the rate or
degree of motor recovery. Drugs, along with other neurostimulatory approaches, may augment gains in slow learners more than in subjects who can
quickly learn a skill.[73,81] Drugs may also activate or inhibit subcomponents
of the distributed sensorimotor system, such as the CPG.[21] Blockers of
dopamine and norepinephrine may inhibit skilled motor gains,[82] perhaps depending on the time of use in relation to the injury.[83] A few studies suggest
that intensive speech therapy combined with a drug that enhances vigilance
or learning may benefit patients who have adequate language comprehen-
sion.[84,85] The rapid growth in knowledge about the molecules that modulate
learning, such as agonists of the NMDA receptor, cyclic nucleotide adenosine
monophosphate (cAMP), and cAMP response element binding protein
(CREB), is leading to the possibility of new lines of drugs to augment rehabilitation strategies.[86,87]

Controlled trials of anti-spasticity agents have varied widely in the target
symptoms managed and the outcome assessments employed.[88–91] Functional
gains related to walking and use of the upper limbs are often marginal. How-

ever, a medication that prevents disabling spasms may improve quality of life. Continued basic studies of the neurobiology of spasticity, such as the windup of flexion reflexes and other physiologic changes induced in the cord by loss of supraspinal input, are needed.[92–94]

Randomized trials that compare a rehabilitation intervention combined with an experimental drug versus a placebo require considerable thought. For example, both the dose of medication and the dose of the rehabilitation strategy need to be optimized and adverse effects need to be minimized. Outcome measures should be sensitive to important changes in function and relevant to the intervention. The choice of pharmacologic augmenting agent, at least for sensorimotor studies, may be developed from TMS, positron emission tomography (PET), and functional magnetic resonance imaging (fMRI) studies that reveal a drug-induced increase in cortical excitability, rapidly induced plasticity in M1, or change in neurotransmitter levels in patients.[95–97]

Neurostimulators and Neuroprostheses

Regional electrical stimulation of the cortex, deep nuclei, spinal cord, and motor unit could augment retraining. Phasic electrical stimulation of nerve-muscle can stimulate genes to increase muscle fiber volume. When optimal afferent stimulation parameters are employed, peripheral electrical stimulation can augment cortical excitability and reorganization to enhance motor skills,[98] especially if coordinated with retraining. Deep brain and vagal nerve electrical stimulators and subdural or implanted cortical arrays may drive excitatory and inhibitory outflow to the forebrain and brain stem.[99] In theory, finding the optimal parameters for stimulation could modulate attentional drives and frontal lobe executive functions[100] and augment the acquisition of procedural or declarative learning. Repetitive TMS is another potential tool to excite or inhibit cortical pathways for sensorimotor[81] or affective and cognitive processes such as hemi-attention.[101,102]

Neuroprostheses have used local cortical potentials to control an electrical stimulator for anticipated movements.[103] Brain-computer interfaces that employ a variety of brain signals to communicate or to control a prosthesis without muscle stimulation[104] and neuroelectronic chips implanted into the brain to make a circuit[105] may both add to our understanding of the neurobiology of the brain and enhance functional outcomes for highly impaired patients.

PLASTICITY INDUCED BY THERAPIES FOR PATIENTS

Functional neuroimaging using PET, fMRI, TMS, and other modalities reveals cerebral synaptic activity that accompanies normal motor and cognitive processing and learning, evolving changes induced by an injury, and reorganization associated with a rehabilitative intervention. These techniques, despite their individual limitations,[1,106] provide a microscopic view of training-related experience-dependent plasticity.

After an experimental sensorimotor cortical stroke in rats, improved neurologic function correlates with the amount of shift of activation from the initial contralesional homologous cortex back to the ipsilesional cortex. Thus, functional gains are most readily associated with sparing of tissue or restoration of synaptic activity by intrinsic and extrinsic mechanisms (TABLE 1).[107] Studies of stroke in patients, mostly assessing upper extremity distal movements, reveal similar findings.[108] Using PET and fMRI, correlations of regions of activation with the amount of recovery have been found for the ipsilesional cerebellum,[109] contralateral premotor and secondary sensory cortices,[110] perilesional activity, and an overall decrease in activity over the course of behavioral gains within the sensorimotor network.[111] Regions associated with working memory, attention, and planning are often more active compared to healthy subjects. Behavioral gains for finer motor skills may run more in parallel to the relative sparing of the corticospinal tract, determined by less wallerian degeneration, than to the balance of activation in ipsilateral compared to contralateral M1.[112]

Insights into relationships between activity in the nodes of the distributed motor system after brain or spinal cord injury and gains in task-related motor skills may be pursued with greater correlative power by evaluating neuroimaging changes associated with a defined rehabilitation strategy and repeated over predefined intervals until no further changes in behavior or representational plasticity are found. The therapy should promote intensive practice of functionally important movements, then employ an activation paradigm that directly uses some portion of the skilled movements that were practiced. A few interventional studies do reveal reorganization within M1[63] and related nodes for upper limb movements[110,113] and for walking.[114] Other specific rehabilitation approaches have revealed associations between behavioral gains and reorganization.[45,115] The relationships, however, between specific motor, language, and other cognitive improvements and the size and location of cortical and subcortical activations are still uncertain.

Functional neuroimaging holds promise for serving as a physiologic marker for whether a physical, cognitive, pharmacologic, or biologic intervention engages regions of interest in a functional network, activates mechanisms of reorganizational plasticity, and leads to adaptations in parallel to the intensity, duration, and efficacy of a therapy. If relationships between cortical maps and important behavioral outcomes can be made for subjects with differing lesions and impairments, then functional imaging protocols may come to have early predictive abilities about whether a treatment is likely to work and how much of a defined rehabilitation therapy is enough.

AUGMENTATION OF REHABILITATION BY NEURAL REPAIR

A variety of models of stroke, TBI, and SCI provide insights into approaches for neural repair–mediated rehabilitation.[1] Axonal sprouting[116,117] and neurogenesis[118] shortly after stroke depend upon signals from the environment that may differ from within the lesion itself, its penumbral periphery, and adjacent normal tissue.[119] Ischemia appears to facilitate LTP, in part by reducing perilesional GABAergic inhibition and increasing glutamate receptor stimulation.[120] Thus, the penumbra is potentially a field for activity-dependent plasticity. The migration and differentiation of neural progenitor cells and regenerating axons and their incorporation into a functional matrix will depend in part on their responsiveness to evolving environmental cues and gene expression.[121]

Experimental interventions to stimulate functional recovery include intralesional grafts of fetal cortex, stem cells, and progenitor cells,[122] as well as intravenous injection of marrow stromal cells.[123] Behavioral gains in animal models have been modest, but increase with exercise and an enriched environment.[124] Such gains may be related more to trophic or other effects of the cells, rather than to new synaptic connections. Near future trials in patients will test the therapeutic potential for targeting myelin-associated inhibitory substances produced by oligodendrocytes, such as myelin-associated glycoprotein (MAG), oligodendrocyte-myelin glycoprotein (OMGP), and Nogo-A. Neurite growth inhibition is caused by their Nogo-66 and amino-Nogo domains when oligodendrocytes, periaxonal CNS myelin, and myelin debris are exposed by an injury. When the receptor complex is signaled by one of these inhibitory substances, a small guanosine triphosphotase (GTPase) called Rho and other cascades of intracellular activity stop support for the growth cone. For example, neurite and axonal outgrowth increased in the adult rat's uninjured cortex associated with improved control of the affected forepaw 6 weeks after an antibody to Nogo-A was injected.[125]

Axonal regeneration after experimental SCI is also increased by injecting antibodies to Nogo and MAG, as well as by blocking the Nogo receptor or its intracellular pathways.[126–130] Partial reversal of this inhibition has been accomplished using an intrathecal infusion of the small peptide NEP1–40, which inhibits binding of Nogo-66 to the Nogo receptor.[128] The inhibition of Rho using small antagonist molecules such as C3-05, which is an ADP ribose transferase, may eventually accomplish the same effect in patients.[130] In addition, inactivation of Rho may lessen delayed cell death, which could be of clinical value in patients with gray matter involvement from a cervical or conus SCI.[131] A related approach is to increase the amount of the second messenger cAMP, which induces genes to activate protein kinase A and to synthesize polyamines.[132] An increasing number of signaling interactions are being found between cAMP, Rho, and neurotrophins for axonal regeneration.

Other animal studies in SCI have aimed to dissolve glycoproteins that inhibit growth cones by local injection of chondroitinase; provide a gradient of neurotrophins or other axon guidance molecules to attract the growth cone; turn on genes that produce growth-, microtubule-, and neurofilament-associated proteins; bridge a cystic cavity with nerve filaments, biopolymers that contain regenerative substances, and neural cells within a nurturing biologic scaffold; implant embryonic neural tissue, stem cells, or neural progenitor cells that may integrate; inject Schwann cells or olfactory ensheathing glia derived from olfactory epithelium that can myelinate axons; implant cells such as fibroblasts genetically modified to secrete neurotrophins; stimulate intrinsic neurogenesis; and reimplant ventral roots from below to above a lesion.[133–135] Human studies have begun to build upon one or more of these approaches.

The first published reports of implantation of a human neuronal cell line into the cavity left by an infarct near the basal ganglia and internal capsule in human subjects demonstrated relative safety[136] and survival of the cells.[137] Efficacy studies are pending. The strategy seems even less likely to reveal functional gains than the slowly emerging human experiments with cell implants for Parkinson's disease, however.[138] In theory, human implants into the brain after stroke may replenish some portion of trophic and other neurohumoral or neurotransmitter substances, provide a bridge for regeneration of host axons, make local synaptic connections, or replace damaged neural elements, but seem unlikely to be incorporated into a complex neural network such as the striatum. Verbal reports describe safety studies of cell implants in patients with multiple sclerosis to remyelinate axons in patients. Unpublished reports from Asia and other regions outside North America tell of transplantation of fetal tissue, olfactory ensheathing cells, and construction of peripheral nerve bridges in humans after SCI (<www.carecure.atinfopop.com>).

Relevance of Animal Models

Much of the neurobiology of rehabilitation is drawn from animal models of injury and repair.[1] The translation of these experiments into rehabilitation interventions is not likely to proceed without discouraging setbacks, if the experience with acute neuroprotective interventions in patients with stroke, SCI and cerebral trauma holds.[139–142]

Type of induced injury, timing of the intervention, location of lesion, relative volume, natural history of recovery, co-morbid conditions, sex and age, levels of activity, and other factors are controlled in laboratory experiments, but not in patients.[140,142–145] Laboratory animals are bred and maintained in relatively unchallenging, impoverished and stressful circumstances, which may make their biologic responses to an injury different from wild rodents and humans.[146,147] Highly inbred rodent strains and transgenic mice allow the study of particular processes of injury and repair, but the cascades of gene expression over time and cellular and molecular changes in the milieu may not unfold in another strain or species, or in humans. Even sensorimotor, locomotor, and cognitive abilities vary between laboratory animal strains,[148] which may confound outcome measurements.

The pathways taken by neural cells and axons during development span distances of a few mm under the outer surface of the neural tube. The paths to targets are both short and sweet—multiple guidance signals that constrain and beckon appear in an orderly sequence within a highly organized, canal-like matrix of capillaries and glia. For neural repair in adults, the distances that cells may have to migrate or axons regenerate differ dramatically between humans and rodents. The surface area of a mouse brain is 1/1000th that of the human brain. About 20 cross-sections of the rat lumbar cord can be superimposed within the cross-sectional area of the human cord.[134] Regenerating axons and collateral sprouts in experiments usually extend only 10–15 mm below a spinal cord lesion. Successful biologic interventions in animal studies reveal only modest numbers of short-lived, regenerating cells in models of stroke[118] and modest numbers of regenerating axons after manipulations for SCI.[149–152] As with transplanted cells, the axons must operate within an environment that lacks the ideal ratio of signaling substances and targets that made survival, migration, and functional connectivity over tiny distances an evolutionary wonder that is the study of developmental neurobiology.

Still, if 10% of a supraspinal pathway can be restored,[153,154] then augmented by collateral sprouting, enough connections for rebuilding simple skills may be in place, even if the new inputs only reach propriospinal pathways below a spinal cord injury. Rehabilitation strategies that make use of the neurobiology underlying skills learning within a flexible, distributed motor system can then incorporate newly connected nodes into the motor controllers that lessen the disability of patients.

REFERENCES

1. DOBKIN, B. 2003. The Clinical Science of Neurologic Rehabilitation. Oxford University Press. New York.
2. DOBKIN, B. 2000. Functional rewiring of brain and spinal cord after injury: the three R's of neural repair and neurological rehabilitation. Curr. Opin. Neurol. **13:** 655–659.
3. RALSTON, D. & H. RALSTON. 1985. The terminations of corticospinal tract axons in the macaque monkey. J. Comp. Neurol. **242:** 325–337.
4. CHENEY, P., J. HILL-KARRER, A. BELHAJ-SAIF, et al. 2000. Cortical motor areas and their properties: implications for neuroprosthetics. In Neural Plasticity and Regeneration. F. Seil, Ed.: 136–160. Elsevier. Amsterdam.

5. BUONOMANO, D. & M. MERZENICH. 1998. Cortical plasticity: from synapses to maps. Annu. Rev. Neurosci. **21:** 149–186.
6. GRAZIAN, M., C. TAYLOR & T. MOORE. 2002. Complex movements evoked by microstimulation of precentral cortex. Neuron **34:** 841–851.
7. NUDO, R., B. WISE, F. SIFUENTES & G. MILLIKEN. 1996. Neural substrates for the effects of rehabilitative training on motor recovery after ischemic infarct. Science **272:** 1791–1794.
8. FROST, S., S. BARBAY, K. FRIEL, et al. 2003. Reorganization of remote cortical regions after ischemic brain injury: a potential substrate for stroke recovery. J. Neurophysiol. **89:** 3205–3214.
9. CLASSEN, J., J. LIEPERT, S. WISE, et al. 1998. Rapid plasticity of human cortical movement representation induced by practice. J. Neurophysiol. **79:** 1117–1123.
10. BUTEFISCH, C., B. DAVIS, L. SAWAKI, et al. 2002. Modulation of use-dependent plasticity by d-amphetamine. Ann. Neurol. **51:** 59–68.
11. EDER, M., W. ZIEGLGANSBERGER & H.U. DODT. 2002. Neocortical long-term potentiation and long-term depression: site of expression investigated by infrared-guided laser stimulation. J. Neurosci. **22:** 7558–7568.
12. GRUTZENDLER, J., N. KASTHURI & W.B. GAN. 2002. Long-term dendritic spine stability in the adult cortex. Nature **420:** 812–816.
13. BURY, S. & T. JONES. 2002. Unilateral sensorimotor cortex lesions in adult rats facilitate motor skill learning with the "unaffected" forelimb and training-induced dendritic structural plasticity in the motor cortex. J. Neurosci. **22:** 8597–8606.
14. RIZZOLATTI, G., L. FOGASSI, V. GALLESE. 2001. Neurophysiological mechanisms underlying the understanding and imitation of action. Nature Rev. Neurosci. **2:** 661–670.
15. KOSKI, L., A. WOHLSCHLAGER, H. BEKKERING, et al. 2002. Modulation of motor and premotor activity during imitation of target-directed actions. Cereb. Cortex **12:** 847–855.
16. VILLABLANCA, J. & D. HOVDA. 2000. Developmental neuroplasticity in a model of cerebral hemispherectomy and stroke. J. Neurosci. **95:** 625–637.
17. BELHAJ-SAIF, A. & P. CHENEY. 2000. Plasticity in the distribution of the red nucleus output to forearm muscles after unilateral lesions of the pyramidal tract. J. Neurophysiol. **83:** 3147–3153.
18. KWON, B., J. LIU, C. MESSERER, et al. 2002. Survival and regeneration of rubrospinal neurons 1 year after spinal cord injury. Proc. Natl. Acad. Sci. **99:** 3246–3251.
19. ROSSIGNOL, S., L. BOUYER, D. BARTHELEMY, et al. 2002. Recovery of locomotion in the cat following spinal cord lesions. Brain Res Rev **40:** 257–266.
20. DE LEON, R., J. HODGSON, R. ROY & V. EDGERTON. 1998. Locomotor capacity attributable to step training versus spontaneous recovery after spinalization in adult cats. J. Neurophysiol. **79:** 1329–1340.
21. ROSSIGNOL, S., C. CHAU, E. BRUSTEIN, et al. 1998. Pharmacological activation and modulation of the central pattern generator for locomotion in the cat. Ann N.Y. Acad Sci. **860:** 346–359.
22. EDGERTON, V. & R. ROY. 2002. Paralysis recovery in human and model systems. Curr. Opin. Neurobiol. **12:** 658–667.
23. CALANCIE, B., B. NEEDHAM-SHROPSHIRE, B. GREEN, et al. 1994. Involuntary stepping after chronic spinal cord injury. Brain **117:** 1143–1159.

24. DOBKIN, B., S. HARKEMA, P. REQUEJO & V. EDGERTON. 1995. Modulation of locomotor-like EMG activity in subjects with complete and incomplete chronic spinal cord injury. J. Neurol. Rehabil. **9:** 183–190.

25. EDGERTON, V., S. HARKEMA & B. DOBKIN. 2003. Retraining the human spinal cord. *In* Spinal Cord Medicine: Principles and Practice. V. Lin, Ed.: 817–828. Demos Medical Publishing. New York.

26. DIMITRIJEVIC, M.R., Y. GERASIMENKO & M.M. PINTER. 1998. Evidence for a spinal central pattern generator in humans. Ann. N.Y. Acad. Sci. **860:** 360–376.

27. GRILLNER, S. & P. WALLEN. 2002. Cellular bases of a vertebrate locomotor system-steering, intersegmental and segmental co-ordination and sensory control. Brain Res. Brain Res. Rev. **40:** 92–106.

28. TILLAKARATNE, N. 2000. Increased expression of glutamate decarboxylase (GAD67) in feline lumbar spinal cord after complete thoracic spinal cord injury. J. Neurosci. Res. **60:** 219–230.

29. TILLAKARATNE, N., R. DE LEON, T. HOANG, *et al.* 2002. Use-dependent modulation of inhibitory capacity in the feline lumbar spinal cord. J. Neurosci. **22:** 3130–3143.

30. BIZZI, E., M. TRESCH, P. SALTIEL & A. D'AVELLA. 2000. New perspectives on spinal motor systems. Nature Rev/Neurosci. **1:** 101–108.

31. POPPELE, R. & G. BOSCO. 2003. Sophisticated spinal contributions to motor control. Trends Neurosci. **26:** 269–276.

32. DIETZ, V. 2003. Spinal cord pattern generators for locomotion. Clin. Neurophysiol. **114:** 1379–1389.

33. CAPADAY, C. 2002. The special nature of human walking and its neural control. Trends Neurosci **25:** 370–376.

34. HARKEMA, S., S. HURLEY, U. PATEL, *et al.* 1997. Human lumbosacral spinal cord interprets loading during stepping. J. Neurophysiol. **77:** 797–811.

35. DUYSENS, J., F. CLARAC & H. CRUSE. 2000. Load-regulating mechanisms in gait and posture: comparative aspects. Physiol. Rev. **80:** 83–133.

36. DIETZ, V., R. MULLER & G. COLOMBO. 2002. Locomotor activity in spinal man: significance of afferent input from joint and load receptors. Brain **125:** 2626–2634.

37. SCOTT, S. 2002. Optimal strategies for movement: success with variability. Nat. Neurosci. **5:** 1110–1111.

38. KWAKKEL, G., R. VAN PEPPEN, R. WAGENAAR, *et al.* 2004. Effects of augmented exercise therapy time after stroke: a meta-analysis. Stroke **35:** 2529–2539.

39. KWAKKEL, G., R. WAGENAAR, J. TWISK, *et al.* 1999. Intensity of leg and arm training after primary middle cerebral artery stroke: a randomised trial. Lancet **354:** 191–196.

40. DEAN, C. & R. SHEPHERD. 1997. Task-related training improves performance of seated reaching tasks after stroke. Stroke **28:** 722–728.

41. DEAN, C., C. RICHARDS & F. MALOUIN. 2000. Task-related circuit training improves performance of locomotor tasks in chronic stroke: a randomized, controlled pilot trial. Arch. Phys. Med. Rehabil. **81:** 409–417.

42. WINSTEIN, C., A. MERIANS & K. SULLIVAN. 1999. Motor learning after unilateral brain damage. Neuropsychologia **37:** 975–987.

43. TAUB, E., G. USWATTE & T. ELBERT. 2002. New treatments in neurorehabilitation founded on basic research. Nature Rev. Neurosci. **3:** 228–236.

44. SULLIVAN, K., B. KNOWLTON & B. DOBKIN. 2002. Step training with body weight support: effect of treadmill speed and practice paradigms on post-stroke locomotor recovery. Arch. Phys. Med. Rehabil. **83:** 683–691.
45. PULVERMULLER, F., B. NEININGER, T. ELBERT, *et al.* 2001. Constraint-induced therapy of chronic aphasia after stroke. Stroke **32:** 1621–1626.
46. BHOGAL, S., R. TEASELL & M. SPEECHLEY. 2003. Intensity of aphasia therapy, impact on recovery. Stroke **34:** 987–993.
47. KARNI, A., G. MEYER, P. JEZZARD, *et al.* 1995. Functional MRI evidence for adult motor cortex plasticity during motor skill learning. Nature **377:** 155–158.
48. KARNI, A., G. MEYER, C. HIPOLITO, *et al.* 1998. The acquisition of skilled motor performance: Fast and slow experience-driven changes in primary motor cortex. Proc. Natl. Acad. Sci. **95:** 861–868.
49. MUELLBACHER, W., U. ZIEMANN, J. WISSEL, *et al.* 2002. Early consolidation in human primary motor cortex. Nature **415:** 640–644.
50. YIN, P. & S. KITAZAWA. 2001. Long-lasting aftereffects of prism adaptation in the monkey. Exp. Brain Res. **141:** 250–253.
51. NUDO, R., G. MILLIKEN, W. JENKINS & M. MERZENICH. 1996. Use-dependent alterations of movement representations in primary motor cortex of adult squirrel monkeys. J. Neurosci. **16:** 785–807.
52. PAZ, R., T. BORAUD, C. NATAN, *et al.* 2003. Preparatory activity in motor cortex reflects learning of local visuomotor skills. Nat. Neurosci. **8:** 882–890.
53. GRIBBLE, P. & S. SCOTT. 2002. Overlap of internal models in motor cortex for mechanical loads during reaching. Nature **417:** 938–941.
54. TODOROV, E. & M. JORDAN. 2000. Optimal feedback control as a theory of motor coordination. Nat. Neurosci. **5:** 1226–1235.
55. SHADMEHR, R. & Z. MOUSSAVI. 2000. Spatial generalization from learning dynamics of reaching movements. Neuroscience **20:** 7807–7815.
56. THOROUGHMAN, K. & R. SHADMEHR. 2000. Learning of action through adaptive combination of motor primitives. Nature **407:** 742–747.
57. DONCHIN, O., L. SAWAKI, G. MADUPU, *et al.* 2002. Mechanisms influencing acquisition and recall of motor memories. J. Neurophysiol. **88:** 2114–2123.
58. BARBEAU, H., K. NORMAN, J. FUNG, *et al.* 1998. Does neurorehabilitation play a role in the recovery of walking in neurological populations? Ann. N.Y. Acad. Sci. **860:** 377–382.
59. DOBKIN, B. 1999. Overview of treadmill locomotor training with partial body weight support: a neurophysiologically sound approach whose time has come for randomized clinical trials. Neurorehabil. Neural Repair **13:** 157–165.
60. VISINTIN, M., H. BARBEAU, N. KORNER-BITENSKY & N. MAYO. 1998. A new approach to retrain gait in stroke patients through body weight support and treadmill stimulation. Stroke **29:** 1122–1128.
61. NILSSON, L., J. CARLSSON, A. DANIELSSON, *et al.* 2002. Walking training of patients with hemiparesis at an early stage after stroke: a comparison of walking training on a treadmill with body weight support and walking training on the ground. Clin. Rehabil. **15:** 515–527.
62. DOBKIN, B., D. APPLE, H. BARBEAU, *et al.* 2003. Methods for a randomized trial of weight-supported treadmill training versus conventional training for walking during inpatient rehabilitation after incomplete traumatic spinal cord injury. Neurorehabil. Neural Repair **17:** 153–167.

63. LIEPERT, J., H. BAUDER, W. MILTNER, et al. 2000. Treatment-induced cortical reorganization after stroke in humans. Stroke **31:** 1210–1216.

64. DROMERICK, A., D. EDWARDS & M. HAHN. 2000. Does the application of constraint-induced movement therapy during acute rehabilitation reduce arm impairment after ischemic stroke? Stroke **31:** 2984–2988.

65. WOLF, S., S. BLANTON, H. BAER, et al. 2002. Repetitive task practice: a critical review of constraint-induced movement therapy in stroke. Neurologist **8:** 325–338.

66. VAN DER LEE, J. 2001. Constraint-induced therapy for stroke: more of the same or something completely different? Curr. Opin. Neurol. **14:** 741–744.

67. KOZLOWSKI, D., D. JAMES & T. SCHALLERT. 1996. Use-dependent exaggeration of neuronal injury after unilateral sensorimotor cortex lesions. J. Neurosci. **16:** 4776–4786.

68. TILLERSON, J.L., A.D. COHEN, W.M. CAUDLE, et al. 2002. Forced nonuse in unilateral parkinsonian rats exacerbates injury. J. Neurosci. **22:** 6790–6799.

69. WINSTEIN, C., J. MILLER, S. BLANTON, et al. 2003. Methods for a multi-site randomized trial to investigate the effect of constraint-induced movement therapy in improving upper extremity function among adults recovering from a cerebrovascular stroke. Neurorehabil. Neural Repair **17:** 137–152.

70. CAURAUGH, J., K. LIGHT, S. KIM, et al. 2000. Chronic motor dysfunction after stroke: recovering wrist and finger extension by electromyography-triggered neuromuscular stimulation. Stroke **31:** 1360–1364.

71. VOLPE, B., H. KREBS, N. HOGAN, et al. 2000. A novel approach to stroke rehabilitation: robot-aided sensorimotor stimulation. Neurology **54:** 1938–1944.

72. FASOLI, S., I. KREBS, J. STEIN, et al. 2003. Effects of robotic therapy on motor impairment and recovery in chronic stroke. Arch. Phys. Med. Rehabil. **84:** 477–482.

73. MATTAY, V., J. CALLICOTT, A. BERTOLINO, et al. 2000. Effects of dextroamphetamine on cognitive performance and cortical activation. NeuroImage **12:** 268–275.

74. GU, Q. 2002. Neuromodulatory transmitter systems in the cortex and their role in cortical plasticity. Neuroscience **111:** 815–835.

75. GOLDSTEIN, L. 1999. Amphetamine-facilitated poststroke recovery. Stroke **30:** 696–697.

76. STROEMER, R., T. KENT & C. HULSEBOSCH. 1998. Enhanced neocortical neural sprouting, synaptogenesis and behavioral recovery with d-amphetamine therapy after neocortical infarction in rats. Stroke **29:** 2381–2395.

77. SCHEIDTMANN, K., W. FRIES, F. MULLER & E. KOENIG. 2001. Effect of levodopa in combination with physiotherapy on functional motor recovery after stroke: a prospective, randomised, double-blinded study. Lancet **358:** 787–790.

78. GRADE, C., B. REDFORD, J. CHROSTOWSKI, et al. 1998. Methylphenidate in early poststroke reovery: a double-blind, placebo-controlled study. Arch. Phys. Med. Rehabil. **79:** 1047–1050.

79. CONNER, J., A. CULBERSON, C. PACKOWSKI, et al. 2003. Lesions of the basal forebrain cholinergic system impair task acquisition and abolish cortical plasticity associated with motor skill learning. Neuron **38:** 819–829.

80. PARIENTE, J., I. LOUBINOUX, C. CAREL, et al. 2001. Fluoxetine modulates motor performance and cerebral activation of patients recovering from stroke. Ann. Neurol. **50:** 718–729.

81. RAGERT, P., H. DINSE, B. PLEGER, *et al.* 2003. Combination of 5 Hz repetitive transcranial magnetic stimulation and tactile coactivation boosts tactile discrimination in humans. Neurosci. Lett. **348:** 105–108.

82. KORCHOUNOV, A., T.V. ILIC & U. ZIEMANN. 2003. The alpha-adrenergic agonist guanfacine reduces excitability of human motor cortex through disfacilitation and increase inhibition. Clin. Neurophysiol. **114:** 1834–1840.

83. GOLDSTEIN, L., A. DROMERICK, D. GOOD, *et al.* 2002. Possible time window for the detrimental effects of drugs on poststroke recovery. Neurology(Suppl. 3) **58:** A5–6.

84. KESSLER, J., A. THIEL, H. KARBE & W. HEISS. 2000. Piracetam improves activated blood flow and facilitates rehabilitation of poststroke aphasic patients. Stroke **31:** 2112–2116.

85. WALKER-BATSON, D., S. CURTIS, R. NATARAJAN, *et al.* 2001. A double-blind placebo-controlled study of the use of amphetamine in the treatment of aphasia. Stroke **32:** 2093–2098.

86. DINSE, H., P. RAGERT, B. PLEGER, *et al.* 2003. Pharmacological modulation of perceptual learning and associated cortical reorganization. Science **301:** 91–94.

87. KANDEL, E. 2001. The molecular biology of memory storage: a dialogue betweeen genes and synapses. Science **294:** 1030–1038.

88. GELBER, D., D. GOOD, A. DROMERICK, *et al.* 2001. Open-label dose-titration safety and efficacy study of tizanidine hydrochloride in the treatment of spasticity associated with chronic stroke. Stroke **32:** 1841–1846.

89. BRASHEAR, A., M. GORDON, E. ELOVIC, *et al.* 2002. Intramuscular injection of botulinum toxin for the treatment of wrist and finger spasticity after a stroke. N. Engl. J. Med. **347:** 395–400.

90. ORSNES, G., C. CRONE, C. KRARUP, *et al.* 2000. The effect of baclofen on the transmission in spinal pathways in spastic multiple sclerosis patients. Clin. Neurophysiol. **111:** 1372–1379.

91. RÉMY-NÉRIS, O., H. BARBEAU, O. DANIEL, *et al.* 1999. Effects of intrathecal clonidine injection on spinal reflexes and human locomotion in incomplete paraplegic subjects. Exp. Brain Res. **129:** 433–440.

92. MIRBAGHERI, M.M., H. BARBEAU, M. LADOUCEUR & R.E. KEARNEY. 2001. Intrinsic and reflex stiffness in normal and spastic spinal cord injured subjects. Exp Brain Res **141:** 446–459.

93. DIETZ, V.. 2000. Spastic movement disorder. Spinal Cord **38:** 389–393.

94. HORNBY, T.G., W.Z. RYMER, E.N. BENZ & B.D. SCHMIT. 2003. Windup of flexion reflexes in chronic human spinal cord injury: a marker for neuronal plateau potentials? J. Neurophysiol. **89:** 416–426.

95. BOROOJERDI, B., U. ZIEMANN, R. CHEN, *et al.* 2001. Mechanisms underlying human motor system plasticity. Muscle Nerve **24:** 602–613.

96. ALPERT, N.M., R.D. BADGAIYAN, E. LIVNI & A.J. FISCHMAN. 2003. A novel method for noninvasive detection of neuromodulatory changes in specific neurotransmitter systems. Neuroimage **19:** 1049–1060.

97. GOERENDT, I.K., C. MESSA, A.D. LAWRENCE, *et al.* 2003. Dopamine release during sequential finger movements in health and Parkinson's disease: a PET study. Brain **126:** 312–325.

98. DOBKIN, B. 2003. Do electrically stimulated sensory inputs and movements lead to long-term plasticity and rehabilitation gains? Curr. Opin. Neurol. **16:** 686–691.

99. TALWAR, S., S. XU, E. HAWLEY, et al. 2002. Rat navigation guided by remote control. Nature **417**: 37–38.

100. SCHIFF, N.& K. PURPURA. 2002. Towards a neurophysiological foundation for cognitive neuromodulaion through deep brain stimulation. Thalamus and Related Systems **2**: 55–69.

101. BRIGHINA, F., E. BISIACH, M. OLIVERI, et al. 2003. 1 Hz repetitive transcranial magnetic stimulation of the unaffected hemisphere ameliorates contralesional visuospatial neglect in humans. Neurosci. Lett. **336**: 131–133.

102. KEMNA, L.J. & D. GEMBRIS. 2003. Repetitive transcranial magnetic stimulation induces different responses in different cortical areas: a functional magnetic resonance study in humans. Neurosci.Lett. **336**: 85–88.

103. TAYLOR, D., S. HELMS TILLERY & A. SCHWARTZ. 2002. Direct cortical control of 3D neuroprosthetic devices. Science **296**: 1829–1831.

104. VAUGHAN, T., W. HEETDERKS, L. TREJO, et al. 2003. Brain-computer interface technology: a review of the Second International Meeting. IEEE Trans. Neural Syst. Rehabil. Eng. **11**: 94–109.

105. ZECK, G. & P. FROMHERZ. 2001. Noninvasive neuroelectronic interfacing with synaptically connected snail neurons imobilized on a semiconductor chip. Proc. Natl. Acad. Sci. **98**: 10457–10462.

106. DOBKIN, B. 2003. Functional MRI: A potential physiologic indicator for stroke rehabilitation interventions. Stroke **34**: e23–24.

107. DIJKHUIZEN, R.M., A.B. SINGHAL, J.B. MANDEVILLE, et al. 2003. Correlation between brain reorganization, ischemic damage, and neurologic status after transient focal cerebral ischemia in rats: a functional magnetic resonance imaging study. J. Neurosci. **23**: 510–517.

108. CALAUTTI, C. & J.-C. BARON. 2003. Functional neuroimaging studies of motor recovery after stroke in adults: a review. Stroke **34**: 1553–1566.

109. SMALL, S., P. HLUSTIK, D. NOLL, et al. 2002. Cerebellar hemispheric activation ipsilateral to the paretic hand correlates with functional recovery after stroke. Brain **125**: 1544–1557.

110. JOHANSEN-BERG, H., H. DAWES, C. GUY, et al. 2002. Correlation between motor improvements and altered fMRI activity after rehabilitative therapy. Brain **125**: 2731–2742.

111. WARD, N., N. BROWN, A. THOMPSON & R. FRACKOWIAK. 2003. Neural correlates of outcome after stroke: a cross-sectional fMRI study. Brain **126**: 1430–1448.

112. FEYDY, A., R. CARLIER, A. ROBY-BRAMI, et al. 2002. Longitudinal study of motor recovery after stroke: Recruitment and focusing of brain activation. Stroke **33**: 1610–1617.

113. NELLES, G., W. JENTZEN, M. JUEPTNER, et al. 2001. Arm training induced brain plasticity in stroke studies with serial positron emission tomography. NeuroImage **13**: 1146–1154.

114. DOBKIN, B., A. FIRESTINE, M. WEST, et al. 2004. Ankle dorsiflexion as an fMRI paradigm to assay motor control for walking during rehabilitation. NeuroImage **23**: 370–381.

115. FRASER, C., M. POWER, S. HAMDY, et al. 2002. Driving plasticity in human adult motor cortex is associated with improved motor function after brain injury. Neuron **34**: 831–840.

116. CARMICHAEL, S. & M.-F. CHESSELET. 2002. Synchronous neuronal activity is a signal for axonal sprouting after cortical lesions in the adult rat. J. Neurosci. **22:** 6062–6070.

117. CARMICHAEL, S. 2003. Plasticity of cortical projections after stroke. Neuroscientist **9:** 64–73.

118. ARVIDSSON, A., T. COLLIN, D. KIRIK, *et al.* 2002. Neuronal replacement from endogenous precursors in the adult brain after stroke. Nature Med **8:** 963–970.

119. KATSMAN, D., J. ZHENG, K. SPINELLI & S. CARMICHAEL. 2003. Tissue microenvironments within functional cortical subdivisions adjacent to focal stroke. J. Cereb. Blood Flow Metab. **23:** 997–1009.

120. CALABRESI, P., D. CENTONZE, A. PISANI, *et al.* 2003. Synaptic plasticity in the ischaemic brain. Lancet Neurol **2:** 622–629.

121. READ, S., A. PARSONS, D. HARRISON, *et al.* 2001. Stroke genomics: approaches to identify, validate, and understand ischemic stroke gene expression. J. Cereb. Blood Flow Metab. **21:** 755–778.

122. SAVITZ, S., D. ROSENBAUM, J. DINSMORE, *et al.* 2002. Cell transplantation for stroke. Ann. Neurol. **52:** 266–275.

123. LI, Y., J. CHEN, X. CHEN, *et al.* 2002. Human marrow stromal cell therapy for stroke in rat: neurotrophins and functional recovery. Neurology **59:** 514–523.

124. JOHANSSON, B. 1999. Brain plasticity and stroke rehabilitation. Stroke **31:** 223–230.

125. EMERICK, A., E. NEAFSEY, M. SCHWAB & G. KARTJE. 2003. Functional reorganization of the motor cortex in adult rats after cortical lesion and treatment with monoclonal antibody IN-1. J. Neurosci. **23:** 4826–4830.

126. MERKLER, D., G. METZ, O. RAINETEAU, *et al.* 2001. Locomotor recovery in spinal cord-injured rats treated with an antibody neutralizing the myelin-associated neurite growth inhibitor Nogo-A. J. Neurosci. **21:** 3665–3673.

127. SICOTTE, M., O. TSATAS, S.Y. JEONG, *et al.* 2003. Immunization with myelin or recombinant Nogo-66/MAG in alum promotes axon regeneration and sprouting after corticospinal tract lesions in the spinal cord. Mol. Cell Neurosci. **23:** 251–263.

128. GRANDPRE, T., S. LI & S. STRITTMATTER. 2002. Nogo-66 receptor antagonist peptide promotes axonal regeneration. Nature **417:** 547–551.

129. FOURNIER, A.E., B.T. TAKIZAWA & S.M. STRITTMATTER. 2003. Rho kinase inhibition enhances axonal regeneration in the injured CNS. J. Neurosci. **23:** 1416–1423.

130. DERGHAM, P., B. ELLEZAM, C. ESSAGIAN, *et al.* 2002. Rho signaling pathway targeted to promote spinal cord repair. J. Neurosci. **22:** 6570–6577.

131. DUBREUIL, C., M. WINTON & L. MCKERRACHER. 2003. Rho activation patterns after spinal cord injury and the role of activated Rho in apoptosis in the central nervous system. J. Cell Biol. **162:** 233–243.

132. CAI, D., J. QIU, Z. CAO, *et al.* 2001. Neuronal cyclic AMP controls the developmental loss in ability of axons to regenerate. J. Neurosci.**21:** 4731–4739.

133. BLESCH, A., P. LU & M. TUSZYNSKI. 2002. Neurotrophic factors, gene therapy, and neural stem cells for spinal cord repair. Brain Res. Bull. **57:** 833–838.

134. DOBKIN, B. & L. HAVTON. 2004. Basic advances and new avenues in therapy of spinal cord injury. Annu. Rev. Med. **55:** 255–282.

135. HOULE, J.D. & A. TESSLER. 2003. Repair of chronic spinal cord injury. Exp. Neurol. **182:** 247–260.

136. KONDZIOLKA, D., L. WECHSLER & C. ACHIM. 2002. Neural transplantation for stroke. J. Clin. Neurosci. **9:** 225–230.
137. NELSON, P., D. KONDZIOLKA, L. WECHSLER, *et al.* 2002. Clonal human (hNT) neuron grafts for stroke therapy: neuropathology in a patient 27 months after implantation. Am. J. Pathol. **160:** 1201–1206.
138. FREED, C., P. GREENE, R. BREEZE, *et al.* 2001. Transplantation of embryonic dopamine neurons for severe Parkinson's disease. New Engl. J. Med. **344:** 710–719.
139. DUMONT, A.S., R.J. DUMONT & R. OSKOUIAN. 2002. Will improved understanding of the pathophysiological mechanisms involved in acute spinal cord injury improve the potential for therapeutic intervention? Curr. Opin. Neurol. **15:** 713–720.
140. FADEN, A.I. 2002. Neuroprotection and traumatic brain injury: theoretical option or realistic proposition. Curr. Opin. Neurol. **15:** 707–712.
141. HUNTER, A.J., K.B. MACKAY & D.C. ROGERS. 1998. To what extent have functional studies of ischaemia in animals been useful in the assessment of potential neuroprotective agents? Trends Pharmacol. Sci . **19:** 59–66.
142. GINSBERG, M.D. 2003. Adventures in the pathophysiology of brain ischemia: penumbra, gene expression, neuroprotection: the 2002 Thomas Willis lecture. Stroke **34:** 214–223.
143. BLIGHT, A. 2000. Animal models of spinal cord injury. Top. Spinal Cord Inj. Rehabil. **6:** 1–13.
144. GREEN, A., T. ODERGREN & T. ASHWOOD. 2003. Animal models of stroke: do they have value for discovering neuroprotective agents? Trends Pharm. Sci. **24:** 402–408.
145. KWON, B., T. OXLAND & W. TETZLAFF. 2002. Animal models used in spinal cord regeneration research. Spine **27:** 1504–1510.
146. VAN DER HARST, J., A.-M. BAARS & B. SPRUIT. 2003. Standard housed rats are more sensitive to rewards than enriched housed rats as reflected by their anticipatory behavior. Behav. Brain Res. **142:** 151–156.
147. WURBEL, H. 2001. Ideal homes? Housing effects on rodent brain and behavior. Trends Neurosci. **24:** 207–211.
148. WEBB, A., K. GOWRIBAI & G. MUIR. 2003. Fischer rats have different morphology, sensorimotor and locomotor capabilities compared to Lewis, Long-Evans, Sprague-Dawley and Wistar rats. Behav. Brain Res. **144:** 143–156.
149. RAMON-CUETO, A., M. CORDERO, F. SANTOS-BENITO & J. AVILA. 2000. Functional recovery of paraplegic rats and motor axon regeneration in their spinal cords by olfactory ensheathing glia. Neuron **25:** 425–436.
150. LI, Y., P. DECHERCHI & G. RAISMAN. 2003. Transplantation of olfactory ensheathing cells into spinal cord lesions restores breathing and climbing. J. Neurosci. **23:** 727–731.
151. MURRAY, M., D. KIM, Y. LIU, *et al.* 2002. Transplantation of genetically modified cells contributes to repair from spinal injury. Brain Res. Rev. **40:** 292–300.
152. TUSZYNSKI, M., R. GRILL, L. JONES, *et al.* 2003. NT-3 gene delivery elicits growth of chronically injured corticospinal axons and modestly improves functional deficits after chronic scar resection. Exp. Neurol. **181:** 47–56.
153. KAKULAS, B. 1999. A review of the neuropathology of human spinal cord injury with emphasis on special features. J. Spinal Cord Med. **22:** 119–124.
154. VILENSKY, J., A. MOORE, E. EIDELBERG & J. WALDEN. 1992. Recovery of locomotion in monkeys with spinal cord lesions. J. Mot. Behav. **24:** 288–296.

Temperament and Early Experience Form Social Behavior

NATHAN A. FOX, PHD

Professor, Institute for Child Study, Department of Human Development, University of Maryland, College Park, Maryland 20742, USA

ABSTRACT: Individual differences in the way persons respond to stimulation can have important consequences for their ability to learn and their choice of vocation. Temperament is the study of such individual differences, being thought of as the behavioral style of an individual. Common to all approaches in the study of temperament are the notions that it can be identified in infancy, is fairly stable across development, and influences adult personality. We have identified a specific temperament type in infancy that involves heightened distress to novel and unfamiliar stimuli. Infants who exhibit this temperament are likely, as they get older, to display behavioral inhibition—wariness and heightened vigilance of the unfamiliar—particularly in social situations. Our work has also described the underlying biology of this temperament and has linked it to neural systems supporting fear responses in animals. Children displaying behavioral inhibition are at-risk for behavioral problems related to anxiety and social withdrawal.

KEYWORDS: temperament; behavioral inhibition; shyness; anxiety; fear

Temperament is thought of as the behavioral style of an individual that is present from birth, fairly stable across development, and influential in the formation of adult personality. The notion of temperament has been around for quite some time. Indeed, Galen, a Roman physician in the second century, described what he considered to be four different types of individuals: melancholic, sanguine, choleric, and phlegmatic. The melancholic individual was thought of as cool and dry because of excess black bile, the sanguine individual was warm and moist because of an excess of blood, the choleric individual was warm and dry because of excess of yellow bile, and the phlegmatic individual was cool and moist because of excess of phlegm. Al-

Address for correspondence: Nathan A. Fox, PhD, Institute for Child Study, Department of Human Development, University of Maryland, 3304 Benjamin Building, College Park, MD 20742-1131. Voice: 301-405-2816; fax: 301-405-2891.

nf4@umail.umd.edu

Ann. N.Y. Acad. Sci. 1038: 171–178 (2004). © 2004 New York Academy of Sciences.
doi: 10.1196/annals.1315.025

though he talked about these four humors and the relative dominance of the derived qualities that were inherited, he also wrote about the susceptibility and the influence of each of these temperaments to external events.[1]

Alexander Thomas and Stella Chess, two child psychiatrists, articulated a formulation of temperament. Thomas and Chess observed over one hundred infants and their parents in their homes, cataloging the infant's behavior around daily routine caregiving. On the basis of these observations they identified nine temperament factors, including adaptability, quality of mood, and activity level.[2] Thomas and Chess claimed that each infant could be rated along each of the nine factors to describe their innate temperament. They also combined these factors to come up with three different temperament types: the slow to warm up child, the child with an easy temperament, and the child with a difficult temperament. By way of example, the difficult temperament would be the child who is high in motor activity, low in adaptability, and with a negative quality of mood. Some research suggests that difficult temperament children are at-risk for maladaptive behavioral outcomes (e.g., conduct problems). The easy child, on the other hand, would be quite the opposite; low in motor activity and high in adaptability. Easy temperament children do not present problems to their parents and generally are viewed as having positive behavioral outcomes. The slow-to-warm up child is one who needs a prolonged period for arousal, is generally not very adaptive and is low on approach behaviors. Children who are shy and retiring may fit into this category.

Mary Rothbart from the Psychology Department at the University of Oregon presented a more contemporary version of temperament theory. She divided temperament into two dimensions: reactivity and regulation.[3] Like traditional models, Rothbart argued that temperament can be measured early on in the first months of life and that it was a stable and influential aspect of a child's behavior. Rothbart measured temperament in terms of an infant's response to sensory stimulation. In addition, she claimed that a second aspect of temperament involved the infant's or young child's ability to regulate a reactive response. She and her colleague Michael Posner have written about the role of attention and the prefrontal cortex in the regulation of reactive responses.[4]

Jerome Kagan at Harvard articulated some twenty years ago a third approach to temperament, one that has guided much of my research. He observed a group of children who when placed in novel or unfamiliar settings, became quiet and watchful, and withdrew from social activity. They did not initiate social interaction and, when they are approached in a social situation, they often withdraw. Kagan argued that these behaviors reflected the temperament of behavioral inhibition.[5] In my laboratory we looked to the neuroscience literature to give us hints as to the neural substrates of behavioral inhibition. The behaviors that these children exhibited including their physiological reactivity to novelty and uncertainty led us to believe that the emotion was fear and the neural structure underlying their behavior was the amygdala. The important work of Joseph LeDoux[6,7] and Michael Davis[8–10] on the neural networks underlying both conditioned and unconditioned fear serves as a basis for our intuition. LeDoux and Davis had described in the rat what they call the fear system, a system of subnuclei that are involved in the rat's behavioral response to conditioned fear. Both workers had shown that the amygdala and its nuclei were important structures in the exhibition of responses of the rat to a conditioned fear response. These responses included freezing, autonomic reactivity, the excretion of stress hormones, and heightened startle response.

In my laboratory we found evidence that behaviorally inhibited children displayed this same pattern of physiology in response to novelty. Specifically, we examined each of these outputs, freezing, autonomic, stress hormones, and startle reflex to see if we could find these particular kinds of responses in the behaviorally inhibited children. We were able to show that these behaviorally inhibited children exhibited elevated salivary cortisol, measured three days in a row early in the morning, relative to non-inhibited children.[11] We also found that behaviorally inhibited seven-year-old children showed a much more dramatic increase in their autonomic responses to anxiety induction compared with non-inhibited children, for example, when they were asked to think about giving a speech about their most embarrassing moment. Most children showed a deceleration response, but the highly inhibited children showed accelerative response.[12] In children as early as nine months of age, behaviorally inhibited children exhibited a heightened startle response. When presented with a sudden loud tone, they showed an enhanced startle response relative to infants who were not behaviorally inhibited.[13]

LeDoux and Davis were also very interested in the modulation of this fear response by the cerebral cortex. LeDoux proposed that there were modulatory effects from the cerebral cortex to the subcortical nuclei. We examined brain electrical activity by recording EEG activity during both baseline resting states and during emotion-elicited states and determined whether there were differences between patterns exhibited by behaviorally inhibited children and those of non-inhibited children. In pre-school children there was more right-sided or right-frontal EEG activity in behaviorally inhibited children than in non-inhibited children, a finding that was very similar to one we had earlier reported with shy adults.[14] Adults who self report as being shy, which is the popular analog, if you will, of behavioral inhibition, show a pattern of EEG activity that is quite the opposite of adults who report themselves as more gregarious or exuberant in their temperament.[15]

The physiological pattern that we described in behaviorally inhibited children, in response to exposure to novelty or uncertainty, involves heightened motor and emotional reactivity. We decided to investigate whether similar responses could be identified in infancy and would be associated with later temperamental behavioral inhibition. Based upon Kagan's work and our own we designed a screening procedure at four months of age that would allow us to examine an infant's reactivity to novel auditory and visual stimuli, and we selected mobiles and played strange sounds to these infants while they sat in an infant seat we coded their fretting and crying behavior, their smiling, vocalization, and motor movement. On the basis of the infants' behaviors, e.g., crying or showing a more positive response to mobiles, we were able to form what we called three temperament groups. The negative group was the one, based upon our previous observations, that we believed would go on to show behavioral inhibition. These infants showed a great deal of motor activity and negative affect in response to the novel auditory and visual stimuli. The low group showed very little response to the auditory or visual stimuli. Serendipitously, I might add, there was another group of infants who were showing a great deal of motor arousal in response to the auditory and visual stimuli but instead of showing negative affect they showed a great deal of positive affect. While we had not intended to form this group or to follow them, they represented about 10% of our population, so we decided to follow them. In fact, they have in some sense turned out to be quite an interesting group. I will describe some of the findings about them below.[16]

The "negative" high distress, high motor infants represented about 15%; the "positive" high positive affect, high motor infants represent about 10%, and the "low" infants represent about 20–25% of our population; those are the three groups of infants we followed in our longitudinal sample. At nine months of age we brought them back into the lab, recorded their brain electrical activity, and looked at the relative difference between EEG power in the left and right hemispheres. What we found confirmed our hypothesis that the negative group was showing greater right frontal EEG activation relative to the low group, which was showing symmetry in terms of EEG power. But also quite interesting is that the positive group was showing a pattern of left frontal EEG activation.[17]

We saw these infants at one year and two years of age and studied their behavioral inhibition. At these ages, behavioral inhibition is inferred from a cluster of behaviors that are involved in ceasing activity in response to novel and unfamiliar events or ceasing activity and withdrawing from social interaction. We presented one- and two-year-olds with a robot to see their response. We had the child crawl through a tunnel to see whether or not the child would do that. And we introduced an unfamiliar adult into the playroom to see whether or not the child would withdraw from the situation. At four years of age, we brought these same children back to our playroom and this time we formed same gender play quartets in which we took our inhibited child and three other children and put them together and observed their play for 15 minutes. Then they had to clean up the toys and each give a speech about their most recent (fourth year) birthday. In the social psychology literature, giving a speech is found to be an anxiety-inducing or anxiety-eliciting event for shy adults, so we reasoned this might be a stressful event for the be-

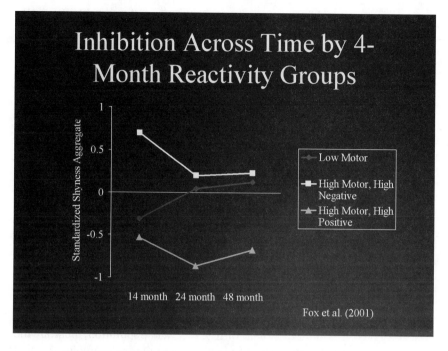

FIGURE 1. Inhibition across time by 4-month reactivity groups.

haviorally inhibited children as well. Finally after another small task, they had another 15 minutes of free play.

When one graphs a standardized measure of behavioral inhibition against age across a four-year period, with three lines each representing the three temperament groups, the children we expected to display behavioral inhibition at 14 months of age, our high motor, high-negative infants, are showing significant behavioral inhibition relative to the other two groups (see FIG. 1). However, by two years of age and then on to four years of age, the mean of the group is no different than it is for our low temperament infants. However, the variability within the high-negative group is quite large at both 24 and 48 months. On the other hand, there is minimal variability within the high-positive infants, those that show no fear and a high degree of social interaction at two years and four years of age.

One of the critical goals of the field of developmental psychology and particularly in the area of temperament and social development is to identify the factors that contribute to the continuity or discontinuity of early temperament. In order to accomplish this goal we divided up the high-negative group into those who showed continuity of behavioral inhibition over the four-year period of time and those that changed or became less inhibited over time. Factors that have been examined include the manner of caregiving that the child receives and the context or quality of the environment in which that caregiving is delivered. As well, within child factors such as the child's sex or birth order have been implicated as having an effect upon developmental trajectories for socialization.

We examined this range of factors in our work and identified caregiving behavior, the context of caregiving and child gender as elements contributing to continuity of behavioral inhibition. In a study of maternal caregiving behavior we found that mothers who were more overprotective and intrusive towards their child were more likely to exacerbate social wariness in their children. Mothers who were less overprotective of their inhibited child actually saw greater discontinuity in these child behaviors over time.[18]

We also examined our data and found that the child's gender and daycare experience were related to patterns of continuity. Boys displaying behavioral inhibition were more likely to remain stable and inhibited over time. We believe that this is because for boys being fearful and shy is a much more salient characteristic for parents, that is, parents may pay more attention to them whereas they do not pay more attention to girls exhibiting the same characteristics. Most interesting for us were the effects of daycare. If the child was placed in daycare, in the first year of life, then those inhibited children were more likely to change as opposed to remain stable.[16]

We also found that the brain activity of the child followed that child's change or stability of behavior. Thus, if the child continued to be inhibited, we continued to find a pattern of activity associated with right frontal activity, but if the child changed, there was a flip in terms of the child's brain activation.

It appears now, from both our study and the research of others that the outcomes of behavioral inhibition include in some instances anxiety disorders and social withdrawal in childhood which involves a lack of friendship relationships, peer isolation, and even reports of being victimized by bullies in middle school, something that at least in the popular press has become of concern recently. Young behaviorally inhibited children typically engage in what we call reticent behavior, watching other children but not engaging them in play—unoccupied and hypervigilant in response. We know that social competence with peers is important in the formation of normative social skills, friendships, and positive adult social relationships. The child with a temperament of behavioral inhibition is at-risk for maladaptive social behavior and perhaps psychopathology.[19]

In sum, individual differences in temperament are readily detected during the first months of life and have a significant effect upon the child's interaction with the world and parent perceptions of that child. Infant temperament is associated with patterns of social behavior in early childhood. Infants displaying a temperament of negative emotionality are likely to exhibit behavioral inhibition and social withdrawal during childhood, and temperamental differences during infancy appear rooted in biology. Yet caregiving environments have a profound impact on the continuity of these differences and on the biology on which they are based.

REFERENCES

1. KAGAN, J. 1994. Galen's prophecy. Basic Books. New York.
2. THOMAS, A., S. CHESS & H.G. BIRCH. 1968. Temperament and behavior disorders in children. New York University Press. New York.
3. ROTHBART, M.K. & D. DERRYBERRY. 1981. Development of individual differences in temperament. In Advances in Developmental Psychology. M. Lamb & A. Brown, Eds., Vol. 1: 37–86. Erlbaum. Hillsdale, NJ.
4. POSNER, M.I. & M.K. ROTHBART. 1998. Attention, self-regulation, and consciousness. Trans. Phil. Soc. London B: 1915–1927.
5. KAGAN, J., J.S. REZNICK, C. CLARKE, et al. 1984. Behavioral inhibition to the unfamiliar. Child Dev. 55: 2212–2225.
6. LEDOUX, J.E. 2000. Emotion circuits in the brain. Ann. Rev. Neurosci. 23: 155–184.
7. LEDOUX, J.E., J. IWATA, P. CICCHETTI & D.J. REIS. 1988. Different projections of the central amygdaloid nucleus mediate autonomic and behavioral correlates of conditioned fear. J. Neurosci. 8: 2517–2529.
8. DAVIS, M. 1986. Pharmacological and anatomical analysis of fear conditioning using the fear-potentiated startle paradigm. Behav. Neurosci. 100: 814–824.
9. DAVIS, M. 1992. The role of the amygdala in fear and anxiety. Ann. Rev. Neurosci. 15: 353–375.
10. DAVIS, M. 1998. Are different parts of the extended amygdala involved in fear versus anxiety? Biol. Psychiatry 44: 1239–1247.
11. SCHMIDT, L.A., N.A. FOX, K.H. RUBIN, et al. 1997. Behavioral and neuroendocrine responses in shy children. Dev. Psychobiol. 30: 127–140.
12. SCHMIDT, L.A., N.A. FOX, J. SCHULKIN & P.W. GOLD. 1999. Behavioral and psychophysiological correlates of self-presentation in temperamentally shy children. Dev. Psychobiol. 35: 119–135.
13. SCHMIDT, L.A. & N.A. FOX. 1998. Fear-potentiated startle responses in temperamentally different human infants. Dev. Psychobiol. 32: 113–120.
14. FOX, N.A., L.A. SCHMIDT, S.D. CALKINS, et al. 1996. The role of frontal activation in the regulation and dysregulation of social behavior during the preschool year. Dev. Psychopathol. 8: 89–102.
15. SCHMIDT, L. & N.A. FOX. 1994. Patterns of cortical electrophysiology and autonomic activity in adults' shyness and sociability. Biol. Psychol. 38: 183–198.
16. FOX, N.A., H.A. HENDERSON, K.H. RUBIN, et al. 2001. Continuity and discontinuity of behavioral inhibition and exuberance: Psychophysiological and behavioral influences across the first four years of life. Child Dev. 72: 1–21.

17. CALKINS, S.D., N.A. FOX & T.R. MARSHALL. 1996. Behavioral and physiological antecedents of inhibited and uninhibited behavior. Child Dev. **67:** 523–540.
18. RUBIN, K.H., C. CHEAH & N.A. FOX. 2001. Emotion regulation, parenting, and display of social reticence in preschoolers. Early Edu. Dev. **12:** 97–115.
19. BIEDERMAN, J., J.F. ROSENBAUM, D.R. HIRSHFELD, *et al.* 1990. Psychiatric correlates of behavioral inhibition in young children of parents with and without psychiatric disorders. Arch. Gen. Psychiatry **47:** 21–26.

Lessons from the Technology of Skill Formation

JAMES J. HECKMAN, PHD

Henry Schultz Distinguished Service Professor of Economics and of Social Sciences, and Director, Center for Social Program Evaluation and Economic Research Center, University of Chicago, Chicago, Illinois 60637, USA

ABSTRACT: This paper discusses recent advances in our understanding of differences in human abilities and skills, their sources, and their evolution over the lifecycle.

KEYWORDS: skills; abilities, lifecycle; skill gaps; remediation policies

The study of human skill formation is no longer handicapped by the taboo that once made it impermissible to talk about differences among people. It is now well documented that people are very diverse on a large array of abilities, that these abilities account for a substantial amount of the variation found among people in terms of their socioeconomic success, and that gaps among children from various socioeconomic groups open up at early ages, and, if anything, widen as children become adults. The family plays a powerful role in shaping these abilities. From a variety of intervention studies, we know that these gaps can be partially remedied if the remediation is attempted at early enough ages. The remediation efforts that appear to be most effective are those that supplement family resources for young children from disadvantaged environments. Since the family is the fundamental source of human inequality, programs that target young children from disadvantaged families have the greatest economic and social returns. I make this case through a series of arguments, bolstered by graphs and tables extracted from Heckman and Masterov (2004) and Cunha and Heckman (2003), and Carneiro and Heckman (2003).

First, *abilities matter.* A large number of empirical studies document that cognitive ability affects both the likelihood of acquiring advanced training and higher education, but also the economic returns to those activities. Abil-

Nobel Prize in Economic Sciences, 2000

Address for correspondence: James J. Heckman, PhD, Department of Economics, University of Chicago, 1126 East 59th Street, Chicago, Illinois 60637. Voice: 773-702-3478.

j-heckman@uchicago.edu

Ann. N.Y. Acad. Sci. 1038: 179–200 (2004). © 2004 New York Academy of Sciences.
doi: 10.1196/annals.1315.026

ities also matter in determining participation in crime, teenage pregnancy, drug use and in other deviant activities. Education has an independent causal effect on participation in crime, the likelihood of producing an out-of-wedlock birth, drug use and the like apart from its role as a conduit of ability. The evidence that cognitive ability matters tells us nothing whatsoever about whether it is genetically determined. The frenzy generated by Herrnstein and Murray's book *The Bell Curve*, because of its claims about genetic determinism, obscured its real message which is that cognitive ability is an important predictor of socioeconomic success.

Second, *abilities are multiple in nature.* IQ has to be distinguished from what is measured by achievement tests, although it partly determines success on achievement tests. Achievement tests in turn have an independent effect on socioeconomic success apart from the effect of IQ, which is strongly correlated with success on achievement tests. Noncognitive skills (perseverance, motivation, self-control and the like) have direct effects on wages (controlling for schooling), teenage pregnancy, smoking, crime, and achievement tests. Both cognitive and noncognitive skills affect socioeconomic success. Both are strongly influenced by family environments.

Third, *ability gaps between individuals and across socioeconomic groups open up at early ages, for both cognitive and noncognitive skills.* They are strongly correlated with family background factors like parental education and maternal ability, which, when controlled for in a statistical sense, largely eliminate these gaps (see FIGURES 1A,B and 2A,B). Inputs of schooling quality and resources have relatively small effects on ability deficits but only marginally account for some of the divergence evident in FIGURE 1A (see De Los Santos, Heckman, and Larenas, 2004). Parenting practices have strong effects on emotional development and motivation.

Fourth, *it is possible to partially compensate for adverse family environments.* Evidence from randomized trials conducted on intervention programs targeted at disadvantaged children who are followed into adulthood suggests that it is possible to eliminate some of the gaps evident in FIGURES 1A and 2A. Enriched early interventions at the youngest ages raise IQ. The Abecedarian program provided an enriched intervention for disadvantaged children starting at age 4 months. The children who received the intervention score consistently higher than the children who do not, even long after the treatment is discontinued (see FIGURE 3). If we wait to intervene until age 4 or later, no lasting effects on IQ have been found (see FIGURE 4 for the Perry Preschool data). However, effects on motivation and, hence, achievement test scores are found. Children are less likely to commit crime and have out-of-wedlock births and are more likely to participate in regular schooling. Early interventions have a substantial effect on adult performance (see FIGURES 5–7) and have a high economic return (see TABLE 1).

Fifth, *different types of abilities appear to be manipulable at different ages.* Thus, while factors affecting IQ deficits need to be addressed at very early

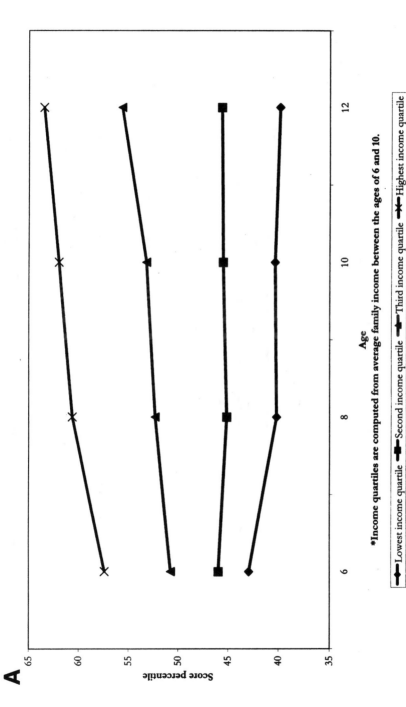

FIGURE 1. Children of NLSY. **A:** Average percentile rank on PIAT-Math score, by income quartile (*). Source for **A** and **B**: Carneiro and Heckman (2003).

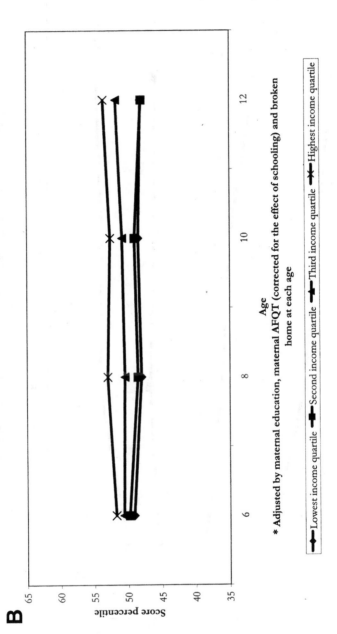

* Adjusted by maternal education, maternal AFQT (corrected for the effect of schooling) and broken home at each age

FIGURE 1 — *continued.* **B:** Adjusted average anti-social score percentile by income quartile (*).

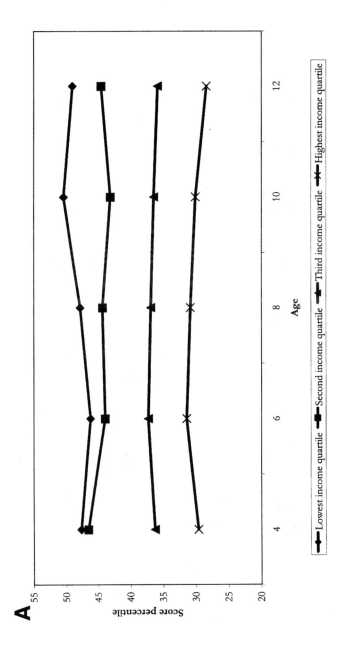

FIGURE 2. Children of NLSY. **A:** Average percentile rank on anti-social score, by income quartile. Source for **A** and **B:** Carneiro and Heckman (2003)

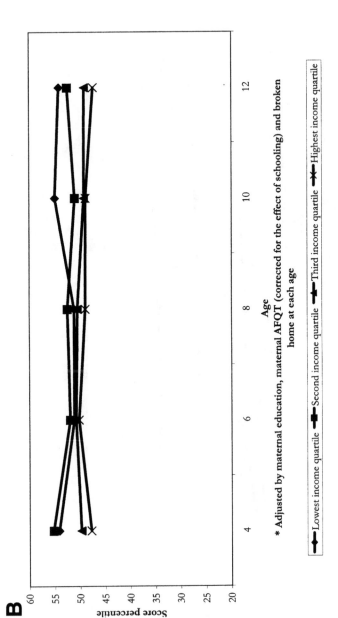

* Adjusted by maternal education, maternal AFQT (corrected for the effect of schooling) and broken home at each age

Lowest income quartile ── Second income quartile ── Third income quartile ── Highest income quartile

FIGURE 2 — *continued*. **B**: Adjusted average anti-social score percentile by income quartile (*).

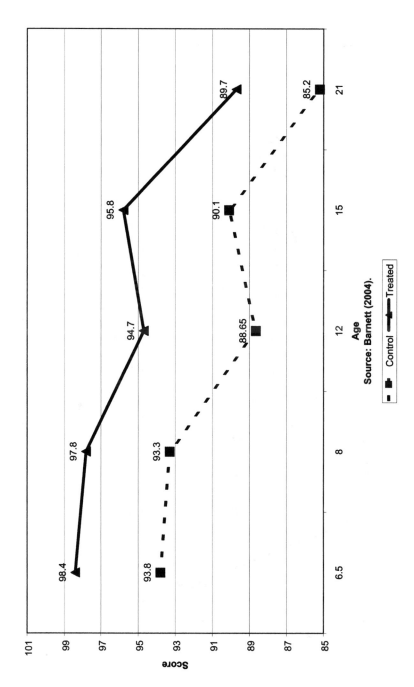

FIGURE 3. Abecedarian IQ scores over time.

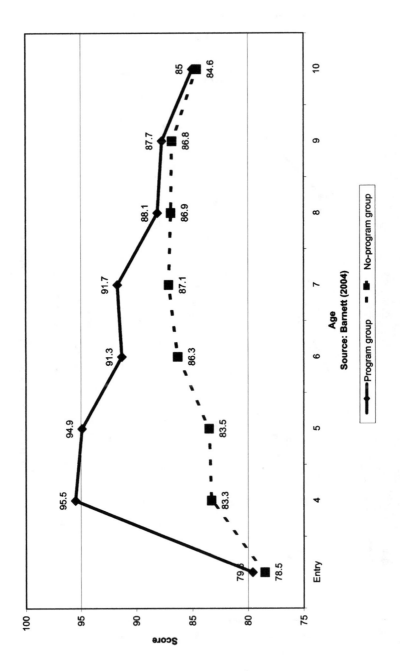

FIGURE 4. Perry Preschool IQ over time.

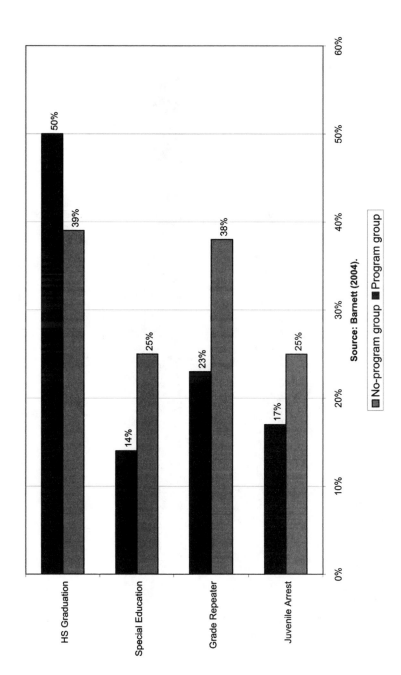

FIGURE 5. Academic and social benefits at school exit for CPC participants.

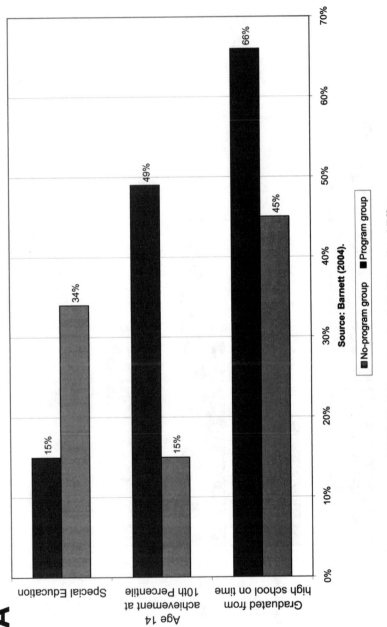

FIGURE 6. Perry Preschool. **A:** Educational Effects.

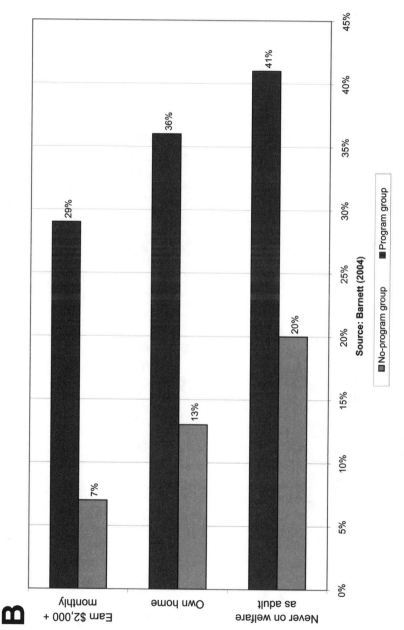

FIGURE 6 — *continued*. B: Economic Outcomes.

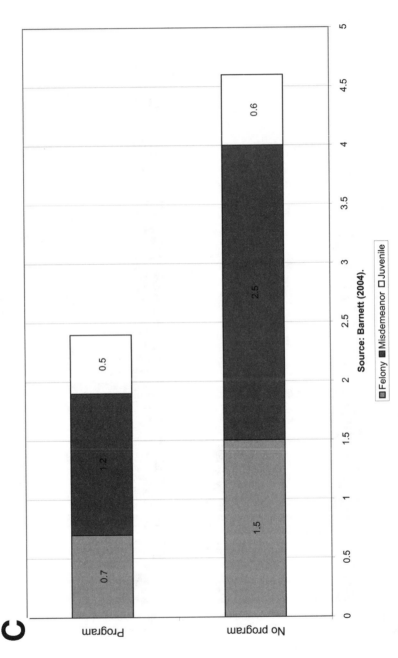

FIGURE 6 — *continued.* C: Arrests per person by age 27.

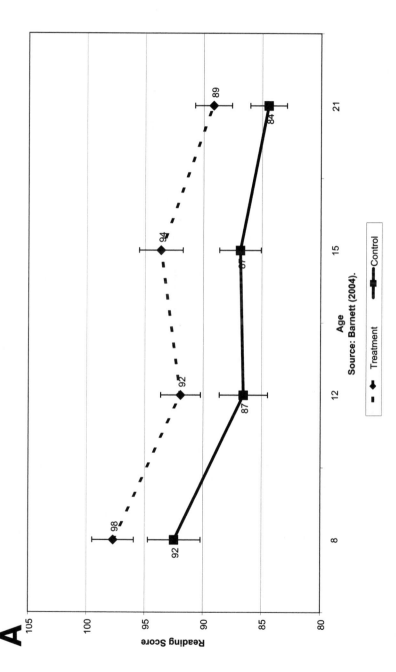

FIGURE 7. A: Abecedarian reading achievement over time.

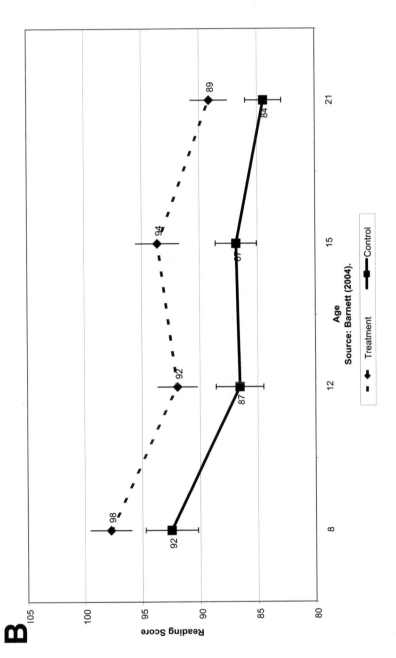

FIGURE 7 — *continued.* **B:** Abecedarian math achievement over time.

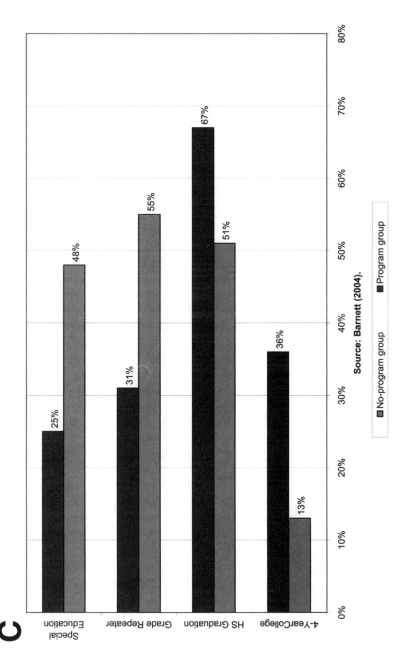

FIGURE 7 — *continued.* C: Abecedarian academic outcomes.

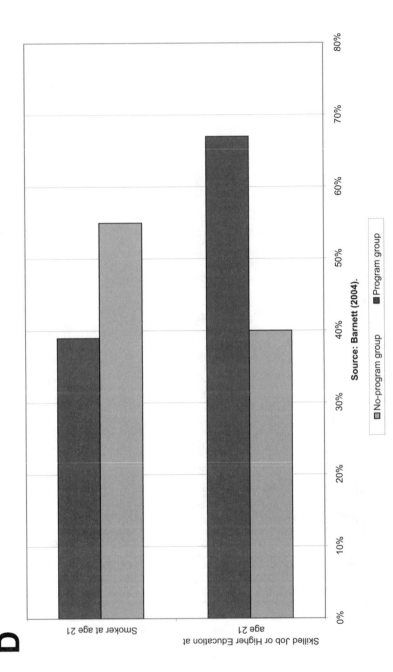

Source: Barnett (2004).

No-program group ■ Program group

FIGURE 7 — *continued.* D: Other benefits of Abecedarian.

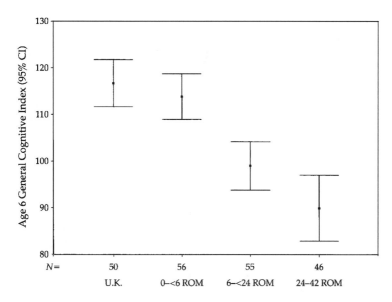

FIGURE 8. Global Cognitive Index (GCI) at 6 years of age as a function of group (age at entry). The means (SD) for the U.K., 0- to <6-month Romanian, <24-month Romanian, and 24- to 42-month Romanian groups were, respectively, 117, (17.8), 114 (18.3), 99 (19.2), and 90 (23.8). U.K. = United Kingdom adoptees; ROM = Romanian adoptees. Source: O'Connor *et al.* (2000).

TABLE 1. Economic benefits and costs

	Perry	Chicago CPC
Child care	986	1,916
Earnings	40,537	32,099
K-12	9,184	5,634
College/adult	−782	−644
Crime	94,065	15,329
Welfare	355	546
FG earnings	6,181	4,894
Abuse/neglect	0	344
Total benefits	150,525	60,117
Total costs	16,514	7,738
Net present value	134,011	52,380
Benefits-to-costs ratio	9.11	7.77

All values are discounted at 3% and are in 2004$. Numbers differ slightly from earlier estimates because FG earnings for Perry and Chicago were estimated using the ratio of FG Earnings Effect to Earnings Effect (about 15%) that was found in Abecedarian. Source: Barnett, 2004.

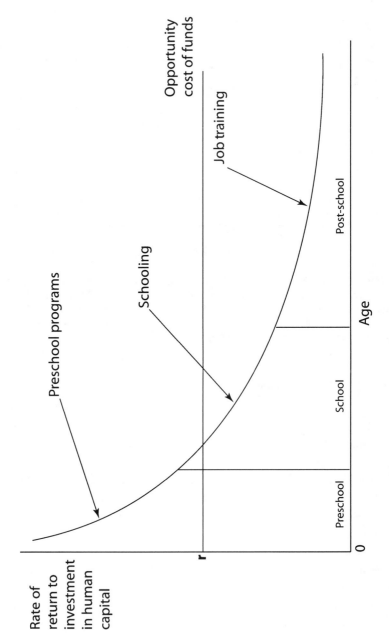

FIGURE 9. Rates of return to human capital investment initially setting investment to be equal across all ages.

ages for interventions to be effective, there is evidence that later interventions in the adolescent years can affect noncognitive skills (see TABLES 2 and 3 for evidence on this point). This evidence appears to be rooted in the neuroscience that establishes the malleability of the prefrontal cortex into the early 20s. This is the region of the brain that governs emotion and self-regulation.

Sixth, *the later the remediation, the less effective it is.* The study by O'Connor and colleagues (2000) of adopted Romanian infants documents this for very early interventions (see FIGURE 8). The later the Romanian orphan is rescued from the social and emotional isolation of the orphanage and placed in an adoptive environment, the lower is his or her cognitive performance at age 6. Moreover, classroom remediation programs designed to

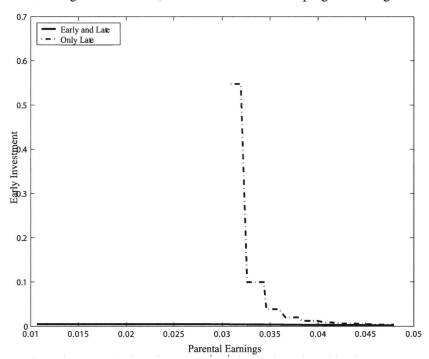

FIGURE 10. The costs of remediation: Late vs. early and late remediation agents that receive zero bequests. Let y denote parental earnings. Let x^*, z^* denote the early and late investments in a complete markets economy. Let $x(y)$, $z(y)$ denote the early and late investments in the Aiyagari/Laitner economy for agents with zero bequests. This economy restricts the ability of families to borrow freely. The early and late remediation are values $\Delta x(y)$ and $\Delta z(y)$ where $\Delta x(y) = x^* - x(y)$, and $\Delta z(y) = z^* - z(y)$. The cost of the early remediation is $C_1 = \Delta x(y) + \Delta z(y)/(1+r)$, where r is the steady state equilibrium interest rate of the Aiyagari/Laitner economy. Let h^* denote the steady state stock of human capital in the complete markets economy. the late remediation is the value δ that solves $g(\delta) = h^* - (\gamma x(y)^\phi + (1-\gamma)\delta^\phi)^{\rho/\phi}$, where the second term is the production function for human capital (ϕ is the substitution parameter, $1/(1-\phi)$ is the elasticity of substitution, and ρ is the scale parameter as estimated in Cunha and Heckman, 2003, 2004). The cost of the late remediation is $C_2 = \delta/(1+\rho)$. Source: Cunha and Heckman (2003).

TABLE 2. Estimated benefits of young adolescent mentoring programs (treatment group reductions compared to control group)

Program	Outcome Measure	Change	Program costs per Participant
Big Brother/Big Sister			$500–$1,500[a]
	initiation drug use	−45.8%	
	initiation alcohol use	−27.4%	
	# of times hit someone	−31.7%	
	# of times stole something	−19.2%	
	grade point average	+3.0%	
	skipped class	−36.7%	
	skipped day of school	−52.2%	
	trust in parent	+2.7%	
	lying to parent	−36.6%	
	peer emotional support	+2.3%	
Sponsor-A-Scholar			$1,485
	10th grade GPA (100 point scale)	2.9	
	11th grade GPA (100 point scale)	2.5	
	% attending college (1 year after HS)	32.8	
	% attending college (2 years after HS)	28.1	
Quantum Opportunity Program			
	graduated from HS or GED	+26%	
	enrolled in 4-year college	+15%	
	enrolled in 2-year college	+24%	
	currently employed full time	+13%	
	self receiving welfare	−22%	
	% ever arrested	−4%	

Source: Carneiro and Heckman (2003).
[a]Costs, in 1996 dollars, for school-based programs are as low as $500 and more expensive community-based mentoring programs cost as much as $1,500. HS = high school.

combat early cognitive deficits have a poor track record. Public job training programs and adult literacy and educational programs, like the GED, that attempt to remediate years of educational and emotional neglect among disadvantaged individuals have a low economic return, and for young males, the return is negative.

FIGURE 9 summarizes the findings of an entire literature. The economic returns to the marginal investment at early ages are high. The economic return

TABLE 3. Effects of selected adolescent social programs on schooling, earnings, and crime

Program/Study	Costs[a]	Program Description	Schooling	Earnings[a]	Crime[a]
STEP (Walker and Viella-Velez, 1992)	N/A	two summers of employment, academic remediation, and life skills for 14 to 15 year olds	short-run gains in test scores; no effect on school completion rates	N/A	N/A
Quantum Opportunities Program[b]	$10,600	counseling; educational, community, and development services for 4 years beginning in 9th grade	34% higher HS graduation and GED attainment rates (2 years after program)	N/A	4% vs. 16% convicted; 0.28 vs. 0.56 average number of arrests (2 years after program)

All comparisons are for program participants vs. non-participants . N/A = not available; HS = high school.
[a]All dollar figures are in 1990 values.
[b]Studies used a random assignment experimental design to determine program impacts.
SOURCE: Heckman, Lochner, Smith, and Taber (1997).

to investment at older ages is lower. The technology of skill formation derived from economic theory and estimated on longitudinal data suggests a strong self-productivity of investment. Investment at an early age produces a high return through this self-productivity. Complementarity (synergy) of investment reinforces self-productivity. Early investment in cognitive and noncognitive skills lowers the cost of later investment by making learning at later ages more efficient. Notice in FIGURES 5, 6A and 7C that those who receive early interventions are less likely to repeat grades or require special education programs while in school. This complementarity highlights the value of early investment. It also demonstrates that there is no trade-off between equity (targeting programs at disadvantaged families) and efficiency (getting the highest economic returns), provided that the investments are made at early ages. There is such a trade-off at later ages.

The empirically established complementarity also suggests that early investments must be followed up by later investments to be effective. Nothing in the new economics of human skill formation suggests that we should starve later educational and skill enhancement efforts. The main finding from the recent literature is that we should prioritize, and shift our priorities, in a marginal fashion by redirecting a given total sum of expenditure on skill investment to earlier ages relative to how it is currently allocated.

The costs of delay implied by the evidence on self-productivity and complementarity are dramatically illustrated by FIGURE 10 from Cunha and Heckman (2003, 2004). Using data from the U.S., they establish that, for children from very poor backgrounds, a strategy of late remediation is economically inefficient. Late remediation, no matter how extensive, cannot restore children from disadvantaged environments to the level of performance they would have attained had they received economically efficient early interventions that compensate for disadvantage in the early years.

Nothing in the recent literature says that investments should not be made in older persons. The phenomenon of neurogenesis informs us that learning can continue into advanced ages. What is missing from that literature is a discussion of the relative costs and returns to investments in older persons compared to younger persons. What we do know is that investments in more able workers at any age generate higher returns than investments in younger workers, and ability is formed at early ages.

REFERENCES

BARNETT, S. 2004. Cost-benefit analysis of preschool education. PowerPoint presentation, <http://nieer.org/resources/files/BarnettBenefits.ppt>

CARNEIRO, P. & J. HECKMAN. 2003. Human capital policy. In Inequality in America: What Role for Human Capital Policy. J. Heckman & A. Krueger, Eds. MIT Press. Cambridge, MA.

CUNHA, F. & J. HECKMAN. The Technology of Skill Formation, presented at Minnesota Federal Reserve, October 2003; AEA meetings, San Diego, January 2004; SEDC meetings, Florence, July 2004 and IRP seminar, University of Wisconsin, November 2004.

DE LOS SANTOS, B., J. HECKMAN & M. LARENAS. 2004. Explaining the gap in achievement test scores for Blacks, Hispanics, and Whites. University of Chicago working paper.

HECKMAN, J., L. LOCHNER, J. SMITH & C. TABER. 1997. The effects of government policy on human capital investment and wage inequality. Chicago Policy Rev. 1(2): 1–40.

HECKMAN, J. & D. MASTEROV. 2004. The productivity argument for investing in young children. Committee on Economic Development, Working Paper #5. September 2004.

HERRNSTEIN, R. & C. MURRAY. 1994. The Bell Curve: Intelligence and Class Structure in American Life. Free Press. New York.

O'CONNOR, T., M. RUTTER, C. BECKETT, et al. and the ENGLISH AND ROMANIAN ADOPTEES STUDY TEAM. 2000. The effects of global privation on cognitive competence: extension and longitudinal follow-up. Child Dev. 7(2): 376–390.

WALKER, G. & F. VILELLA-VELEZ. 1992. Anatomy of a Demonstration: The Summer Training and Education Program (STEP) from pilot through replication and postprogram impacts. Public/Private Ventures. Philadelphia, PA.

Economic Approaches to Understanding Families

GARY S. BECKER, PHD

Professor of Economics and Sociology, University of Chicago, Chicago, illinois 60637, USA

ABSTRACT: The economic approach helps explain the enormous changes in fertility, marriage, divorce, and human capital of families during the past 50 years. Large challenges remain to explain below-replacement fertility in over 60 countries and the consequences of such low birth rates for economic growth and other issues.

KEYWORDS: family; fertility; marriage; divorce; economic analysis

During the last 50 years, the family has probably changed more rapidly than at any other recorded time in history—I could perhaps leave out the "probably" and just make that statement. At the beginning of the 20th century, birth rates in the United States and elsewhere were on the order of four or five children per family. During the last 30 years, birth rates have come down dramatically in almost every part of the world. During the last 50 years, divorce rates have begun to accelerate, a rise that began in the mid-1960s. Now, perhaps one out of three, or two out of five of every first marriages in the United States ends in divorce. At the beginning of the century, divorce was illegal in many states and was rare in most of the country. The participation of married women in the labor force grew continuously in the 20th century, slowly at first and then began to accelerate during the last 50 years. Now, more than two-thirds, maybe three-quarters of all married women in the United States participate in the labor force. At any moment, at any time over the life cycle, their rate is close to 90% or more while they are married.

At the beginning of this century, very few children attended secondary school in the United States. Child labor laws and minimum school laws then came into force, mainly in the 1890s in the United States. It was not until the

Nobel Prize in Economic Sciences, 1992.
Address for correspondence: Gary S. Becker, PhD, Professor of Economics and Sociology, University of Chicago, 1226 E. 59th Street, Chicago, IL 60637. Voice 773-702-8677; fax: 773-702-4849.
gbecker@midway.uchicago.edu
Edited version of oral presentation.

Ann. N.Y. Acad. Sci. 1038: 201–205 (2004). © 2004 New York Academy of Sciences.
doi: 10.1196/annals.1315.027

1920s that a boom in secondary education developed and continued through the 1950s. This trend has stabilized during the last several decades.

Childhood mortality was high even at the beginning of the 20th century. Child health in general was affected by many childhood diseases. When I was growing up, diphtheria and scarlet fever, both of which I had, were not uncommon. Most of these childhood diseases have since been largely eliminated. It is a rare event now when a child dies before the age of 10. These and still other changes, e.g., care of the elderly, social security and the like, have had a revolutionary impact on the family.

How does one explain these changes? There are a variety of different approaches and no one approach has all the answers. I am an economist and I will thus talk about how an economist goes about looking at some of these problems. The economist approach is widely misunderstood. It is usually assumed that when economists discuss marriage, they emphasize only the dollars and cents involved in marriage—how much money does one get out of it and, if there are financial problems, maybe that is the cause of divorces. The material aspects of marriage are indeed a significant part of the approach.

However, the economic approach is not just that; it is based on the assumption that in different aspects of their behavior and most of their activities, people try to make decisions that improve their circumstances as they see them. These improvements may be meeting a man who has better personal interaction with you, having children that you believe will be honest and ethical, participating in jobs that you like; perhaps they do not pay so well but you like the type of work. People try to make decisions in light of the variables and values that are important to them and that will improve their standing with regard to these values. That is the fundamental and a common sense idea on which the economic approach to the family has been built.

In marital decisions, people make choices about which marriages they think will leave them happier than otherwise. Divorce ensues when they are disappointed with the choices they made in the beginning, either because they did not understand themselves so well or they did not understand their mate so well. They began to believe that they can do better by breaking up their marriage, either to stay single or look for another mate. This type of reasoning is also applied to family, fertility decisions. The cost, time, money, energy, and emotion of raising children are all components of the economic cost of having children and they also affect benefits in terms of pleasure from children. Traditionally, benefits were related mainly to old-age support. Now benefits in terms of pleasure from children and their achievements are emphasized. This view of behavior, applying it systematically, forms the economic approach of the family.

We can get a feel for how the research on the family is exploding in economics by calculating the number of articles in which the word family appeared in the title or the abstract in the major economic journals during the 20th century. In the first six decades there are only 20 articles in the 8 to 10 journals that were available over most of this period; that amounts to three articles per decade. In the next decade, that increased to 18 articles in these journals and to 85 articles in the next, after that 148, and then almost 200 articles appeared in the last decade of the 20th century, an enormous increase in the major journals. In a more complete accounting, which does not go back as far, of all the economic journal articles that include family as a keyword, there are about 155 articles or so in the period from 1969 to 1975, then 200 in the next five years, then 300 in the next, then a jump to 1000, then 1800, then to more than 3000 between 1996 and 2000. Thus there has been an enormous increase in economic writing about the family, which in part reflects the enormous change in the family.

Like other researchers, economists are more interested in things that change than things that remain the same. In my final remarks I will concentrate on the tremendous decline in the 20th century in fertility to remarkably low levels. TABLE 1 shows during the period 1980 to 2000 all the nations in the world that had fertility rates below replacement, i.e., the number of children being born were not enough to replace the populations. There are a num-

TABLE 1. Fertility rates for nations with below replacement fertility

	1980	1990	2000		1980	1990	2000		1980	1990	2000
Armenia	2.31	2.62	1.26	France	1.95	1.78	1.88	Netherlands	1.60	1.62	1.72
Australia	1.90	1.91	1.75	Georgia	2.25	2.21	1.08	Norway	1.72	1.93	1.85
Austria	1.62	1.45	1.34	Germany	1.44	1.45	1.35	Poland	2.28	2.04	1.34
Barbados	2.03	1.74	1.75	Greece	2.23	1.40	1.32	Portugal	2.19	1.43	1.51
Belarus	2.03	1.91	1.29	Hong Kong	2.00	1.27	1.02	Puerto Rico	2.55	2.20	1.90
Belgium	1.67	1.62	1.61	Hungary	1.91	1.84	1.29	Romania	2.43	1.84	1.31
Bosnia	2.09	1.70	1.60	Iceland	2.48	2.31	1.98	Russian F.	1.89	1.89	1.21
Bulgaria	2.05	1.81	1.27	Ireland	3.23	2.12	1.87	Singapore	1.74	1.87	1.45
Canada	1.74	1.83	1.55	Italy	1.64	1.26	1.23	Slovak Rep.	2.31	2.09	1.34
Channel Is.	1.41	1.71	1.75	Japan	1.75	1.54	1.36	Slovenia	2.08	1.46	1.22
China	2.54	2.10	1.90	Kazakhstan	2.90	2.72	1.88	Spain	2.22	1.33	1.24
Croatia	NA	1.63	1.39	Korea, Rep.	2.56	1.77	1.43	Sweden	1.68	2.13	1.55
Cuba	1.95	1.69	1.58	Latvia	1.86	2.02	1.16	Switzerland	1.55	1.59	1.46
Cyprus	2.46	2.42	1.91	Lithuania	2.03	2.03	1.27	Thailand	3.48	2.27	1.84
Czech Rep.	2.07	1.89	1.15	Luxembourg	1.50	1.62	1.78	Trin. & Tob.	3.30	2.36	1.75
Denmark	1.55	1.67	1.77	Macao	2.30	1.75	1.15	Ukraine	1.95	1.85	1.20
Dominica	3.92	2.70	1.90	Macedonia	2.51	2.06	1.76	UK	1.89	1.83	1.68
Estonia	2.02	2.04	1.24	Malta	2.05	2.05	1.81	USA	1.84	2.08	2.13
Finland	1.63	1.78	1.73	Moldova	2.39	2.39	1.40	Yugoslavia	2.26	2.08	1.71

ber of interesting facts about these data, such as that there were relatively few countries in 1980 that had below replacement fertility—the United States was one of them. The number grew quite significantly by 1990, and grew further by the year 2000. With very few exceptions, every country that had below replacement for fertility in either 1990 or 1980 was still below in 2000—the United States is one exception. Close to 60 countries, which means almost 50 percent of the world's population, have below replacement fertility rates. Even though Hong Kong is not a country, the latest census enumeration for Hong Kong shows that the total fertility rate was below one, the lowest I have seen. In individual cities like Milano or Tokyo you might expect comparable figures.

Why has fertility declined so much? I believe the decline of fertility is explained in part by the variables I have mentioned. There is an increase in the cost of having children because the value of parents' time has gone up and that is a major cost of raising children through the cost of child care. Very important has been a movement away from having more children to having children with more human capital: healthier and better educated children. This is what economists call substitution of quality for quantity of children (not nice language but that is what is going on).

The growing labor force participation of married women is also a factor, as are high divorce rates, etc. These are clearly important variables, but how does one explain the variation in these low fertility rates between countries? The United States is not that different from Italy, but has much higher fertility rates. We have a study comparing Europe to the United States that is trying to understand these inter-country differences.

What is clear so far is that obvious variables like income and education, labor force participation, and divorce cannot account for the difference. By these variables, the U.S. should have among the lowest fertility rates. The relation of low fertility to still other variables may be the explanation. Do societies with below replacement fertility rates invest more time in their children? We do know in general ever since Jensen's day that the more siblings there are, the lower is the investment per child, so there is some tendency in that direction, in terms of education, health, and some of these other dimensions.

What is the implication of low fertility for macro-economic issues? It is obvious that with low fertility, it is much more difficult to finance the retirement of the elderly. Does this mean that we will continue to extend the age that people have to work before they can get retirement benefits? There is potential for enormous conflict when there are few workers compared with a large number of retired individuals.

Another issue is that, if these low fertility rates continue, populations will begin to decline. What are the consequences of that? The last 200 years has been a world of growing populations; that is the world we know and are familiar with and that is the world in which the world has enjoyed enormous economic progress and development. Is it an accident that economic development and progress has gone along with growing population? Or is there a beneficial effect from higher population to a growing economy? The new economic approach to economic growth suggests some causation from a higher number of people to greater stimulus to research and development. The pharmaceutical industry is a clear example of that. As the number of elderly people in the country and in the world has increased, the drug industry has shifted much of their research from developing drugs for children and the middle aged to drugs for the elderly, following the market, so to speak. This highlights the potential negative consequences of this unprecedented period of low fertility in so many countries throughout the world. Although fertility has declined mainly in rich countries, it is happening in other countries as well and this raises enormous questions that have not yet been answered.

Let me conclude by saying that I believe that the work on the family using the economic approach (I say economic approach rather than economists' approach because many noneconomists use what I have defined as the economic approach) has been productive and certainly has contributed to understanding an important aspects of changes in the family. As we look ahead into the 21st century, a major challenge is to understand the consequences of slowing population growth and even declining population for generational conflict, economic growth, and other macroeconomic questions.

Social and Economic Aspects of Immigration

DOUGLAS S. MASSEY, PHD

Professor of Sociology and Public Affairs, Princeton University, Princeton, New Jersey 08544, USA

ABSTRACT: Flows of people are observed as international migration. Every developed country in the world today has become *de facto* a "country of immigration" whether the country cares to admit it or not. We have surveyed 99 communities in Mexico and 35 in the rest of Latin America and the Caribbean. The datasets contain basic data on 19,850 U.S. migrants originating in Mexico and 3,322 migrants originating elsewhere in Latin America or the Caribbean. As a result of the contradictions of U.S. policy during the 1990s, what used to be a circular flow of able-bodied male workers has been transformed into a permanent migrant migration of families, which will have profound effects on American society for years to come.

KEYWORDS: immigration; cumulative causation; migrants; Caribbean; Latin America; Mexico; social capital

At the beginning of the 21st century, the United States finds itself at the center of an expanding global market economy. Within this global market economy, we see rising transnational flows of all sorts—of capital, goods, resources, commodities, information, and inevitably within a global market, people.[1] Flows of people are observed as international migration. Every developed country in the world today has become *de facto* a "country of immigration" whether the country cares to admit it or not.[2]

In the United States, the volume of immigration has increased geometrically, decade by decade, since the 1940s, and net migration currently accounts for 45 percent of U.S. population growth.[3] As international migration has loomed larger as a component of U.S. population dynamics, the need for accurate and timely immigration statistics has become acute. Unfortunately, of the three sources of demographic change—fertility, mortality, and migration—the last is the least reliably measured and most poorly understood.

Address for correspondence: Douglas S. Massey, PhD, Department of Sociology, 106 Wallace Hall, Princeton University, Princeton, NJ 08544. Voice: 609-258-4949.
dmassey@princeton.edu

Ann. N.Y. Acad. Sci. 1038: 206–212 (2004). © 2004 New York Academy of Sciences.
doi: 10.1196/annals.1315.028

With respect to fertility and mortality, demographers can boast a long history of accurate and precise measurement. In the United States, they can count on well-developed birth and death registration systems to provide reliable yearly tallies of vital events; and if they want to understand the determinants of fertility and mortality, there are excellent surveys that enable the modeling of behavior with respect to child bearing and health using sophisticated statistical methods.

When it comes to immigration, however, measurement is less than ideal. Although U.S. authorities register legal immigrants when they receive their permanent resident visa to generate annual statistics on gross legal immigration, they do not count people who arrive without authorization nor do they measure the actual year of arrival in the country—just the year the residence visa was issued.[4] Moreover, the government maintains no exit controls and does not inspect people leaving country, so that demographers can neither determine how many people become unauthorized by overstaying temporary visas, nor can they directly compute the *net* annual inflow of legal immigrants.

Although the census endeavors to enumerate all residents of the United States, it clearly undercounts those who are present without authorization and it cannot identify the legal situation of any single person, obviously a crucial determinant in modeling social and economic behavior. The census also does not gather accurate information on year of arrival and therefore provides a flawed indicator of cohort characteristics owing to the selectivity of return migration.[5] Immigrants who remain in the United States to be enumerated at any point in time are survivors of a decidedly non-random selection process; they are not a representative sample of those who entered earlier.

In order to overcome these data deficiencies, I developed and currently co-direct two NICHD-funded projects—the Mexican Migration Project (MMP), funded continuously since 1987, and the Latin American Migration Project (LAMP), funded since 1998 (see Massey & Sana[6]). Each year my colleague Jorge Durand and I send teams of interviewers into specific communities located throughout Mexico and other Latin American countries. Within each community we select a random sample of households and from each member we gather basic data on their first and last trips to the United States. Each household head and spouse also provide complete histories of migration and border crossing; and from each head we gather detailed information about the last U.S. trip. These data reveal where migrants from each community go, and we then travel to U.S. destination areas to track down and interview migrants from those communities who have settled abroad, thus creating binational datasets.[3]

To date, we have surveyed 99 communities in Mexico and 35 in the rest of Latin America, including samples compiled in Puerto Rico, the Dominican Republic, Haiti, Nicaragua, Costa Rica, Guatemala, and Peru. The datasets contain basic data on 19,850 U.S. migrants originating in Mexico and 3,322 migrants originating elsewhere in Latin America or the Caribbean. Among the former, 60.9% were in undocumented status on their last trip, whereas among the latter the figure was 18.3%. We also have complete life histories of 6,209 migrants from Mexico and another 889 from elsewhere in the hemisphere. Both the MMP and the LAMP datasets are freely available to users via the world wide web at <http://mmp.opr.princeton.edu/> and <http://lamp.opr.princeton.edu/>, respectively. At present, 315 have registered as users of the MMP database and 95 as users of the LAMP database.

As the older of the two datasets, the Mexican Migration Project has supported far more hypothesis testing and policy analysis to yield many surprising, and often counter-intuitive findings (reviewed in Durand and Massey[3]). In terms of theoretical knowledge, studies have shown that wage differentials are not the all-powerful determinants of labor migration that many believe. Indeed, Mexico-U.S. migration is only weakly related to the size of the binational wage differentials; the poorest communities generally do not send out the most migrants; and pressures for out-migration are most intense in communities undergoing rapid economic development, not in stagnant, poverty-stricken backwaters.[7]

Rather than moving to earn higher wages, Mexican immigrants appear to be using U.S. labor as a means of overcoming missing, failed, or incomplete markets at home.[1] Lacking access to credit markets, they move to accumulate savings to finance consumer expenditures; in the absence of capital markets they migrate to accumulate funds for investment; and lacking insurance markets, households minimize risk by sending members to work in geographically diverse labor markets, thus diversifying their labor portfolios to generate multiple income streams.

This rational calculus corresponds more to a theoretical model known as the New Economics of Labor Migration rather than that of Neoclassical Economics, and data from the MMP have provided critical in adjudicating between the two models. As predicted by the New Economics, Mexico-U.S. migration is more sensitive to secular fluctuations in Mexican interest rates than wages;[7] movement between the two countries is highly circular;[8] U.S. earnings are commonly remitted to family members at home;[9] and remittances and savings are heavily invested in housing and productive enterprises.[10]

Data from the Mexican Migration Project have also been instrumental in establishing the theories of social capital and cumulative causation, which argue that over time migration spreads through social networks to become self-perpetuating and acquire a dynamic momentum.[11] Having a social tie to someone with migratory experience is generally more powerful in predicting migration to the United States—with or without documents—than either wage differentials or interest rates.[7]

These findings are of more than academic interest. If Mexicans enter the United States to solve market failures in their communities of origin and intend to return home rather than maximize lifetime earnings by remaining north of the border, then attempting to discourage undocumented migration

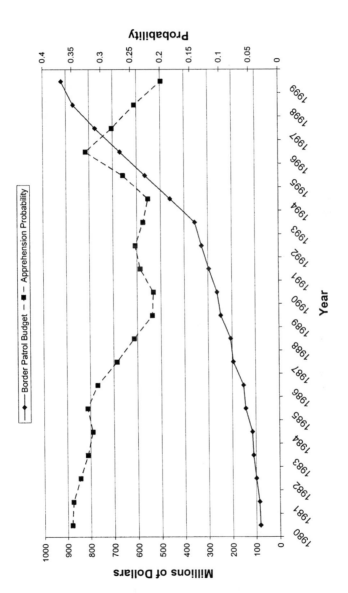

FIGURE 1. Budget of the U.S. Border Patrol and the probability of apprehension by year, 1980–2000.

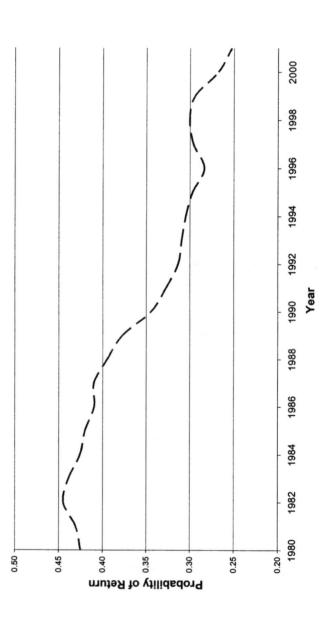

FIGURE 2. Annual probability of return migration by undocumented Mexican migrants, 1980–2000.

by increasing the costs of border crossing may prove counter-productive (see Durand, Massey & Malone[12]). Rather than lowering the likelihood of entry, militarizing the border may simply reduce the odds of return. Data from the Mexican Migration Project show that this is precisely what happened.[12]

FIGURE 1 shows that as the budget for border enforcement increased, the probability of return migration generally fell. The acceleration in border enforcement began with the passage of the Immigration Reform and Control Act in 1986. From 1986 to 1990 the probability of apprehension fell from around .34 to around .21 before leveling off. The launching of Operation Blockade by the Border Patrol in 1993 dramatically increased the level of enforcement and produced a short-term increase the probability of apprehension back up to .34. As migrants adjusted their behavior to the new realities, however, the probability plummeted and by century's end had reached a record low of .20. The odds of getting caught while attempting an unauthorized entry were just one in five.

If Mexicans continue to enter the United States as before, but no longer return home with the same frequency, population growth is the inevitable demographic outcome. As FIGURE 2 demonstrates, therefore, the paradoxical effect of more stringent border enforcement during the 1990s was to accelerate the rate of undocumented population growth in the United States. The annual probability of return migration fell from around .45 in the early 1980s to just .25 in 2000. Rather than solving the problems associated with undocumented migration, U.S. policies only made them worse, producing by the year 2000 the largest undocumented population in American history and laying the foundations for a future underclass of people whose prospects for social and economic mobility are structurally compromised.

In the context of two nations that are growing more integrated economically, which have agreed *by treaty* to promote greater cross-border movements of capital, information, goods, products, and resources, the attempt to draw a symbolic line in the sand to prevent the flow of labor within an otherwise integrated market is doomed to failure, and, indeed, only makes matters worse. As a result of the contradictions of U.S. policy during the 1990s, what used to be a circular flow of able-bodied male workers has been transformed into a permanent migrant migration of families, which will have profound effects on American society for years to come.[12]

REFERENCES

1. MASSEY, D.S., J. ARANGO, G. HUGO, et al. 1998. Worlds in Motion: International Migration at the End of the Millennium. Oxford University Press. Oxford, UK.
2. MASSEY, D.S. & J.E. TAYLOR. 2004. International Migration: Prospects and Policies in a Global Market. Oxford University Press. Oxford, UK.

3. DURAND, J. & D.S. MASSEY. 2004. Crossing the Border: Research from the Mexican Migration Project. Russell Sage Foundation. New York.
4. MASSEY, D.S. & N.J. MALONE. 2003. Pathways to Legalization. Pop. Res. Policy Rev. 21: 473–504.
5. MASSEY, D.S. & D.P. LINDSTROM. 1994. Selective emigration, cohort quality, and models of immigrant assimilation. Soc. Sci. Res. 23: 315–49.
6. MASSEY, D.D. & M. SANA. 2004. Patterns of U.S. migration from Mexico, the Carribean, and Central America. Migraciones Internacionales 2(2): 1–39.
7. MASSEY, D.S. & K.E. ESPINOSA. 1997. What's driving Mexico-U.S.Migration? A theoretical, empirical and policy analysis. Am. J. Sociol. 102: 939–999.
8. MASSEY, D.S. & A. SINGER. 1995. New estimates of undocumented Mexican migration and the probability of apprehension. Demography 32: 203–213.
9. MASSEY D.S. & E. PARRADO. 1994. Migradollars: the remittances and savings of Mexican migrants to the United States. Pop. Res. and Policy Rev. 13: 3–30.
10. DURAND, J., W. KANDEL, E. PARRADO & D.S. MASSEY. 1996. International Migration and Development in Mexican Sending Communities. Demography 33: 249–264.
11. MASSEY, D.S. & R. ZENTENO. 1999. The dynamics of mass migration. Proc. Natl. Acad. Sci. 96(8): 5328–5335.
12. DURAND, J., D.S. MASSEY & N.J. MALONE. 2002. Beyond Smoke and Mirrors: Mexican Immigration in an Age of Economic Integration. Russell Sage Foundation. New York.

Social Change and the American Family

LARRY L. BUMPASS, PHD

Norman B. Ryder Professor Emeritus of Sociology, Center for Demography and Ecology, University of Wisconsin-Madison, Madison, Wisconsin 53706, USA

ABSTRACT: Major changes affecting American family life must be seen in historical and international perspective. Most are shared with other industrialized societies and are rooted in our past and culture. This brief presentation provides an overview with respect to family instability, unmarried sex, unmarried childbearing, cohabitation, and single-parent families. Changes across these behavioral domains are seen as mutually reinforcing in creating diverse family experience and family types. At the same time, even given important differences on the average, the various family types overlap considerably with respect to both their nature and consequences.

KEYWORDS: family; marriage; divorce; sex; childbearing; cohabitation; single-parent

I would like to begin by recognizing the role NICHD has played in the transformation of family research from a cottage industry into a serious scientific endeavor. Obviously peer review, center grants, and training grants have been central to this. But equally important has been a major investment in large-scale surveys with national samples, and with broad substantive coverage of both family life and measures relevant to antecedents and consequences. These data are an essential core resource for hundreds of researchers from a broad range of disciplines, and the result has been an extensive literature documenting and analyzing critical aspects of family life.

This overview will paint with a broad brush and, in the process, must leave out many extremely important topics, such as the parenting of young children and intergenerational relationships with aging parents. Changes with respect to family instability, unmarried sex, unmarried childbearing, cohabitation, and single-parent families are well known. My goal is to provide a sense of scale for each, and to outline some general perspectives for thinking about these changes.

Address for correspondence: Larry L. Bumpass, Norman B. Ryder Emeritus Professor of Sociology, Center for Demography and Ecology, University of Wisconsin-Madison, 4412 Social Science Building, 1180 Observatory Drive, Madison, WI 53706. Voice: 608-262-2182; fax: 608-262-8400.
    bumpass@ssc.wisc.edu

Ann. N.Y. Acad. Sci. 1038: 213–219 (2004). © 2004 New York Academy of Sciences.
doi: 10.1196/annals.1315.029

PERSPECTIVES

First, I must emphasize that changes across these various domains are interdependent. While the strengths of the ties vary, none of the changing behaviors can be properly understood apart from the others. Recognizing these linkages is critical for social policy as well as for research. Second, this package of family change has deep historical and social roots: i.e. the basic trends are not the product of something that happened in the 1960s, 1970s, or any other period. Third, these changes are widely shared across industrialized societies, suggesting that common forces are at work.

Finally, in this context of increasing diversity, marriage has become a variable in family life, and not the defining characteristic. Obviously it is an extremely important variable, but we miss much that is important when families are defined solely in terms of marriage. How marriage makes a difference for families is a central question, and one we are pursuing. In doing so, we must compare differing family configurations (e.g., married, cohabiting, or single-parent) and recognize that family types overlap with respect to both their nature and consequences. Research has consistently found important differences across family types.[1] Too often ignored, however, is the extent to which the populations being compared are similar, despite statistically significant differences in means.[2]

Divorce

Turning now to the changes themselves, I begin with divorce because it illustrates perspectives outlined above. As displayed in FIGURE 1, the proportion of marriages ending in divorce followed an accelerating curve that began in the 19th century.[3] There have been periodic fluctuations and divorce rates reached a plateau around 1980. This aspect of family change is deeply rooted in the evolution of our modern society, and consequently the acceleration in the 1960s needs to be seen in the context of the long-term trend. Indeed, there was no upward inflection in the curve associated with the introduction of no-fault divorce laws in the early 1970s. Quite the contrary, disruption rates have remained stable since the late 1970s at about half of all marriages. I believe that this trend reflects a broader social change affecting other aspects of family life, and indeed social relations more generally. Briefly stated, it has become increasingly legitimate for an individual to make decisions in their own best interest. This is part of an argument about the role of individualism and the individualizing effects of our society and market economy.[4] When children are involved in a divorce, a conscious choice has been made to create a single-parent family. As divorce became more common, so did single-parent families, and the stigma associated with being a single parent eroded. Following the steep increase in divorce after 1960, there was a substantial rise in the

FIGURE 1. Percent of marriages divorced or estimated to ever divorce, by marriage year.

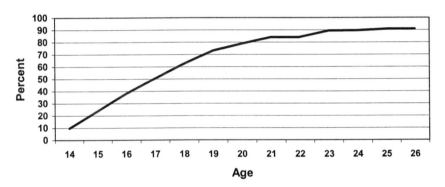

FIGURE 2. Percent of never married females who ever had intercourse, 1995.

proportion who agreed that unhappy marriages should not stay together for the sake of the children. This reduced stigma, in turn, may well have extended, in time, to single-parent families created by unmarried childbearing.

Unmarried Sex

A particularly important factor among these interwoven changes has likely been the increase in sexual intercourse among unmarried young people. FIG-URE 2 illustrates a life course pattern across ages in which 80 percent of un-married women are sexually active by their late teens, and 90 percent by their early twenties (National Survey of Family Growth data, Alba et al.[5]). There is a strong consensus that the onset of sex at the earlier ages should be de-layed, and there has been progress in that regard. On the other hand, it is quite another matter to expect much reduction in the proportion sexually active among those in their late teens and twenties. This issue must be seen in the context of the progressively older ages at which people are marrying. Delaying sex until marriage is unlikely for many when the majority remains unmarried until after age 25 and unmarried sex is widely approved, as it especially is among those under age 30. Unmarried sex is now simply a part of our culture, and this establishes a context for thinking about changes in unmarried childbearing and unmarried cohabitation.

Unmarried Childbearing

The stigma against unmarried childbearing has weakened greatly. In our most recent round of the National Survey of Families and Households, over 40 percent of young people in their twenties agreed that it would be all right for them *personally* to have a child without being married. The shock that was once associated with unmarried pregnancy was, in no small part, that it provided clear evidence of unmarried sex. That is no longer news. It is also important to recognize that the majority of unmarried births result from unplanned pregnancy, and that the delay in marriage has contributed to the increase in unmarried births, *ceteris paribus*. With marriage at older ages, those who wish to avoid pregnancy must do so for a longer period of time.

One third of all births in the United States are now born to unmarried mothers, and we are not at all unique in this regard. Rather, it is clear in FIGURE 3 that the U.S. falls in the middle of the distribution of European countries on the proportion of births that are nonmartial.[6] Further, all of these countries experienced very large increases in this proportion during the 20 years that followed 1975. Virtually no one in the early 1970s thought that the U.S. might follow the Swedish pattern, because Scandinavian history and culture were so different in this regard. Ironically however, the level in the U.S. now is about the same as that of Sweden in the mid-1970s.

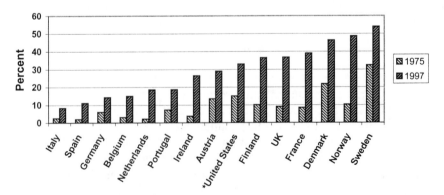

FIGURE 3. Percent of births nonmarital: 1975 and 1997.

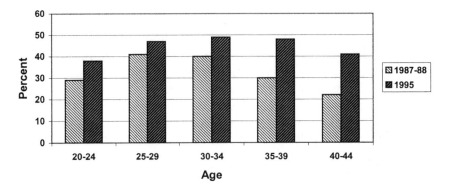

FIGURE 4. Percent of women who had ever cohabited: 1987–1988 and 1995.

Cohabitation

It seems likely that the high prevalence of unmarried sex has also played a role in reducing stigma associated with unmarried couples living together. Cohabitation was once commonly referred to as "living in sin." As does unmarried birth, living together provides evidence that a unmarried couple is having sex. These days, the presumption that a couple is already sharing a bed leaves little room for shock when they decide to share a kitchen.

As we see in FIGURE 4, over half of all adults in the U.S. under age 45 have lived with someone of the opposite sex without being married. The proportion has increased in all age groups and will continue to do so as the younger cohorts move through the age structure. In over half of all marriages, the couple has lived together before marrying. Almost half of all cohabitations involve children. Indeed, almost half of all children in the U.S. spend some time with a cohabiting parent, many of them born into two-parent, albeit unmarried, families. The linkage across the various changes is illustrated in the fact that two-fifths of births to unmarried mothers are born into cohabiting two-parent families. Even among those children born into married families, one out of five will spends some time in a cohabiting family as the parent divorces and subsequently lives with a partner without being married.[7] It is instructive in this regard that in two-thirds of all married stepfamilies the parents cohabited before they married.

The higher divorce rate of marriages preceded by cohabitation has received a great deal of attention. Especially in the context of debates over family values, many have argued that the relationship is causal. This literature is complex and some of the most sophisticated statistical modeling finds no causal relationship. A straightforward demographic observation strongly supports this conclusion. If cohabitation before marriage causes higher rates of divorce, the increasing proportion of all marriages preceded by cohabitation would predict that divorce should have increased. However, it is exactly during the period when cohabitation was becoming much more common that the divorce rate remained constant. The reason, I believe, is that many of the relationships that at an earlier time would have resulted in marriage and then divorced now dissolve prior to marrying. The testing of relationships by cohabitation may well be pruning off divorces in a way that has helped prevent a continued increase. When cohabitation is considered jointly with marriage, family instability has increased among both adults and children during the period of the divorce plateau.[7] Including cohabitation is especially important when examining the family lives of African-Americans.[8]

Consequences

All of the changes considered here have consequences for the family life of children and adults. Less than half of all children live in a traditional nuclear family with both biological parents and no half or step siblings—only a quarter of African-American children do so. Most well known is the doubling since 1970 in the proportion of children in single-parent families, resulting from both divorce and unmarried childbearing.[9] About a quarter of all children live in single-parent families and half will do so at some time in their lives. The reduced economic well-being of women and children in these circumstances is well documented. Further there is an extensive literature finding that children from single-parent families do less well on the average across a broad array of young adult outcomes.[1]

Two points warrant emphasis here. The first is that the children's family contexts have become increasingly unequal as unmarried childbearing, cohabitation, and divorce have increased most among the less well off.[10] To the extent that these family experiences impose hardships on children and limit their life chances, they amplify social inequality. On the other hand, it is essential to recognize that the differences in consequences, even in multivariate models, exist in the context of a large overlap in dispersion around central values. Most children from the least advantageous family contexts turn out all right, and many from the most advantaged have serious problems.[2] The point is obvious, but too often forgotten. Family types are very far indeed from exclusive and monolithic statuses with respect to either their nature or consequences.

CONCLUSION

The dramatic changes in family life discussed here have deep historical roots and are shared with virtually all Western industrialized societies. In short, they are here to stay. Social policy may ameliorate some of the consequences and affect behavior at the margin, and swings in the national mood with respect to these issues may have marginal effects as well. It is instructive, however, to consider the potential feedback effects of these changes on the social context in which young people make family-related decisions.

Over the past thirty years, the proportion of the population that is unmarried has increased greatly as a consequence of both delayed marriage and divorce. Over half of adults in their late twenties are unmarried, as are about a third of those in their early thirties. These young people constitute a large market for media and marketing that likely influence the content of both. In any event, their very numbers and family-related behaviors are a significant component of American life.

I have only been able to overview some of the topics on which there is a great deal of research supported by NICHD. We must first know what the facts are before we can explain them, and the attempt at causal understanding is very difficult indeed. The causal direction of effects between correlated variables is often ambiguous or reciprocal, and unmeasured variables often generate theoretically predicted relationships that are spurious. We must be exceedingly humble about what we know. Nonetheless, it is essential to the health and well-being of the nation's families, and thus the nation at large, that we enter into the public dialogue relevant to policy affecting families.

REFERENCES

1. SELTZER, J.A. 1994. Consequences of marital dissolution for children Ann. Review Sociol. **20:** 235–266.
2. CHERLIN, A. 1999. Going to Extremes: Family Structure, Children's Well-being, and Social Science. Demography **4:** 421–428.
3. CHERLIN, A. 1992. Marriage Divorce and Remarriage. Harvard University Press. Cambridge, MA.
4. LESTHAEGHE, R. & J. SURKYN. 1988. Cultural dynamics and economic theories of fertility change. Pop. Dev. Rev. **14:** 1–45.
5. ALBA, A. W. CHANDRA, L. MOSHER, et al. 1997. Fertility, Family Planning, and Women's Health: New Data from the 1995 National Survey of Family Growth. Vital and Health Statistics, Series 23, No. 19. National Center for Health Statistics.
6. KIERNAN, K. 2001. European perspectives on nonmarital childbearing. *In* Out of Wedlock. L. Wu & B. Wolfe, Eds. Russell Sage Foundation. New York.
7. BUMPASS, L. & H.H. LU. 2000. Trends in cohabitation and implications for children's family contexts in the U.S. Pop. Studies **54:** 29–41.
8. RALEY, R.K. & L. BUMPASS. 2003. The topography of the divorce plateau: levels and trends in union stability since1980. Demographic Res. Volume 8, Article 8.
9. FIELDS, J. 2001. Living Arrangements of Children. Current Population Reports P70-74, U.S. Bureau of the Census.
10. MCLANAHAN, S. 2004. Diverging destinies: how children fare under the second demographic transition. Demography. In press.

Development of the Home Pregnancy Test

JUDITH L. VAITUKAITIS, MD

Director, National Center for Research Resources, National Institutes of Health, Bethesda, Maryland 20892, USA

ABSTRACT: The home pregnancy testworks by measuring human chorionic gonadotropin (hCG) hormone in urine. This hormone was initially studied in NICHD intramural laboratories as a reliable marker of certain tumors. Refinement of the assay for hCG detection to enhance specificity enabled its ready application to pregnancy detection.

KEYWORDS: home pregnancy test; reproductive endocrinology; human chorionic gonadotropin; hCG

Am I pregnant? The answer to this age-old question once demanded a combination of guesswork, intuition, and time. In 1978, however, the long wait to know for sure became a thing of the past. Trumpeted by advertisements as "a private little revolution," the first home pregnancy tests started appearing on drug store shelves that year.

The pregnancy test works by identifying the presence of the "pregnancy hormone," human chorionic gonadotropin (hCG), in urine. Research that led to a sensitive, accurate test for hCG was done in the Reproductive Research Branch of the National Institute of Child Health and Human Development at NIH. For young researchers interested in reproductive endocrinology in the late 1960s, the NICHD was an ideal location. Glenn Braunstein and I were both medical residents at different Boston hospitals in 1969 interested in reproductive endocrinology. From our respective mentors, we each heard the same message: go to Bethesda and talk to physician scientists Mort Lipsett and Griff Ross. The NIH was one of the few places in the country where one could do reproductive endocrinology; it was really a new field.

Human chorionic gonadotropin (hCG) was a fascinating hormone to study in 1970, partly because not much was known about its behavior or makeup. We did know that the human body secretes hCG only during pregnancy or during certain kinds of cancers. If we could find a way to precisely measure

Address for correspondence: Judith L. Vaitukaitis, MD, Director, National for Research Resources, National Institutes of Health, Building 31, Room 3B11, 9000 Rockville Pike, Bethesda, MD 20892-2128. Voice: 301-496-5793; fax; 301-402-0006.

judyv@ncrr.nih.gov

Ann. N.Y. Acad. Sci. 1038: 220–222 (2004). © 2004 New York Academy of Sciences.
doi: 10.1196/annals.1315.030

this hormone, we would have a reliable tumor marker, as well as a way to identify problems with a pregnancy. The National Cancer Institute's Dr. Roy Hertz was studying a cancer called choriocarcinoma at the time. In this disease, patients exhibited tumors that secreted hCG and if blood samples could be tested reliably for the presence of hCG, tumor response during treatment could be tracked.

We knew that the existing bioassay was very crude and insensitive, though it was better than anything else available at that time. We needed another way of measuring hCG in the presence of a finite amount of luteinizing hormone (LH). While we were doing this, we had no idea of the impact on early pregnancy detection. I was working at separating the subunits of hCG and determining their biological function and characteristics. In 1970 and 1971 we generated an antibody that was specific to the beta-subunit of hCG and that could therefore be used in a radioimmunoassay and would not cross-react with other hormones. The first rabbit to produce the antibody was called "SB6" and became the baseline for future experiments.

It was critical for Dr. John Robbins of NICHD to be involved in this, because John had the immunology background. We tried two doses of immunogen to make the antibody, 10 and 50 micrograms, and the animal that had the first dose of 50 micrograms of immunogen was labeled SB6, since it was the sixth rabbit. There were five rabbits immunized with 10 micrograms, and we were told they would never make antibody at 10. However, we went down as low as 2 micrograms and documented a response at that dose. The first animal immunized with 50 micrograms, SB6, yielded the classic antiserum that had the best relative specificity and was used for years. In 1972, we were ready to publish our paper on hCG research, in which we described the methodology for using antibodies to the beta subunit of hCG in a radioimmunoassay to identify and measure hCG in the presence of LH. This became the basis for the home pregnancy test which is so widely used today.

The following website contains a history of research related to the home pregnancy test:
<http://www.history.nih.gov/exhibits/thinblueline/>.

BIBLIOGRAPHY

BRAUNSTEIN, G.D., J.L. VAITUKAITIS & G.T. ROSS. 1972. The in vivo behavior of human chorionic gonadotropin after dissociation into subunits. Endocrinology 91(4):1030–1036.

VAITUKAITIS, J.L., G.D. BRAUNSTEIN & G.T. ROSS. 1972. A radioimmunoassay which specifically measures human chorionic gonadotropin in the presence of human luteinizing hormone. Am. J. Obstet. Gynecol. 113(6):751–758.

RAYFORD, P.L., J.L. VAITUKAITIS, G.T. ROSS, et al. 1972. Use of specific antisera to characterize biologic activity of hCG-beta subunit preparations. Endocrinology 91(1):144–146.

VAITUKAITIS, J.L., G.T. ROSS, J.G. PIERCE, et al. 1973. Generation of specific antisera with the hormone-specific beta-subunit of hTSH or hFSH. J. Clin. Endocrinol. Metab. **37**(5): 653–659.

VAITUKAITIS, J.L. 1973. Immunologic and physical characterization of human chorionic gonadotropin (hCG) secreted by tumors. J. Clin. Endocrinol. Metab. **37**(4): 505–514.

GOLDENBERG, R.L., E.O. REITER, J.L. VAITUKAITIS & G.T. ROSS. 1973. Hormonal factors influencing ovarian uptake of human chorionic gonadotropin. Endocrinology **92**(5): 1565–1567.

HODGEN, G.D., W.E. NIXON, J.L. VAITUKAITIS, et al. 1973. Neutralization of primate chorionic gonadotropin activities by antisera against the subunits of human chorionic gonadotropin in radioimmunoassay and bioassay. Endocrinology **92**(3): 705–709.

BRAUNSTEIN, G.D., J.L. VAITUKAITIS, P.P. CARBONE & G.T. ROSS. 1973. Ectopic production of human chorionic gonadotrophin by neoplasms. Ann. Intern. Med. **78**(1): 39–45.

VAITUKAITIS, J.L. & G.T. ROSS. 1973. Recent advances in evaluation of gonadotropic hormones. Annu. Rev. Med. **24**: 295–302.

HODGEN, G.D., W.W. TULLNER, J.L. VAITUKAITIS, et al. 1974. Specific radioimmunoassay of chorionic gonadotropin during implantation in rhesus monkeys. J. Clin. Endocrinol. Metab. **39**(3): 457–464.

VAITUKAITIS, J.L. 1974. Human chorionic gonadotropin as a tumor marker. Ann. Clin. Lab. Sci. **4**(4): 276–280.

MORGAN, F.J., R.E. CANFIELD, J.L. VAITUKAITIS & G.T. ROSS. 1974. Properties of the subunits of human chorionic gonadotropin. Endocrinology **94**(6): 1601–1606.

VAITUKAITIS, J.L. 1974. Changing placental concentrations of human chorionic gonadotropin and its subunits during gestation. J. Clin. Endocrinol. Metab. **38**(5): 755–760.

VAITUKAITIS, J.L. 1975. Editorial: When is a tumor marker not a tumor marker? N. Engl. J. Med. **293**(26): 1370–1371.

CATT, K.J., M.L. DUFAU & J.L. VAITUKAITIS. 1975. Appearance of hCG in pregnancy plasma following the initiation of implantation of the blastocyst. J. Clin. Endocrinol. Metab. **40**: 537–540.

VIGERSKY, R.A., D.L. LORIAUX, A.E. ANDERSEN, et al. 1976. Delayed pituitary hormone response to LRF and TRF in patients with anorexia nervosa and with secondary amenorrhea associated with simple weight loss. J. Clin. Endocrinol. Metab. **43**(4): 893–900.

VAITUKAITIS, J.L.& E.R EBERSOLE. 1976. Evidence for altered synthesis of human chorionic gonadotropin in gestational trophoblastic tumors. J. Clin. Endocrinol. Metab. **42**(6):1048–1055.

VAITUKAITIS, J.L., G.T. ROSS, G.D. BRAUNSTEIN & P.L. RAYFORD. 1976. Gonadotropins and their subunits: basic and clinical studies. Recent Prog. Horm. Res. **32**: 289–331.

ALBERTSON, B.D. & J.L. VAITUKAITIS. 1977. Role of cyclic nucleotides in modulating ovarian hCG action. Endocr. Res. Commun. **4**(6): 367–378.

Development of the Pill

CELSO-RAMÓN GARCÍA, MD†

William Shippen Jr. Emeritus Professor of Obstetrics and Gynecology, Department of Obstetrics and Gynecology, Hospital of the University of Pennsylvania, Philadelphia, Pennsylvania 19104, USA

ABSTRACT: The history of development of the first oral contraceptive reveals the coalescence of scientific and social forces in the late 1950s that led to his major advance in reproductive freedom for women. Improved knowledge of basic reproductive endocrinology, the development of oral compounds by pharmaceutical companies, and careful clinical trials to document efficacy each played pivotal roles in the story. In addition to industry, the National Institute of Child Health and Human Development and the U.S. Food and Drug Administration provided the research and regulatory support structures to nurture the field along its ultimately highly successful path. Still, it remains important to note that more than 500,000 women die each year from complications of child-bearing, a problem that is particularly acute in Africa. A significant portion of this mortality would be prevented by better knowledge of and access to oral contraceptives.

KEYWORDS: oral contraceptive; reproduction; progesterone; estrogen; public health

May 9th, 2003, marked the 43rd anniversary of the approval of the first oral contraceptive by the Food and Drug Administration. This was at the time when the care of women, especially maternal care, was believed to be best supported through the National Institute of Child Health and Human Development. Maternal care was to include the preconceptual time as well.

In the 40 or 50 years preceding the beginning of the development of the oral contraceptive, many efforts had been made to modify the ovulatory mechanisms, mainly in animals. Many years later in Boston, Fuller Albright and Sommers Sturgis intimated that a combination of diethylstilbestrol fol-

†Deceased. Please see *In Memoriam*, this volume.

Address for correspondence: Stephen G. Kaler, MD, MPH, Clinical Director, Intramural Research Program, National Institute of Child Health and Human Development, NIH, Building 10, Room 9S-261, 10 Center Drive, MSC 1834, Bethesda, MD 20892.

kalers@mail.nih.gov

Ann. N.Y. Acad. Sci. 1038: 223–226 (2004). © 2004 New York Academy of Sciences.
doi: 10.1196/annals.1315.031

lowed by intramuscular progesterone, a regimen they used to diagnose and treat patients with endometriosis, could probably be relied on to avoid pregnancy. The political and social climate was such that it was strictly unlawful in Massachusetts to advise, prescribe or instruct on the use of contraceptives. John Rock, a professor at Harvard Medical School, technically broke the law by lecturing at the medical school on every contraceptive modality available at the time.

It is difficult to comprehend the aura that surrounded contraceptive practices in that era, given that, today, well over 100 million women worldwide rely on oral contraceptives as their method of family planning. Indeed, it is the most popular not only in the United States, but also in Western Europe, where it is estimated that over one-half the married women avail themselves of the oral contraceptive.

Mrs. Stanley McCormick, an engineering graduate from MIT and a staunch feminist, had decided to change her focus of supporting studies in schizophrenia to an oral contraceptive. Mrs. McCormick's Boston friends suggested Gregory Pincus would be the one who might be able to do this. Both suffragettes descended on Pincus with a meager budget. Nonetheless, he agreed to proceed with a preliminary review. She persuaded Pincus to explore various courses of action. She made numerous visits to the Worcester Foundation for Experimental Biology in Shrewsbury, Massachusetts, and he to her home office on Beacon Street opposite the Harvard Club. She always had Mrs. Delaney take very careful notes in short hand, which Mrs. Delaney then transcribed and a read to Mrs. McCormack at each subsequent visit and she did that for everyone that she had contact with.

Gregory Pincus reviewed the target organs that might be modified in the female to prevent pregnancy. It should be noted in passing that, several years before, Pincus had written the definitive monograph on *The Eggs of Mammals*. He was very experienced in handling ova as well as embryos, techniques that he taught John Rock and Arthur Hertig, who studied the earliest human embryos that had been seen. It was thus natural that he should focus on the mechanisms of inhibiting ovulation. He turned his attention to an assay that had proven effective at the University of Pennsylvania and began screening the inhibition of ovulation in rabbits with various steroids. The screening studies were carried out by Min Chueh Chang and Ann Merrill at the Worcester Foundation of Experimental Biology. The steroids were obtained from various pharmaceutical companies. Pincus discarded the corticoids and androgens and focused his attention on estrogens and progestagens.

Pincus's research was preceded by the work of Russell Marker, who developed the ability to synthesize steroids from diosgenin in wild Mexican yams. From these came the original two or three progestational compounds that were applied in the early contraceptive formulations. Marker commercialized the production of progesterone in Mexico with the help of the small pharmaceutical company Laboratorios Hormona.

In the process of creating the drugs Norethynodrel and Norethinodrone, the 3-methyl ether of ethynyl estradiol was inadvertently carried over. The first 50 women to whom I administered the medications had indirect indices of inhibition of ovulation. However, the results were confounded by the 3-methyl contaminant of ethynyl estradiol, which could have suppressed ovulation by itself. Such a contaminant was suspected by the chemists at Syntex, where it had been demonstrated in the lab of Alexander Zaffroni. These data were not mentioned at the official presentations during the Laurentian Hormone conference at Mount Tremblant in Canada but were discussed with the Food and Drug Administration during the intermissions.

Subsequently, we obtained carefully purified agents and it was obvious that they themselves could inhibit ovulation, but pesky side reactions such as various types of uterine bleeding made them very impractical. Therefore estrogens were added to those original compounds to create the early oral contraceptives. The dosages were high, but as time went by the dosages were reduced.

Before I joined Gregory Pincus and John Rock in New England, I had carried out studies using crystalline oral progesterone on volunteer women medical students at the School of Medicine at the University of Puerto Rico, where I was a faculty member at the Department of Obstetrics and Gynecology at that time. Pincus, Rock, and I selected Puerto Rico for the larger trials because, at that time, the inhabitant migration to other parts of the world was very infrequent. Thus, there was a stable cadre of reproductively active women who desired reversible contraception. Even though tuboligation ("La Operación") was exceptionally popular, there was much interest in this new reversible method that appeared foolproof if taken consistently. Pincus had tried some of these agents at the Worcester State Hospital, but the menstrual habits of those patients were very erratic for other reasons. Some of these studies were carried out at the John Rock Reproductive Center in Brooklyn before we took them to Puerto Rico. In Puerto Rico, we went to the family planning group Pro Bienestar de Familia in Rio Pedras, Puerto Rico. During the course of this program in Puerto Rico, the renowned biostatistician and pioneer in reproductive endocrinology Dr. Christopher Tietze visited the center as a tourist. He asked to see the format of the study and the record-keeping, since this was an area of his expertise. He commented that he had never seen such careful documentation of patients' past history, medical problems, medication histories including tablet(s) missed, etc. Independently, Dr. Adeline Pendleton-Satherthwaite, a missionary physician, set up similar studies at the Humacao Hospital under the sponsorship of Dr. Clarence Gamble. Subsequent studies took place also in Port-au-Prince, Haiti.

These experiences offer case studies of partnerships between the private sector, industry, and investigators. It soon became apparent that the application of this modality of regulation of fertility in women with proven fertility required mechanisms for reporting to the Food and Drug Administration as a necessary part of the process, and application for an IND and other government requirements was needed to gain the approval of the use of this medical approach. Industry was in the best position to carry out this important function and that is what we let them do. I wish to emphasize, however, that it was Mrs. Stanley McCormick who supported the first five years or so of the basic studies, not industry. Our experiences with industry, with G.D. Searle, Wyeth-Ayerst, Park-Davis, Ortho, and Syntex, were invaluable, but they came much later.

Numerous variations in lowering dosage and content have yielded the present oral contraceptives, each one claiming to be better then the others. The last contraceptive approach uses a similar steroid, not orally but by the percutaneous approach known as the patch.

My experience as a member of NICHD council, a consultant to the contraceptive development program at the Rockefeller Foundation, as well as the contraceptive development program at NICHD reinforced the prime importance of industry's depth of experience and expertise in dealing with the Food and Drug Administration. In fact, the Contraceptive Development Branch of NICHD created a contract research program, which invited industry to become a copartner in contraceptive development, a form of partnering in the creation of new compounds that would be screened as potential contraceptives. Many contraceptive regimens were evaluated for their efficacy. Dr. Gabriel Bialy had a very broad view of a contraceptive development program with excellent interactions between the scientists of NIH, the FDA, and industry. GNRH analogues were one of the positive developments that came out of the NICHD contraceptive program. While they may not be useful as contraceptives, they have many other uses.

I am often amused by those who claim to be the father of the pill, the godfather of the pill, or the grandfather the pill. Most of these accounts are by Johnny-come-latelies or those who allege that they have researched the history of the pill and publish monographs on the subject but allow poetic license to run wild.

It is reported that in developing countries more than half a million women die each year from maternal complications. In many countries, unsafe abortion contributes heavily to the maternal deaths that could and should be avoided by the use of effective contraception. The hazards of contraception have to be weighed against these other hazards, particularly those of pregnancy itself.

Factors Influencing Perinatal Outcomes

ROBERT L GOLDENBERG, MD

*Charles E. Flowers Professor, Department of Obstetrics and Gynecology, The
University of Alabama at Birmingham, Birmingham, Alabama 35233, USA*

ABSTRACT: Important pregnancy outcomes include stillbirth and neonatal
mortality, long-term neurologic handicap, and maternal mortality. Research conducted with the support of NICHD and other agencies in the last
four decades has provided us with the ability to substantially improve
many of these outcomes. In fact, in recent years, in the U.S. and other developed countries, childbirth has become a relatively safe undertaking for
the mothers, and the vast majority of infants are born healthy and survive.
In many developing countries, the risk of each of the adverse outcomes
mentioned above is increased 10- to 100-fold compared to U.S. rates, with
many of the differences explained by inadequately organized healthcare
systems and low levels of health expenditures. At present, we have the
knowledge to substantially reduce adverse pregnancy outcomes throughout the world; so far we have not had the will.

KEYWORDS: maternal mortality; infant mortality; stillbirth; neonatal
mortality

Although excess population growth is not thought of as one of the standard
adverse outcomes of pregnancy, it may be one of the most important. In the
year 2000, the earth's population was about 6 billion people, about 4 billion
living in developing countries and about 2 billion in industrialized countries.[1] Population growth either has either begun to decrease or will soon decrease in many developed countries. But with large portions of the
population in developing countries under the age of 15, there will continue
to be very large population increases in those countries (FIG. 1).[2] With continued population growth, there is increased pollution, and on a per person
basis, less fresh water, less affordable energy, fewer health care resources,
and less food. With one-third of the world's population already malnourished, continued population growth will only contribute further to the conditions mentioned above.

Address for correspondence: Robert L. Goldenberg, MD, Charles E. Flowers Professor,
Department of OB/GYN, 1500 6th Avenue South, Suite 379, Birmingham, AL 35233-1602.
Voice: 205-934-3273.
rlg@uab.edu

Ann. N.Y. Acad. Sci. 1038: 227–234 (2004). © 2004 New York Academy of Sciences.
doi: 10.1196/annals.1315.032

United Kingdom   Pakistan

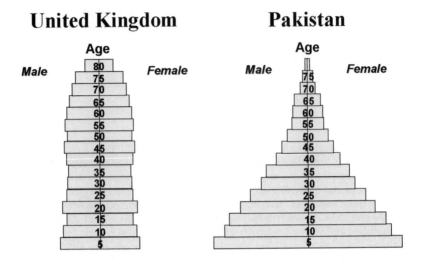

United States Census Bureau,
International Programs
Center[2]

FIGURE 1. Population age distribution by 5-year intervals for the United Kingdom and Pakistan.

When describing differences between developed and developing countries, it is important to remember that far and above any other factor, the outcomes of pregnancies are influenced by where in the world they take place.[3–5] The last speaker mentioned that of the approximately 600,000 women who die each year during pregnancy or childbirth, 99% live in developing countries. The maternal death rate in the U.S. is about eight per hundred thousand births. In many areas of sub-Saharan Africa, it approaches 1,000 per hundred thousand births, and in some areas of Africa such as in Ethiopia, maternal deaths occur as frequently as 1,500 per hundred thousand pregnancies (TABLE 1).[6]

TABLE 1. Maternal death

Country	Maternal Mortality Ratio 100,000 (per live births)
United States	8
Mexico	187
Indonesia	331
Tanzania	770
Gambia	1005
Ethiopia	1528

Data from Tracy & Tomich.[6]

TABLE 2. Preventing maternal mortality

Antibiotics for infection
Blood for hemorrhage
Cesarean section for obstructed labor
D & C for complications of miscarriage and abortion
Eclampsia prevention

In many places in Africa, the average woman has a one in ten lifetime chance of dying in childbirth. The major causes of maternal mortality are the same throughout the world: hemorrhage, sepsis, preeclampsia, obstructed labor, uterine rupture, and complications of abortion.[7,8] If those problems could be solved, the death rate would approach that seen in the U.S. now, where of the few deaths that occur, many are secondary to pulmonary embolism or anesthesia complications. Preventing maternal mortality is relatively easy. Providing blood in the case of hemorrhage, treating infections with antibiotics, preventing obstructed labor with caesarian sections, treating complications of miscarriage and abortion, and treating preeclampsia, will substantially reduce the number of maternal deaths (TABLE 2). In the U.S. through the 1930s, maternal mortality rates were nearly the same as they are now in many parts of Africa. In the 1940s and 1950s, in the U.S. we learned how to induce labor and perform cesarean sections. We began to do blood transfusions, developed antibiotics and began to use magnesium sulfate to treat preeclampsia. With those interventions, maternal mortality has fallen dramatically—not to zero, but very close (FIG. 2).[9] I come from Alabama, which has around 60,000 births per year. In an average year, there may be six or eight maternal deaths.

Stillbirth is defined as an infant born without a heartbeat, respiration, or any movement. In the U.S., most states used a lower gestational age cut-off about 20 weeks.[10] Since about half of the deaths from 20 weeks to one year of age in the U.S. are fetal deaths, this is the pregnancy outcome that is most under-appreciated and certainly the most understudied. The discrepancy between stillbirth rates in developing countries, such as sites in Africa, and developed countries, such as Scandinavia and the U.S. are dramatic, with often a 20-fold difference. The causes of stillbirth include fetal asphyxia often associated with placental insufficiency, fetal growth retardation, preeclampsia, congenital anomalies, and, especially in developing countries, intrauterine infections such as syphilis and malaria. Some of the other causes include Rh disease, diabetes and trauma. With all the recent emphasis placed on HIV, it is often forgotten that syphilis is a huge problem in developing countries. In Zambia, 15% of all pregnant women test positive for syphilis, and of the women who test positive for syphilis, about a third will have a stillbirth. This means that in Zambia, a stillbirth rate of up to 50 per thousand is explained

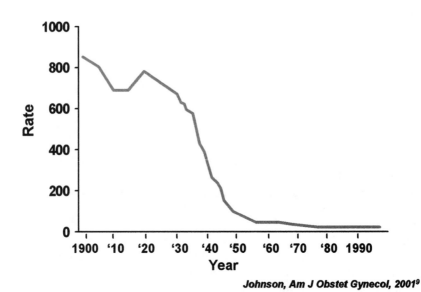

Johnson, Am J Obstet Gynecol, 2001[9]

FIGURE 2. Maternal mortality rate per 100,000 live births, United States—1900–2000.

by syphilis alone, compared to the overall stillbirth rate in the U.S. of about 5 per thousand births. The very large reductions in stillbirth rates in developed countries over the last several decades have occurred because of improvements in medical care. Those improvements include the ability to monitor fetuses, especially for growth retardation and preeclampsia, with early delivery of those at risk, and reduction of post-term pregnancies. Rh disease has virtually been eliminated with the use of Rhogam, and there is far better medical care for those women with preeclampsia and diabetes. Because of better prevention of perinatal infections, these now rarely are a cause of death. These types of medical interventions have reduced fetal deaths from about 40 per thousand births in Alabama 25 years ago to 7 per thousand births at the present time.

Another important pregnancy outcome is neonatal death, or deaths that occur within the first 28 days of life. Globally, there are about 4 million neonatal deaths per year, with almost all occurring in developing countries.[4] The major causes of death worldwide include birth asphyxia, pneumonia and encephalitis, congenital anomalies and the complications of preterm birth. In developing countries, much of the neonatal mortality is due to infection.[11] The large number of malnourished mothers and malnourished babies, frequently with no access to medical care, sets the stage for these deaths.

Similar to outcomes throughout the U.S., statistics from the University of Alabama in Birmingham, from 1975 to the present, show that there was a

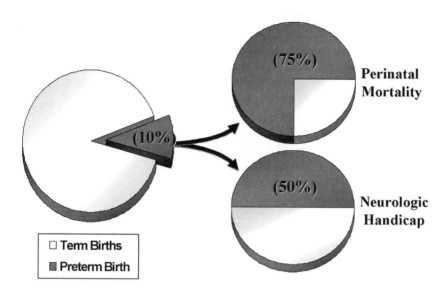

FIGURE 3. Sequelae of preterm births.

marked improvement in neonatal survival during that time. The ability to keep very small babies alive often depended on being able to transfer their mothers to a place that could provide appropriate care. This in turn depended on the combination of a regionalized transport system plus the life-saving technologies available at the newborn intensive care unit. It thus became clear to many of us in the 1970s and 1980s that receiving care at the appropriate type of institution was crucial for improving pregnancy outcome.

In the U.S., because of the improved survival of larger infants, much of the residual mortality currently occurs in the smallest babies. Thus, at this point, if we are going to reduce neonatal mortality in the United States, we will have to focus on the babies being born weighing between 500 and 1,000 g. About 10 percent of all babies are premature, and prematurity accounts for 75 percent of perinatal mortality and about 50 percent of neurological handicaps (FIG. 3). Much of this is due to the terrible prognosis for babies that are born right at the edge of survival and survive, i.e., those born at 23 to 24 weeks and weighing 500 to 700 grams at birth. About a quarter of these babies will end up with a long-term handicap.

Looking at preterm birth in the United States over the last 30 years, public health and medical programs have had no impact on reducing preterm birth[12] (FIG. 4).[13] It is becoming clear now that many of the early preterm births, those occurring before 30 or 32 weeks, are due to various kinds of maternal intrauterine infections that we have not yet found a way to prevent. Overall, when we look at the preterm birth scorecard, we have had substantial reduc-

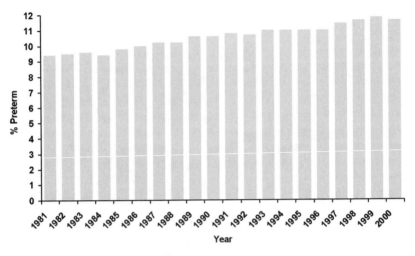

Source: Natl Vital Statistics Report, Vol. 50, Feb 2002[13]

FIGURE 4. Preterm birth in the United States.

tions in mortality but we have failed in our attempts to reduce spontaneous preterm birth. The other failure, as already mentioned, is that there has been little or no reduction in long-term handicap among the smallest survivors. So there is a lot of work still to be done.

My own U.S. experience is in Alabama. There, the infant mortality rate in the 1970s was essentially the worst in the country. When we started looking into the reasons for the high mortality in the mid-1970s, it became clear that the babies were dying because they did not receive appropriate medical care. A group in Alabama came together and organized a system of care that guaranteed prenatal care for every woman in the state through the public health department, something that had not been available before. They designated regional centers that could provide what was then state-of-the-art newborn intensive care. They devised a maternal and infant transport system and they educated providers in use of the system. All this took about one year to put in place. By 1979, the infant mortality rate in Alabama had dropped by about one-third from 20 to about 14 per thousand (FIG. 5). More important, although improvements were occurring throughout the United States, Alabama did much better than a number of the states that by demographic characteristics should have been doing better. This experience taught us that an organized medical care system and access to appropriate medical services for mothers and infants were crucial for improving survival for Alabama's infants.

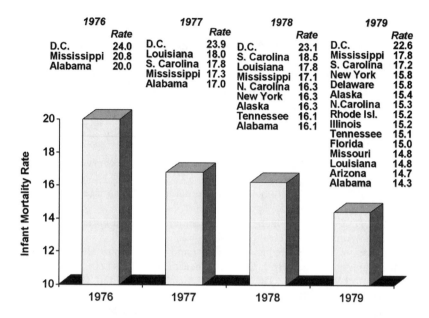

FIGURE 5. Infant mortality in Alabama 1976 to 1979 and also in the states with higher rates of infant mortality than Alabama.

In translating this lesson to developing countries, it is clear that the most obvious barriers to improving pregnancy outcomes are the lack of organized systems of care and the current low level of expenditures on health. In the poorest countries, the average health expenditure is $13 per year. In Zambia it is even lower—$4 per year. The health officer for Lusaka, the capital city in Zambia, who is responsible for medical care for 40,000 births, has a total budget of $180,000 a year with which to manage those births, $4.50 per birth. $180,000 would be about the cost of providing one premature baby newborn intensive care in the U.S.

More than 9 million fetuses and infants and 600,000 of their mothers will continue to die each year before or just after birth, unless the international health community employs programs to reduce their numbers by applying the research that has been done at NICHD and many other places over the last 40 years.[14] We all know what to do to fix the problems associated with poor pregnancy outcomes in many developing countries. It is really just a matter of our having the will to do it.

REFERENCES

1. GOLDENBERG, R.L. & A.H. JOBE. 2001. Prospects for research in reproductive health and birth outcomes. JAMA **285**(5): 633–639.
2. Adapted from Global Population Composition, United States Census Bureau, International Programs Center, 2002.
3. SCIARRA, J.J. 1993. Reproductive health. Am. J. Obstet. Gynecol. **168**: 1649–1654.
4. NOWAK, R. 1994. New push to reduce maternal mortality in poor countries. **269**: 780–782.
5. FATHALLA, M.F. 1991. Reproductive health: a global overview. Ann. N.Y. Acad. Sci. **626**: 1–10.
6. TRACY, E.E. & P.G. TOMICH. 2002. Maternal mortality: an international crisis. ACOG Clin. Rev. **7**: 15.
7. MAINE, D. & A. ROSENFIELD. 1999. The safe motherhood initiative: why has it stalled? Am. J. Public Health **89**: 480–482.
8. LILJESTRAND, J. 1999. Reducing perinatal and maternal mortality in the world: the major challenges. Br. J. Obstet. Gynaecol. **106**: 877–880.
9. JOHNSON, J.W.C. 2001. The millennial mark, presidential address. Am. J. Obstet. Gynecol. **185**(2): 261–267.
10. GOLDENBERG, R.L., R. KIRBY & J.F. CULHANE. 2004. Stillbirth: a review. J. Matern. Fetal Neonatal Med. **16**(2): 79–94.
11. STOLL, B.J. 1997. The global impact of neonatal infection. Clin. Perinatol. **24**: 1–21.
12. GOLDENBERG, R.L. & D.J. ROUSE. 1998. The prevention of premature birth. N. Engl. J. Med. **339**: 313–320.
13. National Vital Statistics Report, Vol. 50, Feb. 2002.
14. Child Health Research Project special report: reducing perinatal and neonatal mortality.199. *In* Proceedings of the USAID's Child Health Research Project and Maternal and Neonatal Health Program Meeting. Johns Hopkins University Office of Design and Publications. Baltimore, MD.